CINEMA SEATBACK KICKER

20-22k/pa negotiable   **Grade 3**

- Are you unable to sit still for more than 30 seconds?
- Do you have a staggering lack of spatial awareness?
- Can you demonstrate a high level of proficiency in ignoring aggressive glances?

If you answered YES to all of these questions, then FIDGETCUNT PLC have an exciting opportunity for you to work as a Grade 3 CINEMA SEATBACK KICKER.

At Fidgetcunt PLC, we've been kicking the backs of cinema seats since 2004, and we are currently looking to expand our fast-growing and dynamic team of restless movie theatre chair nudgers.

If you are an enterprising and energetic young arsehole looking to gain valuable experience in ruining other people's cinema trips, then we want to hear from you TODAY.

Send your CV to vacancies@fidgetcuntplc.org.

FIDGETCUNT PLC
Where kicking the backs of cinema seats is all about PEOPLE

RUSTLE, RUSTLE, RUSTLE & MUNCH ASSOCIATES

A vacancy has arisen for an experienced...

UNNECESSARILY LOUD EATER

£32k pa plus benefits

We are an established noisy playhouse food consumption firm looking for a forward thinking and highly motivated cunt to join our rapidly expanding Loud Eating team.

The successful candidate will have...

* At least three years' experience of taking way too fucking long to open a bag of Maltesers

* A proven track record of masticating at a volume of 150 decibels or higher

* Little to no self-awareness

The ability to spend up to nine minutes rummaging about for a fistful of popcorn is essential, and a willingness to breathe loudly or belch between bites would be a bonus. Applicants must be willing to noisily consume EVERY kind of cinema food and/or beverage presently on sale in the UK, including but not limited to: popcorn (salted/sweet/caramel), nachos, hot dogs, ice cream, sweets, chocolate, fizzy drinks and Slush Puppies.

Send CVs to: Rustle, Rustle, Rustle & Munch Associates, PO Box 719, Sunderland, SR1 6PQ. Closing date for applications is 17 June 2020. Rustle, Rustle, Rustle & Munch is an equal opportunities employer.

FUCKWITTED LATE ARRIVER

Required immediately at the

ODEON CINEMA TIPTON   £12 p/h

Odeon Cinema Tipton is currently recruiting a part-time **FUCKWITTED LATE ARRIVER** to assist in the erosion of our customers' cinematic enjoyment. Working 25 hours per week (with flexible overtime), you will be required to:

- Arrive 10 minutes after the start of each scheduled film, breathing heavily and sweating through your clothes
- Switch on your iPhone torch and clumsily shine it around the furious audience in search of a free seat
- Select the seat that will require the largest number of people to stand up whilst muttering 'For fuck's sake' as you squeeze past

A willingness to immediately get up and go to the toilet as soon as you've sat down would be an advantage, but is not essential.

Send CV and the names of two referees who think you're a fucking arsehole to: **Odeon Cinema Tipton, HR Dept, PO Box 389, TP7 6HJ.** Remember to mark your envelope *'FUCKWITTED LATE ARRIVER APPLICATION'*.

VIEWBLOCK HATWANKER GROUP

TRILBY CLAD BELLEND

28-30k pa
ref: Viz294/005

VWG are the UK's largest provider of wankers in hats who block cinema screens.

We are currently seeking a young, self-motivated **TRILBY CLAD BELLEND** to sit in a busy 300-seater East Yorkshire screening room, annoying the piss out of the person behind them.

This is an ideal first step on the cinema arsehole career ladder for an ambitious young film ruiner.

The successful candidate will own their own trilby (straw boaters, top hats and fezzes may also be accepted) and will be able to demonstrate a proven track record of refusing to take it off, even when threatened with physical violence.

Apply online at www.vwg. co.uk, using the reference 'Viz294/005'

Viewblock Hatwanker Group *Blocking cinema screens with hats TODAY for a brighter TOMORROW*

THE TALKING DURING FILMS CO.

EXECUTIVE SPOILER & MUTTERER

(Grade IV)

Salary based on experience
Benefits + company car

TDFC requires an **EXECUTIVE SPOILER & MUTTERER** to give away vital plot points during some of the UK's biggest forthcoming summer blockbusters.

A minimum of TEN YEARS experience of talking loudly during films is essential, and an ability to demonstrate spoiler dissemination - either online or in public - would be an advantage.

The successful applicant will have a proven track record of illegally downloading films before they are released, and then loudly revealing what's about to happen in a cinema environment.

So if you've ever been...

- **Violently assaulted during a Star Wars screening**
- **Beaten unconscious in a Marvel movie**
- **Hospitalised at a Harry Potter premiere**

... then we want to hear from YOU.

The Talking During Films Co.
We talk... *during films*

PHONEGLANCE TOSSPOTS LTD
Cinema Annoyance Solutions

YOU ARE:
- On a phone contract with free texts and data
- Willing to work 40 hours per week
- A fucking cunt

WE ARE:
- Phoneglance Tosspots Ltd, Britain's foremost supplier of twats in cinemas who can't stop checking their phones.

At PTL we work with more than SIXTY top cinema chains across the UK, providing them with expert mid-film phone glancers who are highly trained to send texts, make calls and even watch YouTube videos during the latest big screen releases. If you have the attention span of a fucking goldfish and you enjoy raising strangers' blood pressure, then you could be EXACTLY the kind of narcissistic dickhead we're looking for.

Send your CV to: info@phoneglancetosspots.com.

Phoneglance Tosspots:
You wouldn't want your cinema trip ruined by anyone else.

I CAN'T BELIEVE YOU ONLY HAVE A SINGLE BEDSIDE TABLE

OH, YOU HAVE TO KEEP BRINGING UP MY ONE NIGHTSTAND

NOTHING!

Mind where you're stepping. It's

Viz

THE
ZOOKEEPER'S BOOT

A Wellyful of Pages Caked with the Foulage of Issues 292~301

In the Elephant House
Graham Dury and Simon Thorp

Great Apes

Mark Bates, Alex Collier, Terry Corrigan, Simon Ecob, Ivan Edwards, Tom Ellen, Chad Elliot, Barney Farmer, Ray Fury, Matt Haydock, Lee Healey, Rob Hitchmough, Jacob Hutchinson, Davey Jones, Marc Jones, Aiden Kelly, Paul Kelly, Lee Kern, Shaun Madrid, Luke McGarry, Steve McGarry, Brian Milburn, Richard Milne, Alex Morris, Paul Palmer, Tom Paterson, Tom Richmond, Mathew Shepherd. Paul Solomons, Kent Tayler, Nick Tolson and Stevie White and Rhydderch Wilson.

Small Mammals
David Saunders and Lee Boyman

Published by Diamond Publishing Ltd
7th Floor, Vantage London, Great West Road, London, TW8 9AG
ISBN 978-1-91642-192-9
First Printing Summer 2022

Subscribe online at www.viz.co.uk
Find us at facebook.com/vizcomic and twitter.com/vizcomic

2

3

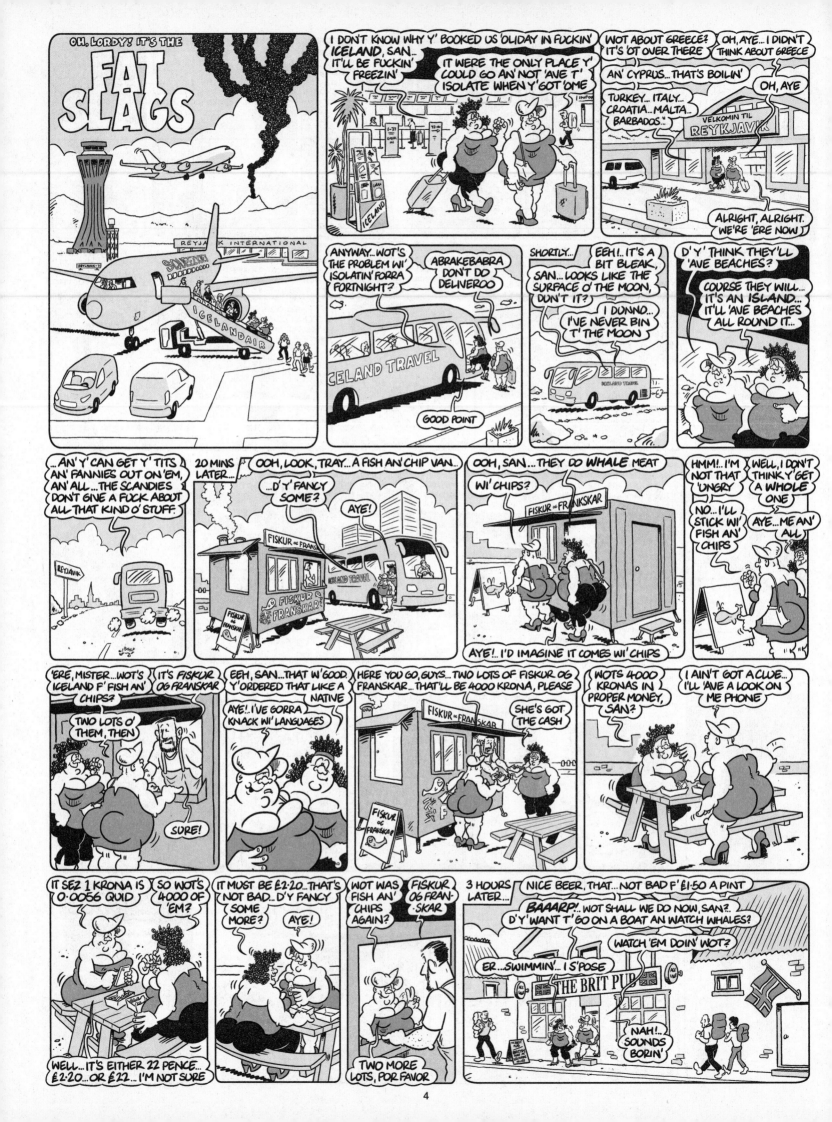

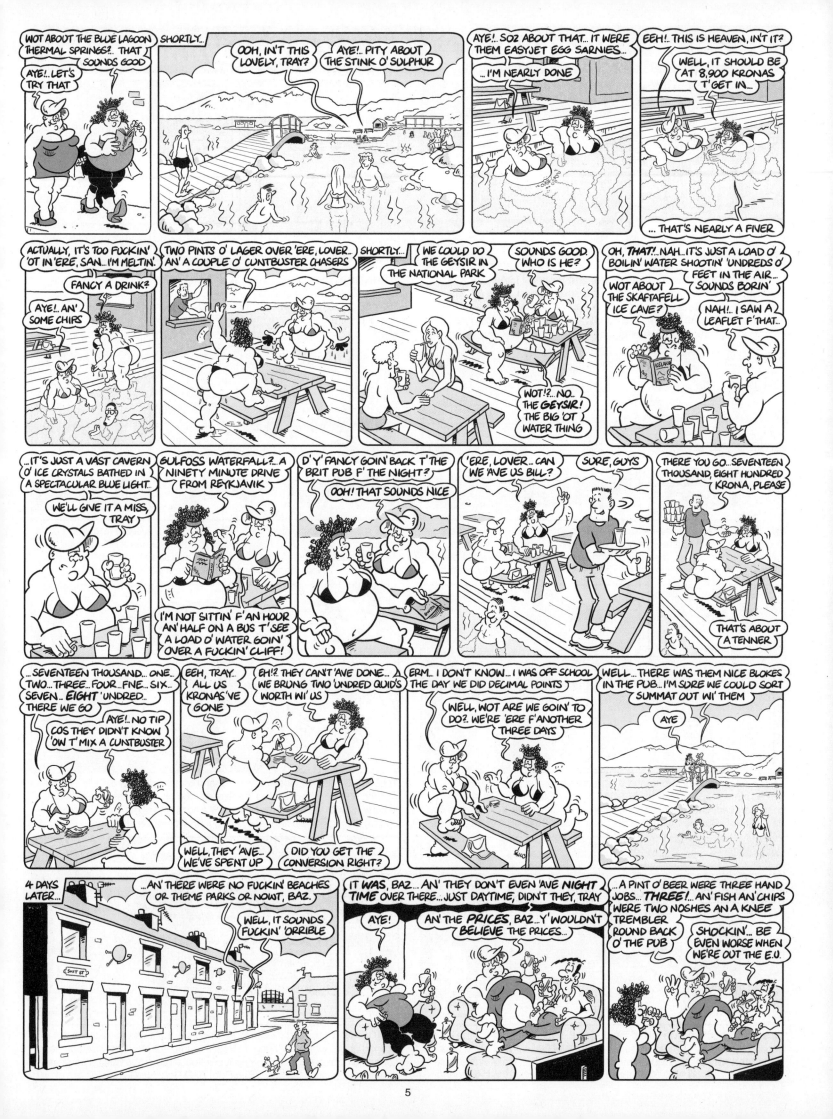

5

Bad Bob  The Randy Wonder Dog

IT WAS Christmas Eve in Glenpeebles, and Sergeant Greenock was patrolling the village with his faithful Jack Russell terrier, Bob. All was peaceful as the villagers slept in their beds. But suddenly, the silence of the festive night was broken by shrill cry, "Help! Help ma boab! Fire!"

ROUNDING the corner, the sergeant saw flames licking out of the window of Miss McCulloch's cottage, her Christmas tree ablaze. And upstairs, the lady of the house was trapped in her bedroom. "Dinnae worry, Miss. I'll call the fire brigade straight awa'!" he shouted.

WITHIN minutes, the Glenpeebles Fire Brigade had arrived on the scene and set to work. "We'll hae ye oot o' there in nae time, Miss McCulloch!" called Chief Fraser. His men got to work with their hosepipe to put out the flames, while the chief himself set about rescuing the frightened woman.

BUT AS Fraser ascended the ladder, Bob suddenly leapt and clung on to the fire chief's leg. "Och! Get yir dog aff ma leg, Greenoch!" he cried, as the mutt pumped away for all he was worth. "Git aff him, Bob!" shouted the sergeant. "How many times hae I got to tell ye? BAD Bob!"

THE FIRE chief was strong and eventually shook the dog free. Bob picked himself up and ran towards the house. "Stop, Bob! Dinnae go in!" cried Sergeant Greenock. "It's too dangerous, and there's nothing ye can do tae help!" But the brave little dog was already running into the flames.

THE FIRE chief reached the window, and with practised ease, lifted Miss McCulloch onto his shoulder. But the terrified woman didn't just have the flames to contend with, as the randy terrier had a tight hold of her calf. "There's a dog on ma leg!" she cried. "And he's got his wee wet lipstick oot!"

MISS McCulloch tried to shake the dog free, and as she did so, the ladder began to wobble. "Hold still, lassie!" cried Chief Fraser. "You'll hae us aff the ladder!" But the young woman was near hysterical. Chief Fraser lost his balance, and he, Miss McCulloch and Bob all tumbled to the ground.

SERGEANT Greenoch tried to prise Bob free, but it was too late, as the randy mutt approached his vinegar strokes. "Och, no! The dirty wee bas has spongled oan ma leg!" cried Miss McCulloch. The embarrassed sergeant could only chastise his dog. "Bad Bob! BAD Bob! Nae Mince Pie fir ye!"

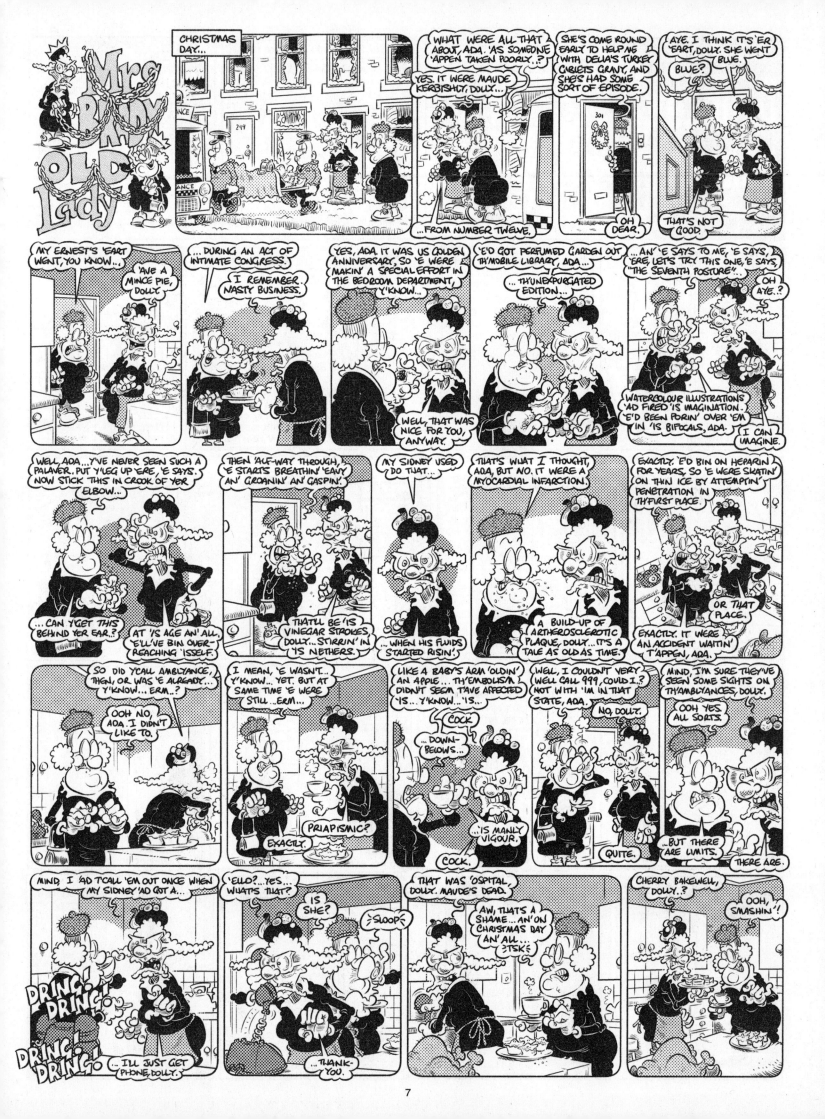

7

letterBOCKS

Viz Comic, P.O. Box 841 Whitley Bay, NE26 9EQ : letters@viz.co.uk

HOW come when a train is cancelled, the rail operator puts on a replacement bus service, but when my bus to work doesn't show up, the bus company doesn't provide a replacement train? As always, it's one rule for middle class, toffee-nosed commuters, and another one for ordinary plebs who work locally.

T. O'Neill, Glasgow

HOW come you never see anyone buffing an apple on their jumper before eating it any more? I don't even do it myself, as no doubt the PC lobby has now deemed it a 'hate crime' or some such, and I have no wish to be hauled up before the courts.

Two Jackets, Waterford

I THINK I've just walked past Bill Oddie, but it might have just been a dumpy old bloke with a beard. To be honest, you would think he would have the common decency to walk around doing the Funky Gibbon, or perhaps a few bird songs, so we know it's definitely him.

Mark Brook, Paignton

I'VE watched the last series of *The Apprentice*, and I have honestly not seen that many twats in one place since my son's fifth birthday party.

Terry Tittybiscuits, Leeds

I'VE always assumed that you need to be big and strong to be a bouncer, but observing them at work while out last night, I realised that the main part of their job is spoiling people's fun by pointing out what they are doing wrong. I think I'd actually be very good at that.

Jane Hoole Garner, St. Ives

IF the tolerance for speed limits is 10% +2mph, why don't they just update the speed signs to 35, 46 etc., so that people can concentrate on driving, rather than doing sums to work out how fast they can go?

Mat, Westhill

MY wife came home recently to find me dressed in her clothes, shoes and underwear. We had a right laugh, when we realised the mistake I had made, as our wardrobes look very similar.

Terry Farricker, Blackpool

ACCORDING to the illustration on Fox's Glacier Mints wrappers, polar bears have been stranded on little melting blocks of ice since they were first manufactured back in 1918, long before climate change was invented. And the mints are probably still the same size now as they were in my childhood. What a con this so-called 'global warming' is.

Phil Kitching, Isle of Jura

"THA mecks a muckle and tha's got t'muck a meckle", my old Yorkshire Grandma used to say. As a result of this and other nonsensical babblings, we had her put away.

Eldon Furse, email

WHEN someone is shot in a TV drama, the medics always count to three before lifting them from the gurney to the operating table. Surely they could build the suspense up a bit if they counted to ten?

Bertrum Hubris, Croydon

IF you want to watch the television whilst sitting on the lav, I suggest you put a television in the bathroom rather than install a toilet in the living room which, frankly, hasn't gone down very well with my wife.

H Crumb, Goole

IT'S all very well Bryan Adams going on about how great the summer of '69 was, but that was when I got hit by a car which broke my leg and put me in hospital for 10 weeks, meaning I missed all the school holidays and didn't get to see the live broadcast of the Apollo 11 moon landing. Mind you, Bryan Adams is Canadian, and he probably grew up on a farm in the back end of fuck knows where, so he may have been singing with rose-tinted glasses on.

Derek Coster, Watford

I FIND it nice that the abusive chant of "You're shit and you know you are" at least acknowledges the intended victim's level of self-awareness. Credit where it's due and all that.

Two Jackets, Waterford

ON a wildlife programme recently, David Attenborough stated that adult elephants will drink fifty gallons of water a day. At the same time, we saw them roaming the African plains in a desperate search because all the water holes were depleted. Now I'm no wildlife expert, but surely if the elephants weren't such greedy bastards, there wouldn't be a problem.

Bartram Twelves, Ely

HOW come astronauts from the 1960s always seem to be wearing their spacesuits inside the spacecraft? Surely when they go on their spacewalks outside they're not going to feel the benefit.

Two Jackets, Waterford

I DON'T think I'd have been any good if I was fighting in WWI. I need my eight hours every night, and all that shelling and early starts would have put me in a bad mood all day. Plus, I hate the smell of cigarette smoke, and I'm no historian, but they all seemed to be heavy smokers and they don't seem to have had any 'No Smoking' trenches.

Rock Brazilliano, Kent

THEY say more people are killed by cows in England each year than are killed by sharks worldwide. What a load of bollocks. I don't even think cows can swim, and even if they can, I've certainly never seen one in the ocean.

Angus, Bishops Stortford

I'M tired of everyone harping on about how long giraffes' necks are. I saw a snake the at London Zoo the other day and its neck went all the way down to its arse. That's where the plaudits should go.

Billy Driptray, Surrey

I HAD a look at the Periodic Table the other day and Christ, what a load of rubbish. Who's ever heard of Molybdenum or Astatine or Hafnium? Come on scientists, stick to everyday elements that we are all familiar with, like wood, glass and sand.

Ben Nunn, Caterham

HOW about a picture of that bloke kissing that Phoebe Waller-Bridge off of the BBC's *Fleabag*'s arse?

Brucie Bonus
St. Leonards on Sea

* *Would YOU like to see a celebrity getting kissed on the arse by that bloke in that picture? Simply write and tell us which celebrity you would like to see getting their arsed kissed and why, and if your letter is chosen, we'll print the picture in the next issue. Mark your envelope or email "That picture of that bloke kissing that star's arse."*

"YOU only get an Ooooh with Typhoo" the advert says. But my missus went "Ooooh" when I stuck two fingers in her balloon knot. Actually it was more of an *"Arrghfuckoff!"*, but that would sound stupid in a tea advert. Frankly, I don't think they've thought it through.

Ian Baker, Weston-super-Mare

SO, to reverse all this global warming we must stop flying on holiday, stop using the car, stop using gas and electricity, and stop eating meat. This is indeed a heavy price to pay and I for one would rather drown with all the polar bears.

Stuart Achilles, Wigan

I BET most of them aliens in films such as *Star Trek* and *Star Wars* have really bad breath. And I also reckon that their farts are pretty terrible too.

R Devereux, Hereford

TOP TIPS

A CABBAGE attached to your scrotum with duct tape makes an ideal scrotum-stretching weight. If it is too heavy and causing over-stretching, simply remove a few of the outer leaves.

Kirk Flatus, Filey

RUIN the reputation of a new co-worker by starting to steal from colleagues and leaving massive shits unflushed in the works toilets soon after they arrive, and then refraining from these activities whenever they are off.

Mike Tatham, St. Andrews

ENGLAND rugby team. Intimidate your opponents by performing a Morris dance before every game.

James Wallace, Belper

INSTALL a swear box at work, get £50 in change and spend the day telling everyone to fuck off.

Malcolm Alcock, email

IMPRESS supermarket checkout assistants by buying goods to the value of £15.97. When the they say "1597 please", you can immediately reply that 1597 is both a prime and Fibonacci number, and the year in which the English defeated the Spanish Armada.

Martin Harwood, Bradford

FOOTBALL grounds. Save energy by fitting motion sensors to the floodlights. They will only come on and illuminate the half where the play is, thus cutting electricity bills by 50%.

Paul Swinfield, Sale

TRADESMEN. Whatever your trade, advertise that you are a painter and decorator on the side of your van. That way, would-be thieves know that inside they will only find some old paint brushes and women's underwear.

William Allen, Hove

toptips@viz.co.uk

☐ **WHEN** they're on the slack, horses' cocks are very small, almost invisible in fact. I don't know what all the hoo-har is about.

Fat Al White, Wrenthorpe

☐ **IN** solidarity with Extinction Rebellion protesters, I smashed the windows and slashed the tyres of my neighbour's new BMW to prevent its exhaust polluting the planet. I set fire to his shed as well, but that was because he's a right cunt, nothing to do with the climate.

D F Kant, email

☐ **IF** we all turn veggie, what will happen to all the cows and sheep? Surely they would just start overpopulating the countryside. Then nature would come up with some way of keeping their numbers in check by evolving a massive bird thing that picks them off. However, this beast wouldn't be too choosy and would almost certainly eat ramblers and small children too, meaning we'd all have to stay indoors, properly shitting it. I think we should all stick to eating meat as the cabbage-chompers haven't really thought this one through.

Willy Balls, Banbury

☐ **DOES** anyone know if Bamber Gascoigne is still alive? Only, last night I had a dream where I was visiting a stately home and he was taking a shit in the garden. I want to know for certain if it was him.

Ed Win, Corby

☐ **IN** a dream last night, I was out for a walk in the country when I had an urgent shit in someone's outdoor toilet. Later in the dream, the police tracked me down and gave me a stern warning. What, exactly, is the law in this regard?

Mike Bell, Chelmsford

＊ *Two very interesting letters involving shitting in dreams. Are there any lawyers amongst our readers who could say if any crimes had been committed in those dreams, or any psychotherapists who could interpret them?*

☐ **THE** amount of pornography freely available on the internet nowadays makes me very concerned. There isn't nearly enough. Come on grumble merchants, at least make a bit of effort.

Craig Scott, East Calder

☐ **I DON'T** understand why films about lighthouse keepers always portray them as dark, disturbed, miserable souls. Sounds like the ideal job to me. If I could spend all day watching telly, having a wank with the curtains open and getting pissed every night, that sounds spot on.

Trev, Glossop

☐ **WHY** are there charity shops called 'Cats Protection'? I can understand raising money to save snow leopards and whales and so on, but since when have we been running out of cats? And if we're talking about protection, where's the charity shops for mice?

Barry Truncheons, Goole

☐ **"WHY** not re-use your towels?"** suggested the sign in the bathroom of the hotel. Yet when I cut one up for dusters and used the other to clean my shoes, they were noticeably fucking cross. I think more clarity is needed from the hospitality industry.

Gail, Minchinhampton

☐ **WHY** America has invested billions to develop a camera so powerful it can read a newspaper headline from space is anyone's guess. Why don't they just send astronauts up with a Kindle and pay the subscription fee for an electronic copy of their preferred newspaper? This would also allow them to read the full article and not just the headline.

Paul Padre, Walkington

☐ **HOW** do seals drink fresh water to survive? Perhaps the gobshite scientists and religious cock suckers could answer me that.

Charles the Ninth, Rimsville

☐ **A LOCAL** caravan retailer on the radio uses the slogan "As passionate about caravans as you are". Quite frankly, I couldn't give a fuck about caravans, which makes their company look rather unprofessional.

Graeme Clark, Crook

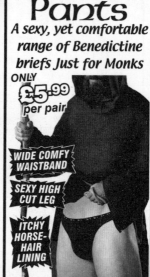
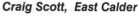

Continued over...

14

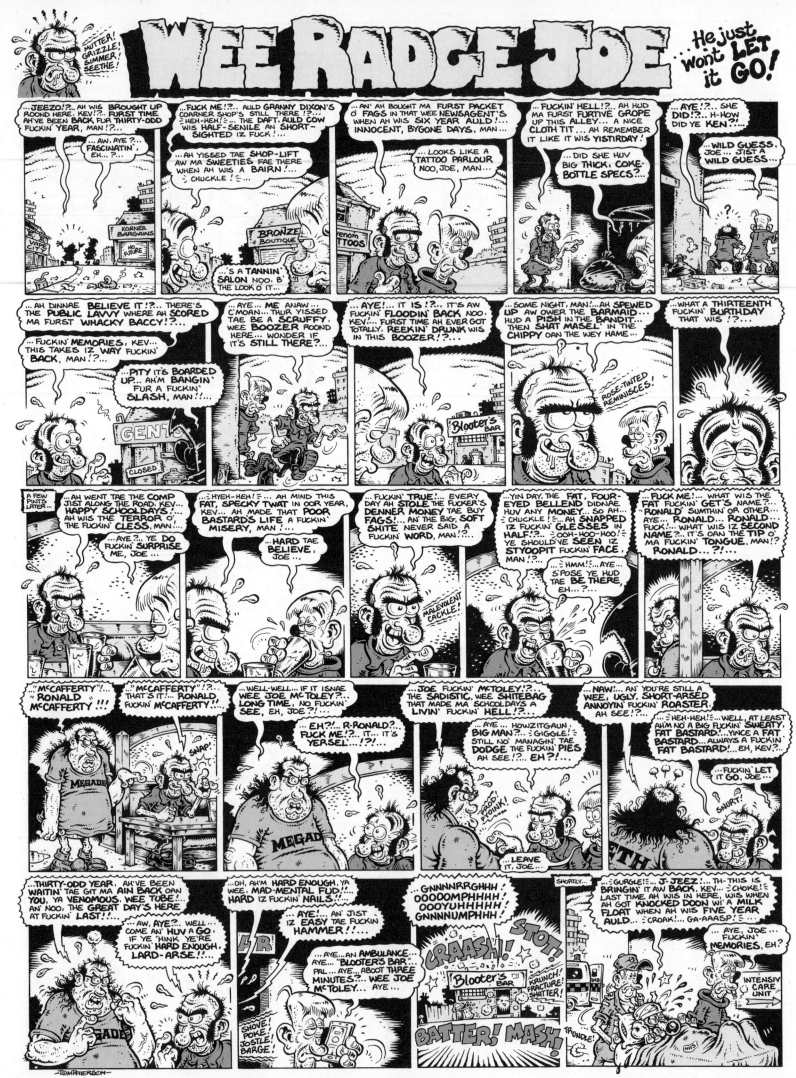

16

NO SUSSEXES PLEASE

THE WORLD was rocked last month by Prince Harry and Meghan Markle's announcement that they plan to retire from royal life and earn their own living across the Atlantic.

The selfish pair's spiteful broadside, timed to spoil the 38th birthday celebrations of the wonderfully British Duchess of Cambridge, reportedly broke the Queen's heart. The 93-year-old monarch, who has selflessly sat on the throne for nearly six decades, was consumed with grief after her ungrateful grandson and his American divorcee wife decided to sever all ties with the UK monarchy and scuttle off to the US, after being "upset" by wholly reasonable press coverage of their disgraceful and shameless lifestyle.

According to their announcement, Harry and Meghan intend to make their own way in the world, working to earn their livings like normal people.

But what will they do?

Apart from Meghan having a hugely successful acting career, and Harry being a qualified helicopter pilot, both are completely unskilled, and they might find holding down a normal job a bit more tricky than they expected.

It's time to take a look at some of the employment opportunities on offer in the Viz Job Centre window, to weigh up whether Harry and Meghan can earn a living doing work that matches their rarified skillsets.

HARRY

Helicopter Pilot

LIKE all male members of the royal family, Prince Harry is a skilled chopper pilot. He saw action flying Apaches in the Gulf under the pseudonym "Captain Wales," so he might well fancy being employed as an "eye-in-the-sky" traffic reporter on a US commercial radio station called something like WZRP or WKPX.

In between a limited playlist of eighties MOR ballads and shouted ads for Chrysler dealerships and slimming tablets, the Prince - now simply known as "Harry in the Sky" - would spend his days hovering above busy interstate junctions, passing on reports about traffic congestion and freeway pile-ups.

However, it's not impossible that combat veteran Harry could experience a frightening *Apocalypse Now*-style flashback above the freeway, and find himself believing he is back under Taliban attack in the Middle East theatre of combat. If he mistakes a queue of innocent sedans and trucks waiting their turn to leave the freeway for a hostile insurgent convoy, he might inadvertently swoop down and open fire, unleashing hell out of a clear blue sky onto hundreds of hapless stateside commuters.

Job suitability: 6

Porn star

AS any tabloid reader knows, back in his carefree bachelor days Harry was photographed romping naked round a billiard table with a bevy of scantily clad Las Vegas beauties. As someone who is clearly comfortable taking off his clothes in front of the camera, perhaps a new career in the stateside 'Silicone Valley' porn business would suit the self-exiled sixth in line to the throne.

Celebrity lookalikes are highly sought after in the adult entertainment industry, meaning that a genuine royal such as Harry could command top dollar to strip off and get down and dirty on camera. Off-colour scud movie titles such as *Some Day My Prince Will Cum*, *Fucking 'em Palace*, and *Right Royal Rogering* would fly off the sex shop shelves as royal fans queued up to spend their hard-earned wads on the Prince's blue-blooded blue movies. Even Harry's trademark ginger hair would prove no obstacle to his hardcore success, as the first job of the day for any modern porn star is to shave their pubes for a more streamlined look on camera.

However, as a Prince, Harry is accompanied everywhere by six heavily armed security officers, and to avoid "breaking the fourth wall" these minders would be forced to strip off and join in the hardcore on-screen antics, turning all Harry's productions into crowded seven-way gang bangs. Not only that, but the first six participants would be heavy-set men with dark glasses and curly earpiece wires, a scenario that might prove a little too "niche" even for the famously diverse stateside porn market.

Job suitability: 4

Maître D'

IN the course of his formal royal duties, Prince Harry has met tens of thousands of people, greeting each of them in a charming manner, making them all feel special and not swearing. In fact, he's exactly the sort of personable, well-presented gent who would make an excellent Maître d' at a fashionable high-end New York eaterie. If guests were met, shown to their table, and had their napkins flicked open and placed on their laps by the sixth in line to the throne, they would know they were in for a pretty special dining experience.

Thanks to his expensive public school education, the prince could charm diners as he used his posh British accent to explain which menu items were off, offer to grind a ludicrously big pepper mill over their main course, and apologise about flies in the soup; what's more the restaurant would save money, as it's quite likely that Harry owns his own white tie, posh shirt, tail coat and shiny dress shoes.

But as well as in the soup, there could be a fly in the ointment. As a member of the royal family, the Prince is not allowed to carry money on his person, so any customer attempting to tip him by slipping a tightly folded dollar bill into his hand, would be a serious breach of court protocol, leading to an awkward scene in the restaurant and a potential diplomatic incident.

Job suitability: 7

Ribbon factory worker

THROUGHOUT his years of formal royal engagements, Harry has cut countless ribbons at opening ceremonies for hospitals, schools and supermarkets. So if a major US-based ribbon manufacturer was looking for someone to snip their products to length at the end of a factory production line prior to them being rolled onto spools, packed into cardboard boxes and delivered to shops, the Prince would be a shoe-in for the position.

There would be no need for costly on-the-job training, as the royal recruit would be snipping away like a time-served pro from the start of his first shift until the hooter went at six o'clock.

But there is a potential pitfall, and it's a big one. The Duke may find old ceremonial habits hard to shake off, and after each snip of his scissors, Harry would feel compelled to make a long-winded, humourless and patronising speech before walking up and down the production line, shaking hands with his factory colleagues and enquiring if they'd come far. Consequently, he would quickly fall behind on his targets, and it wouldn't be long before he found himself being called into the manager's office for a right royal bollocking.

Job suitability: 3

GOOD RIDDAN

18

WE'RE BRITISH (AND AMERICAN)

MEGHAN

Beauty Queen

THE beauty pageant circuit is a huge national industry across America, with countless millions of dollars in prize money given away to the country's prettiest girls each year. Once Harry and Meghan take up residence in the exclusive upstate Hamptons district, the famously attractive Duchess will find herself eligible to compete in - and doubtless win-the "Miss New York State" contest, taking home not just a silk sash, a diamante tiara and a bunch of flowers, but also a cool million dollar prize.

And with the couple owning luxury weekend homes dotted all around the country, including a ski-lodge in Aspen, Colorado, a beachfront condo in Miami, Florida, and a luxury ranch in Texas, Meghan could find herself picking up plenty more big money prizes in similar contests all over her home country.

However, it's possible that outspoken feminist Meghan may look upon beauty pageants as outdated "meat markets" that are sexist and demeaning to women. But she needn't worry her pretty little head about such matters, because modern day contests are not simply concerned with outward appearances. As well as the swimsuit rounds and those all-important vital statistics, Meghan will get the chance to show her other skills for the judges. Doing a little tap-dance in an Uncle Sam leotard, or singing a patriotic song whilst dressed as the Statue of Liberty will see the 36-24-36 princess walking away with first prize whilst remaining true to her all-important feminist ideals.

Job suitability: 9

Actor

BEFORE she donned a tiara to become a member of the British monarchy, Meghan Markle was a highly successful actress, with an impressive rollcall of starring roles in shows such as *Suits, CSI Miami* and *Knight Rider*. And as acting is one of those careers that is 'in the blood', she could easily step back into showbiz and make her living once again on the screen. But it's fair to say that since her marriage to Harry, she has found herself 'typecast', and she may struggle to be taken seriously by audiences as any character other than the Duchess of Sussex. A New York cop, an astronaut scientist, or a hard-bitten hooker from the Bronx are all bread and butter roles for female actors, but they are now ones which Meghan would find herself unable to play with any conviction.

Fortunately, Hollywood has always had a love affair with the British monarchy, and there will never be any shortage of cheap, made-for-TV biopics about our royal family. And who better to cast in the role of Meghan Markle than the woman herself? However, such is the competition for viewers these days that many film makers feel compelled to include sex scenes to boost ratings. Even if the titillating shots were essential to the plot, it is unlikely that Meghan would bring shame on the institution of the monarchy by getting them out for the cameras and romping naked with her "husband", played by an actor you've never heard of doing an English accent that sounds like Dick Van Dyke in *Mary Poppins*.

Job suitability: 3

Whitehouse Spokesperson

SINCE he took office, President Trump has seen off two White House Press Secretaries - Sean Spicer and Sarah Huckerby-Sanders - who between them presided over dozens of press briefings in their combined two-and-a-half years on the job. The current incumbent, Stephanie Grisham, has yet to take a briefing, and commentators wonder if she will ever get to stand behind that famous podium before following her predecessors out of the door of 1600 Pennsylvania Avenue. And when the role does become vacant, who better to fill it than Meghan Markle?

The 45th POTUS is a great fan of both British royalty and attractive women a third his age, so the Duchess would almost certainly be appointed if she applied for the post. As a former actress, she would immediately feel comfortable in front of the world's cameras, seamlessly explaining to the Washington Press Corps that what the president said actually meant the opposite of what they thought it meant, or denying that he had said it at all.

But Meghan is famously an outspoken critic of the Trump regime, and as such would be unlikely to take up such a key position in her long-time bête noir's administration. Unless, of course, she took the job as a clever ruse, using her first and only briefing to denounce her orange-coloured boss in front of the world's press, before being wrestled to the ground with unnecessary force by CIA agents.

Job suitability: 2

Door-to-door Salesperson

ONE of the biggest obstacles faced by door-to-door hawkers is homeowners pretending they aren't in when they ring the bell. It makes their working lives more difficult, but they accept it as part of the job. Every one of us is guilty of doing it at one time or another, but how many of us would hide behind the sofa if we saw the former Duchess of Sussex heaving a suitcase of wares up our garden path? Immediately, Meghan would have an enormous advantage over her colleagues, an edge which would probably see her take the office Salesperson of the Month award time after time.

Admittedly, some products would be more suited to her sales patter than others; having spent countless hours in make-up before shoots during her acting days, she would make an excellent Avon lady, for example, advising clients knowledgeably about skin creams, blushers and lipsticks. However, with Frogmore Cottage servants having done all her cleaning for the past three years, she probably doesn't know her Astonish from her Cif, so she might struggle to shift many of the products in her Bettaware suitcase.

Whatever she sells, Meghan is sure to be a hit with the housewives of Middle America, although she might find herself facing one problem. Being of mixed race and walking around affluent areas of America, there is quite a high chance of her being shot for no reason by police, who would later be acquitted of any wrongdoing.

Job suitability: 6

...CE TO BAD RUBBISH

says Daily Mail journalist
CHARLIE PONTOON

SO Harry and Meghan are turning their backs on Britain and scuttling off to the other side of the Atlantic.

Well, I say GOOD!

After all we've done for them, this is how they say thank-you, is it? Let's hope they go to the West coast, so they're a little bit further away from the rest of us.

I for one am glad that we're finally seeing the back of this vile couple. Especially her.

Let's face it, Meghan never really fulfilled the criteria of what we British people demand from our Princesses.

She was American. She was Catholic. She was a divorcee.

And she was some other things.

And don't let her sob-story about right wing press intrusion fool you into feeling the slightest shred of sympathy for her.

She knew full well that she would be vilified the moment she fell in love with Prince Harry.

Vitriolic abuse goes with the territory and she signed up for it the moment she said "I do."

Now it turns out she can't stand the heat, and she wants to get out of the palace kitchen. Well I for one am glad.

Good riddance to bad rubbish.

With her gone, it will free up column inches in our newspapers for stories about proper Princesses. *British Princesses.*

And when I say British, I think you know what I mean.

21

WE all love a walk in the countryside. But no amble along a British riverside path or woodland track is complete without coming across a pile of illegally dumped household waste. Whether its a load of stained mattresses, a heap of ripped-out kitchen units or half a ton of smashed-up plasterboard, picking our way around a big pile of shite is a part of any walk in the great outdoors.

Despite being socially, morally and environmentally unacceptable, fly-tipping is just as popular now as its ever been, with an estimated 1-in-5 of us regularly dumping vanloads of illegal waste in areas of natural beauty.

But how much do we actually know about this quintessentially British practice? When did it start? What is the most fly-tipped product? Who is the smallest person ever to do it? It's time to answer all those questions and 17 more. Here's...

20 THINGS YOU NEVER KNEW ABOUT FLY-TIPPING

1 **FLY-TIPPING** probably came over to Britain with the Romans in around 220 BC. Historians like Mary Beard probably believe that provincial governors imposed taxes on the population, perhaps requiring them to pay a levy to Julius Caesar on any goods they needed to dispose of. Unable or unwilling to pay these possible taxes, canny Britons would more than likely have loaded up their ox-carts with the refuse, conceivably dumping it under cover of darkness at the side of Roman roads.

2 **BACK** in the Middle Ages, the offence of 'flye typping' was punishable by death, and by a strange legal quirk this punitive measure has never been taken off the legal statute book. This is, of course, a legal anomaly, and the last execution for the offence took place way back in 1978. These days, offenders escape with their lives, a fine of up to £1000 and 200 hours community service.

3 **IF YOU** think the practice of fly-tipping is restricted to unlicensed tradesmen and DIY-ers too cheap to hire a skip, you may be surprised to hear that many Tinseltown A-listers have been prosecuted for illegally dumping their rubbish. In 2007, Clint Eastwood was fined $1500 by Carmel magistrates for dumping half a ton of builder's rubble in the Hollywood Hills after ripping out his patio to put in some decking. And last year, socialite and IT-girl Paris Hilton was given a $2,000 fine and ordered to attend a social awareness course after being caught by Bel Air police emptying a bath, a toilet, a sink and twenty yards of copper pipe out of her van in a back street off Sunset Boulevard.

4 **HOLLYWOOD** stars who have never been prosecuted for fly-tipping include *Spiderman* star Toby McGuire, straight-to-DVD king Wings Hauser, and Tim Roth, who portrayed *Reservoir Dogs*'s Mr Orange.

5 **ONE BIRMINGHAM** couple loved fly-tipping so much that they actually took their wedding vows whilst illegally dumping rubbish. Andrew Mould and Olive Mildew gathered with their guests in a secluded layby off the A42 for the unusual marriage ceremony. As the couple took their vows, the best man and three ushers began emptying a vanload of cardboard packaging onto the verge. The vicar even got in on the act by throwing some old prayer cushions into a hedge before pronouncing Andrew and Olive man and wife.

6 **THE MOST** valuable fly-tippage ever recorded was a pile of Fabergé Eggs dumped in a layby in St. Petersberg in 1912. The haul, worth over £85million, was owned by Tsar Nicholas II, who decided to get rid of them during a clear out of the attic at his Winter Palace. The notoriously thrifty Tsar asked his treasury ministers for 35 Roubles to hire a skip, but took care of the matter himself that night and pocketed the cash.

7 **ILLEGALLY** dumping your rubbish is cheaper than hiring a skip, but you could be hit with a hefty fine, as council officials often go through fly-tipped refuse looking for material that will point to the perpetrator. "For this reason, make sure you pick through your crap first to take out any addressed envelopes, utility bills and prescriptions etc," says Money Saving Expert Martin Lewis.

8 **POPULAR HBO** series *Game of Thrones* filmed a scene where the character Jon Snow, played by Kit Harrington, was ordered by The Maester to clear out a storeroom at Castle Black and dispose of everything properly. In the sequence, rebellious Snow loaded the contents of the room, including old barrels, broken chairs and mouldy sack cloth, onto a cart and dumped everything in a wood on the other side of The Wall. As one of the most popular characters in the series, Snow was seen as a role model for many of the show's young fans, and *GoT* producers worried that his actions would set a bad example. After a meeting of the show's producers the scene was cut and replaced with some sex.

9 **THE SMALLEST** man ever to be prosecuted for fly-tipping was Calvin Phillips who, in 1986, was caught by police dumping a Tonka truck full of tiny flat-pack wardrobes that he had ripped out of the dolls' house where he lived. Despite the pile of illegally dumped waste being smaller than a shoebox, the fine imposed on Phillips by Cardiff magistrates was of normal size – £800, plus 200 hours community service.

L₁ Y₄ T₁ I₁ P₃ P₃ I₁ N₁ G₂ ... FLY-TIPPING

10 ONE YORKSHIRE couple loved fly-tipping so much that they held the christening of their first child whilst illegally dumping some old floorboards and two mattresses in woods near Osset. Janet Soupspoon held her baby and the godparents made their pledges while husband Frank dragged the wooden planks from his transit van and lobbed them into undergrowth. And, after making the sign of the cross on the baby's forehead to welcome him into the family of Christ, the vicar helped Frank drag the heavy mattresses into the bushes.

11 IF YOU are caught fly-tipping in Germany, you may be accused of 'Fliegenkippen'. On the other hand, you may not. That's because Fliegenkippen is the literal Google translation of 'fly-tipping', whilst for all we know the Germans may in fact have their own colloquial terms for the practice, such as bad dumping ('schlechtes Dumping') or dump and run ('dump und lauf').

12 SCIENTISTS believe that by the year 2050, the practice of fly-tipping will have changed beyond all recognition. Gone will be the white Transit van pulling into a layby in the middle of the night to offload a couple of settees and a fridge. Instead, silver hover vans will glide silently to a halt before offloading a couple of settees and a fridge behind a crater on the Moon, or perhaps even Mars.

13 TOP OF the list of most popular items fly-tipped by Britons comes old carpets, closely followed by broken chairs, old washing machines and builders' rubble. Down at the bottom of the list comes jewels, gold bars and bags of cash.

14 A FEW adventurous people like to combine their love of fly-tipping with another activity closely associated with laybys and secluded spots – *dogging*. Dog-tippers dump their rubbish before watching a couple engage in sex in the back of a Vauxhall Astra. Or they may indulge in sex in the back of their now empty van, inviting other dog tippers to watch while masturbating in their trousers.

15 PUT DOWN the word FLYTIPPING on a scrabble board and you'll get a respectable 21 points. And if the F or the Y sit on a double letter score, you can make that 25. If the word spans the triple word square, you'll bag 63, and using all your letters in doing so will get you a bonus 50 on top, making a game-winning 113 points. However, fly-tipping is actually two separate words, albeit hyphenated, so it's not allowed.

16 A COUPLE from Newcastle loved fly-tipping so much that, when Stan Cheesehole passed away, rather than bury or cremate him, his wife Edna decided to have him fly-tipped. Mourners gathered down a dirt track in Plessey Woods to celebrate Stan's life. And whilst the local vicar read a eulogy, undertakers dragged the coffin out of the van along with a pile of grass cuttings, some roofing felt and 24 square yards of perished carpet underlay, and pushed them all in the bushes.

17 WHEN scientists at Oxford University conducted research into illegal waste dumping throughout the United Kingdom, they found that laybys with a sign saying "No Fly-tipping" were equally likely to contain illegally dumped material as those with no signs. The researchers concluded that all fly-tippers are in some degree illiterate.

18 IF ALL the illegally dumped waste in the UK was gathered together in one big fly-tipped pile, it would need a white transit van the size of Rutland to move it all, and a layby the size of Wales's Gower Peninsula to dump it in.

19 IN CONTRAST to rubbish that is fly-tipped in the countryside, refuse that is disposed of responsibly is dealt with

under the government's UK Managed Waste Strategy scheme; that is to say, it is taken away by local authorities and dumped in the countryside.

20 BY AN extraordinary coincidence, as well as describing an offence under section 33 (1)(a) of the Environmental Protection Act 1990, both "fly" and "tipping" are words connected to restaurant waiters and soup. A "fly" is what you might complain about after finding one floating in it, whilst "tipping" is the awkward process of adding a small gratuity to your bill in the hope that no-one wanks in it next time you visit.

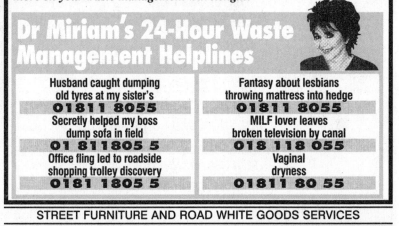

STREET FURNITURE AND ROAD WHITE GOODS SERVICES

ALLOTT OF NOOKIE!

THANKS to the recent flu pandemic affecting fruit and veg growers, fresh produce has been in short supply in recent months. And with no sign of any improvements to the currently unreliable supply chain in sight, British families are currently facing the prospect of a shortage of fresh produce.

But one Doncaster allotment holder says the Coronavirus food shortages have led to a nookie bonanza for him. According to **GORDON EGGBOUNDS**, 58, empty supermarket shelves have meant a bumper crop of MILFs at his shed door, all eager to do whatever is necessary to keep their larders stocked with fresh produce from his allotment.

"The local birds will do anything to get their hands on my fruit and veg," Eggbounds told his local newspaper *The Mexborough Infarction and Embolism*. "And believe me, when I say anything, I actually *mean* everything."

"I mean all the stuff you see on the mucky videos. Not that I've ever seen any mucky videos. They don't do anything for me, those sorts of things," he added.

> *Goodness only knows what the other allotment holders were thinking as I led this yummy mummy in her short skirt and high heels down the path alongside the coldframes.*

Spring to Attention

Gordon first got lucky in the Spring, when his bumper crop brought him an unexpected nookie harvest that was beyond his wildest expectations. He told the paper: "I'd grown a load of winter kale, and there was far more than me and the wife could eat. Me and the other allotment holders normally swap our excess produce, leaving anything we don't want in a box by the gate as a sort of honesty system."

> As I was digging a trench to put some onions in, I heard a woman's voice shouting, 'How much do you want for the kale?' I put down my fork and wandered over to the gate, where a very attractive woman in her early thirties was eyeing up my leafy greens. I recognised her as one of the mums from the local primary school across the road, who I had occasionally seen from my shed.

I explained to her how the allotments barter system works, with the members taking a bunch of kale out the box and leaving me half a dozen apples or some runner beans, for example. The woman looked at me imploringly. 'I don't grow anything in my garden, but surely there's something I can give you in return for some kale,' she said, doing that face that the women do in the mucky films, probably. I wouldn't know, as I've never watched one.

Anyway, it was obvious what she was suggesting. My wife Doris and I have a very modern, open relationship, and I didn't need asking twice. Goodness only knows what the other allotment holders were thinking as I led this yummy mummy in her short skirt and high heels down the path alongside the coldframes and into my shed to complete the transaction.

Obviously, I'm too much of a gentleman to reveal exactly what I got in return for that kale, but I will say this; we both left that shed extremely satisfied, thirty seconds later.

Mucky Business

News of Eggbound's earthy allotment transaction must have quickly got round the local school-run mums, and it wasn't long before the local women were beating a path to his shed door in a bid to get their five-a-day. He told the paper: "Word had clearly got round the Mexborough school gate MILFs that I would let them get fresh in return for my greens, and there was often three or four of them a week offering me how's-your-father."

> In March, I'd had a particularly big crop of early-sprouting broccoli; I'd dug a load of pig shit into the trenches, and it had come up a treat. There was loads of the stuff, and we don't eat much of it at home because it makes Doris fart, so I put a load of it in the trade box by the gate. I was just relaxing with a couple of cans, when there was a knock on my shed door.

I opened it to find one of the local mums stood there in a leopard skin mini-skirt and fishnet tights. She looked like something out of a contact magazine, not that I've ever seen one. Some people probably buy those sorts of things, but not me.

'I was just looking at your thick-stemmed broccoli in the box by the gate,' she said. 'You can't get it in the supermarket, so I was wondering if perhaps we could come to some sort of arrangement…' Her words trailed off as she fluttered her false eyelashes, seductively. Heaven knows what the other allotment holders thought if they saw me inviting this shapely siren into my shed to complete the transaction. Their suspicions would have been confirmed just moments later, when they saw the whole shed rocking for a good half minute to 45 seconds.

Gone to seed: Eggbounds' gardening experience led to him laying more than simply turf.

Honesty is the breast policy: Gordon's allotment honesty box attracted the interest of the local yummy mummies.

Shed for figures: Gordon's allotment shed doubled as a luxury shag pad.

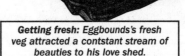

Getting fresh: Eggbounds's fresh veg attracted a contstant stream of beauties to his love shed.

I'd had that much action in there recently, that I'd moved the compost bags away from the back wall and put an old mattress down instead. Despite the smell of turkey manure fertilizer, which is very difficult to get rid of, it was a proper Casanova's boudoir.

That was a bumper crop of broccoli and let me tell you, by the time I'd got rid of it all, I was weak at the knees and my back was going. **"**

Green Tops and Fingers

As the spring rolled on and Gordon continued to reap his carnal harvest, he unexpectedly fell foul of the allotments committee. He told the paper: "There's a big waiting list for these plots, and they're very particular about you keeping the weeds under control. And I was spending too much of my time on assignations in the shed and not enough keeping the dandelions at bay.

" I got a letter from the committee telling me that I had a week to clear the weeds from my plot, or I'd be asked to give it up. Well, I didn't want to lose my allotment, as with Doris on the hormone tablets due to her flushes, my produce-based transactions in the shed were the only way I could slake my sexual thirst. I determined to

In the sack: Compost wasn't the only thing that Eggbounds 'bagged up' up in his allotment shed.

spend a whole day getting my allotment spick and span again, ready for the committee's inspection.

However, I'd only been going with the Dutch hoe for five minutes when I heard voices from the gate. It was a pair of busty MILFs, on their way back from the school run. One of them was wearing a tight leather mini-skirt and a boob tube, whilst her pal had a bright red, skin-tight spray-on dress. They explained that they had just heard that Sainsburys was out of potatoes, and they desperately needed some as they were both making bangers and mash for tea.

As luck would have it, I'd got more spuds than I knew what to do with, because I grow them in car tyres, adding another tyre full of muck each time the leaves reach the top to encourage more tubers. They were both giving me those 'come to shed eyes,' so I gave them each a couple of pounds of King Edwards, and invited them into my larchlap boudoir to complete the transaction in the customary manner.

They were both giving me those 'come to shed eyes,' so I gave them each a couple of pounds of King Edwards, and invited them into my shed to complete the transaction in the customary manner.

It's only a six-by-four, and half of it is taken up with 50lb bags of blood, fish and bone, so our threesome orgy was a little cramped to say the least. But even so, it was the most mind-blowingly erotic sixty seconds of my life. As I lay on the mattress in the afterglow of our triste, exhausted and spent, the yummy mummies pulled up their clouts, grabbed

their spuds, and left. As I listened to their high heels clattering off down the path, I was left wondering if the whole erotic episode had merely been a dream. **"**

A Blow For a 'Snip

Gordon may have wondered if he had been dreaming, but he was brought back down to earth with a bump a few days later, when he arrived at the allotments to find another letter from the committee pinned to the door. He told the paper: "It said I'd failed my final plot inspection, and even worse than that, someone had complained that I'd been using my shed for immoral purposes."

" I resolved there and then to lodge an official appeal with the committee. Unfortunately, I got a bit sidetracked because I'd arrived at my shed with one of the primary school mums off the local estate. She'd seen a recipe on a TV cookery show the night before for parsnip soup. But they'd sold out of that particular root vegetable in Morrisons, so she'd come down to my allotment to see if I would swap her half a dozen for a blowjob.

Well, my wife hasn't given me oral pleasure since back when she had her own teeth, and I can't stand parsnips. I was only growing them because I'd got a packet of free seeds on *Gardeners' World* magazine, so it was a win-win situation for me. And I must admit that during that next minute-and-a-quarter of sensual oblivion, my problems with the allotments committee went completely out of my head. **"**

Turn-ip for the Boobs

Gordon's life for the past three months had been a heady whirlwind of lust and vegetables. He told the paper: "Honestly, if Casanova had had an allotment, he wouldn't of had more nookie than me. And anyway, he was in Venice, and they probably don't have allotments there."

" But little did I know that my sex harvest was about to fail. I was at it in my shed with a busty blonde who wanted some turnips to mash, when suddenly the door burst open just as I hit the vinegar strokes. I turned to see two coppers, who were eyeing up the woman I was in the middle of doing on my mattress. They seemed to recognise her.

'Get your knickers on, Roxy,' they said. 'You're going for a ride.' Although the police seemed to know her, my yummy mummy certainly didn't seem very pleased to see them. In fact, she gave them a right mouthful of four-letter language that I hoped she didn't use in front of the other mums' kids at the primary school gates.

I had to go with them in the car to make a statement at the station, and while I was there they accused me of paying a prostitute for sexual services. I pointed out that I was entirely innocent, as no money had changed hands, just turnips.

However, I had a final plot inspection due that afternoon, so I was keen to get back and weed my beds before the committee came round, so I admitted eighteen specimen offences, and accepted a caution so I could get back to my allotment. But it was all in vain, as they said my neglected plot was likely to spread weeds and pests to other allotments. I knew it was just sour grapes, as for years they'd all been jealous about the size of my veg. My recent romantic trysts in my allotment shed had merely given the excuse they needed to trump up the charges and get rid of me. **"**

NEXT WEEK: Crust Lust. Gordon sets up an artisan bakery in his garage, and swaps fresh bread for hot sex with the local mums while his wife is at the bingo.

27

CAN THE WOKE TAKE

ASK any upstanding Brit to name their favourite day of the year that isn't Christmas Day, Boxing Day, Easter Sunday, St George's Day, Valentine's Day, New Year's Eve, Halloween or their birthday, and you'll get the same answer every time: *April Fools' Day*. Or Pancake Day.

April 1st is the wacky 24 hours in which we are permitted – or even *encouraged* – to play good-natured pranks on our nearest and dearest. And from Land's End to John O'Groats, this traditional day of merriment makes every one of us proud to be British.

Well… perhaps not *quite* every one of us.

For the humourless, virtue-signalling, liberal elite, PC Brigade, snowflake remoaner **CELEBS** would have you believe that April Fools' Day is an offensive archaic custom.

These toffee-nosed 'woke' A-Listers are intent on sucking the fun out of every great British tradition – be it eating meat, driving fast cars or pursuing lengthy campaigns of thinly veiled racial abuse through the tabloid press. And as such, it would be no surprise if, this year, the 'elf-n-safety'-obsessed showbiz loony left wanted to cancel April Fools' Day altogether.

Ask any sane person and they'll tell you: *it's political correctness gone MAD!* April Fools' is our last bastion of Englishness – a glorious comedic ritual that dates back to the building of Stonehenge – and we at *Viz* are not going to sit idly by and let it be trampled into the dust by a load of pompous fucking hypocrites in their elitist Hampstead bubbles.

So we sent our award winning investigative reporter, **MAHATMA MACAROON**, undercover to play a few cheeky, light-hearted April 1st japes on the UK's highest profile snowflakes – to see if these sanctimonious stuck-up arseholes **REALLY** consider our National Day of Laughter a step too far.

See what Mahatma uncovered when he asked the question… *Can the WOKE take a JOKE?*

BY **VIZ** UNDERCOVER REPORTER
MAHATMA MACAROON

WOKE CELEB No. 1: *Gary Lineker*

NOT satisfied with regaling us with his opinions about football on *Match of the Day*, Lineker feels the need to be a political pundit too. In the run up to Brexit, he forced his opinions down our throats on his Twitter feed, informing us that we made the wrong decision in deciding to leave Europe. He would most likely say that the 17.6 million people who like a giggle on April Fools' Day are also wrong. So I set out to prank him and give him the chance to join the fun.

Arriving at Lineker's Leicestershire mansion at 4:00am, I take a jemmy and quickly pop open the window of his downstairs bathroom.

Lifting the plush, soft-close lavatory seat, I fix a piece of invisible clingfilm over the bowl, stretching it tight before lowering the seat and climbing back out into the garden.

At 5:30am, I hear someone enter the bathroom and, judging by the silhouette cast on the window, I guess that it is Lineker himself.

The thought of the former England captain standing at his toilet with urine bouncing everywhere has me silently rocking with laughter, and I hope Lineker will join in the merriment when he realises he's been pranked.

But instead of laughter, I'm greeted with sour, bad-tempered foul language. "What the f***ing…AARGH! F*CK!" I hear him scream.

I peep into the top window and see that rather than standing up for a number 1, the Leicester City number 10 had sat down for a number 2.

The sight of Lineker stumbling round his bathroom in a lake of urine with faeces smeared across his buttocks is one which would crack anyone up.

But not snowflake Lineker, whose bad temper at being the 'butt' of the joke simply has to be seen to be believed. Judging from his language, I would imagine the former striker would rather the EU legislate to stop British citizens playing such hilarious japes on each other. I take a couple of snaps of his chucklesome predicament on my phone and make my escape.

Lineker may famously have never received a yellow card during his playing career, but I'm afraid he gets a straight RED for Ungentlemanly Conduct from me.

WOKE CELEB No. 2: *Marina Hyde*

PRINT journalist Marina regularly uses her weekly columns to speak out in support of ILLEGAL immigrants, while simultaneously lambasting upstanding salts-of-the-earth like Nigel Farage, Boris Johnson and Rupert Murdoch.

But surely the *Grauniad* hack is not so blinded by 'wokeness' that she can't still enjoy a zany April Fools' prank?

I arrive at Hyde's sprawling north London mansion at 6am after stopping off at a landfill en route, where I've managed to procure four large seagulls using a baited sack.

These things go absolutely mental when they're kept in a confined space, so by the time I approach the journo's house, the noise – and stench – is overpowering.

As luck would have it, Hyde is in the shower as I creep round the back of her house, so I quickly jemmy open the bathroom window and shake the birds inside before slamming it shut.

I have to chuckle as I hear the terrified creatures flapping wildly around the small bathroom, knocking bottles off shelves and showering the place with their foul-smelling faeces as the startled Hyde – with shampoo dripping in her eyes – tries vainly to throw a towel over them. It's a delightful prank that anyone in their right mind would be thrilled to be part of.

Still giggling uncontrollably, I take a few pics on my phone of her flailing about, covered in feathers and bird droppings. Then I spray-paint the words 'APRIL FOOL!' in six-feet high letters across her front door, before leaping over the fence to await her ecstatic reaction.

But instead of the peals of laughter I was expecting, I hear only violent screams of terror over the incessant squawking and shattering of glass. Before long, they are joined by the sound of *sirens* as a troupe of police cars screeches into the columnist's street.

I simply can't believe what I'm seeing. Yet another miserable A-List snob has retreated so far up their own backside that they can't take a simple, well-intentioned JOKE.

I feel myself shiver with despair as I flee the scene. Hyde is very happy to make fun of our cabinet members week in, week out in her tawdry rag, but STOP PRESS: When the joke is on her, it's suddenly not funny!

A JOKE?

We put snowflake celebs to the humour test with light-hearted April Fools' pranks

WOKE CELEB No. 3: *Billy Bragg*

THE so-called 'Bard of Barking' has spent his three-decade so-called 'career' railing against such Great British Institutions as the Conservative party, *The Sun* newspaper and the National Front. As such, it would be no surprise to discover that April Fools' Day was next on Billy's humourless Marxist hit list. We have to ask: in the Trotskyite troubadour's 'New England', would our beloved April pranks still be permitted? It's high time we found out...

Having fled Marina Hyde's plush pad, I arrive at Stalinist Bragg's vast two-bedroom semi-detached Essex mansion just after 7am. Using my trusty crowbar, I quickly break into the downstairs loo and locate the bog roll.

I extract three extra-hot 'Scotch Bonnet' chilli peppers from my combat trousers, and, wearing thick gloves and protective goggles, I rub their scorching flesh vigorously across the first sheet of loo paper.

I can't help chuckling to myself as I clamber back out of the window: even a woolly liberal killjoy like Bragg will *surely* find this classic prank priceless. The look on the *Sexuality* singer's face when he realises he's been had will be an absolute picture.

Concealing myself out of view, I see the Bolshevik balladeer enter the bathroom and begin doing his business. When the job is done and it's time for the paperwork, he tears off the chilli-smeared sheet and crams it straight up his leftie arse.

I brace myself for the tinkling sound of joyous laughter... But none is forthcoming.

Instead, the comedy-phobic vocalist screeches in agony and begins writhing about frantically on the bathroom floor. "Oh f***! Oh Jesus! My a***! My f*cking arse is on fire!" Bragg shrieks, whilst clutching his, admittedly, inflamed-looking anus.

I shake my head in tragic desperation. Yet another high-and-mighty A-List snowflake so in thrall to the politically correct 'thought police' that they can't even enjoy a *simple practical joke*.

I'm so upset that I can barely hold my hand steady as I film Bragg on my phone as he thrashes about like a freshly landed pike.

Billy wowed fans with his 1983 hit 'To Have And To Have Not'. And when it comes to a sense of humour, we can clearly file this fun-sucking sourpuss firmly in the LATTER category.

WOKE CELEB No. 4: *James O'Brien*

SMIRKING, liberal-elitist radio show host James enjoys nothing more than mocking and taunting decent British Leave voters on his tawdry LBC talk show. But will *he* 'Remain' quite so smug when the joke is on *him*?

To find out, I arrive at the Brexit-loathing socialist's swanky Islington pad at 8am on April 1st. Shinning up the drainpipe in a balaclava and combat gear, I jemmy open the bathroom window and sneak inside.

Quick as a flash, I pluck O'Brien's toothbrush from its cup, and insert it – bristles first – into my rectum. I can't help chuckling as I slide the brush repeatedly in and out of my anus. This same cheeky prank will be being played in a million homes up and down the country today, and any normal, right-thinking Brit would find it *hilarious*.

After ten minutes of intense sphinctal swiping, I place the soiled brush back in its glass and hop out onto the window ledge to watch the comedy unfold. Moments later, O'Brien enters the bathroom, squeezes toothpaste onto the tainted brush and begins brushing his teeth. He freezes instantly as he realises something is wrong.

But rather than shaking his head and roaring with laughter at the delightful jape that's been played on him, the priggish snowflake grimaces, drops to his knees and begins vomiting into the toilet.

'What the fuck's happened to my toothbrush?!' I hear the horseplay-intolerant broadcaster howl between retches. Disappointment, fury and disgust course through my veins: clearly, this pompous snob considers the great British April Fools' tradition *beneath him*.

I snap a few pictures of James puking on my iPhone and then slide back down the drainpipe, disappointed, but not surprised.

O'Brien made his name as the celebrated author of the book 'How To Be Right'. But in his ultra-woke hatred of April Fools' Day, he's proven himself dead WRONG.

WOKE CELEB No. 5: *Hugh Grant*

PLUMMY-VOICED 'actor' Grant famously failed to see the funny side when some cheeky journalists light-heartedly hacked his mobile phone a few years ago. While most Brits would have found this show of interest flattering and endearing, the pathetic *Four Weddings* snowflake ran sobbing to his lawyers.

But is the floppy haired A-Lister really SO lacking in humour that he can't appreciate a good, old-fashioned April Fool...?

Having made my escape from James O'Brien's house, I arrive outside Hugh's elegant Surrey homestead at around 9.30am. My spies tell me that the *Mickey Blue Eyes* icon is as regular as clockwork and will be sat on his thunderbox at 9:37 exactly.

I've brought an illegal Chinese firework the size of a bucket that I plan on popping through his bathroom window whilst he's dropping his morning fudge, a rib-tickling slice of tomfoolery that would put a grin on even the most miserable leftie's face.

But I must have dropped my jemmy whilst fleeing the scene of my last prank, so I am forced to light the enormous pyrotechnic and pitch it straight through the glass.

The ensuing flashes, bangs and screams are absolutely hilarious, and when the floppy-haired *Notting Hill* fave comes tumbling out of the broken window, trousers round his ankles, I expect him to be bent double with mirth.

I snap a pic of him collapsed on the ground in what I assume is hysterical laughter, and shout 'April Fool!'

But instead of joining in the fun, the thin-skinned thespian launches a furious four-letter tirade in my direction. Within seconds, he is on the phone to the police, and yet again I'm left shaking my head in disappointment as I hightail it into the surrounding woodland.

Hugh keeps his fans rolling in the aisles with his humorous performances in comedy films. But when it comes to the funniest day of the year, this conceited spoilsport doesn't want to know.

But what should have been an enjoyable day of fun, laughter and practical jokes is about to turn into a nightmare.

I am approached by police in the woodland near Grant's house and, unable to speak for laughing, I explain that the 'firework attack' they are investigating was merely a light-hearted April Fools' prank.

However, the police don't seem to find my practical joke funny and I am arrested on some trumped up charge of causing actual bodily harm.

I simply cannot believe my ears. The plague of politically correct 'wokeness' has apparently now spread beyond our ivory-tower-dwelling arsehole celebs and into Britain's police force. *It's nothing short of a national tragedy.*

As they search me back at the station, the joyless coppers examine my phone, looking for evidence of various 'crimes' that have supposedly been committed against a string of celebrities this morning.

I try to explain that these were all good-natured April Fools' japes, too, but the whiny wet blankets won't listen to reason, and I am charged with three counts of assault and five counts of voyeurism. Unbelievable.

Britain is officially broken, ladies and gentlemen. And make no mistake... it was the 'woke' wot broke it.

NEXT WEEK: Posing as a doctor, Mahatma gives the stars a full, physical examination to EXPOSE the secret bodies they are trying to hide from us beneath their clothes.

CLUNESIUM

SCIENTISTS were excited this week to announce that jug-eared funnyman **MARTIN CLUNES** may in fact be the next element to make an appearance in the Periodic Table of Elements.

The scientific chart, originally produced in 1869 by Russian chemist Dimitri Mendeleev, categorises all of the atomic building blocks which make up the fabric of our universe. Since its conception, scientists have added to the table as new elements have been discovered and classified according to their properties, and it is thought that the *Doc Martin* actor is set to be the latest addition.

tissue

Clunes, 58, recently went to his GP for a routine checkup, during which a small section of tissue removed from a small mole on his neck was sent to a laboratory in the east Midlands. The results confirmed that Clunes was as fit as a fiddle, but found that a small proportion of the *Men Behaving Badly*

EXCLUNESIVE!

star's flesh was in fact constructed from an element that had never before been seen by scientists.

"It appears to be a previously undiscovered alkali metal with the atomic number 119," said Professor Tibor Tsakaz, head of the Nottinghamshire laboratory that carried out the tests.

"Up until now, this has been a theoretical element, appearing on the Periodic Table as the placeholder 'Unununennium'," he continued.

"Now, we will finally be able to give it a permanant name – Clunesium."

"Though scientists had assumed it was only a matter of time before element 119 was discovered, none of them expected to find it hidden within Martin Clunes, who is most famous for playing Gary Strang in nineties sitcom Men Behaving Badly," Professor Tsakaz added.

"We're always thrilled to discover a new element," said Dr Adrian Street, head of Chemistry at Nottingham Baths University. "These days we usually only discover superheavy elements synthetically through nuclear fusion, so to just find one sitting there in the skin of the actor and dog enthusiast Martin Clunes is a real treat," he continued.

attendant

Clunes said he was excited to discover that he is the source of a brand new chemical element. "Everyone has always said that I've got a funny face. But I never thought it was because it contained an element that has more in common with the Group-1 metals rubidium, caesium and francium with a single electron in their s-orbital," he quipped.

And he said he was thrilled that his

119
?
Clunesium

In his element: Clunes excited to be at heart of scientific breakthrough.

name would now sit on the Periodic Table for all time. "It's quite an honour to think that the atomic structure of my own flesh is a legacy that will see my name remembered for hundreds of years to come," he told us. "And that's something that my iffy 2009 remake of The Fall and Rise of Reginald Perrin was never going to do, so that's something at least."

MAJOR MISUNDERSTANDING

DJ '20

Panel 1: ...YEAH, ON MY WAY HOME NOW, LOVE. I GOT A GREAT BARGAIN AT B&M'S... / ...A BIG SET OF SAUCEPANS FOR EIGHT QUID!

Panel 2: SWERVE! / JESUS! / MEE YOW!

Panel 3: CRASH! CLANG! CLATTER! / WAH! / CLING! CLANG! CLONG!

Panel 4: AAH, OH GOD! CAN SOMEBODY CALL AN AMBULANCE? / I THINK MY LEG IS BROKEN!

Panel 5: FOR CHRIST'S SAKE, PUT A SOCK IN IT. / STOP PRETENDING THAT YOUR INFANTILE POSTURING IS A TRIBUTE TO THE NHS.

Panel 6: IF YOU REALLY WANT TO SHOW YOUR APPRECIATION OF FRONTLINE WORKERS, A FEW MOMENTS OF RESPECTFUL CLAPPING WOULD DO. / ALL THIS BANGING OF POTS AND WEARING NOVELTY HATS IS SELF-INDULGENT SHOWING OFF!

Panel 7: I DON'T GIVE TWO HOOTS IF YOU'RE FEELING A BIT BORED! / JUST PUT UP WITH IT! SHOW A BIT OF BACKBONE, FOR CRYING OUT LOUD!

Panel 8: HOW HARD CAN IT BE TO SIT QUIETLY IN YOUR OWN HOUSE FOR A LITTLE WHILE? / SLAM! / YOU'RE NOT BEING ASKED TO GO OVER THE TOP IN THE BLOODY SOMME!

Letterbocks

Viz Comic, P.O. Box 841 Whitley Bay, NE26 9EQ : letters@viz.co.uk

ONE of my goldfish has an uncrimped turd twice his own body length trailing from his arse. In human terms, that's the equivalent of roughly 12 feet of continuous shit being dragged around. I think we underestimate fish.

Peter Busby, Australia

IT'S estimated that on any given day, 300 million people have it off. But with the world population at approximately 7.2 billion, I calculate that to be only a 4.1666%, or about 1/20, chance that it will be me. Are any other readers able to check my maths to see if that's correct? With odds like that, it's no wonder my missus had been keeping me at arm's length for so long.

Barry Bunting, Queef-upon-Sea

ORCHESTRA conductors make me sick. They want to be centre stage with all eyes on them while they're waving their arms about, but they make sure that everyone can see that all the musicians are reading from the music in front of them. That way, if they fuck up, they can always blame the orchestra and say that someone wasn't reading the music correctly.

Billy Rattle, Looe

WE are told in the Bible that when Samson got all his hair cut off, he lost all his strength and wasn't even tough any more. However, most of the bouncers I see outside clubs have heads like billiard balls, and they're supposed to be nails. Either the Bible was lying or bald doormen are a bunch of soft-arses masquerading as hard men.

Newton Spermetre, Squared

THANK you for the calendar that was given away free with the December issue of *Viz Comic*. Would it be possible, on next year's, to print the day on which I should put out each bin in my area, including garden waste and recycling? I would write them in myself but I've lost the leaflet.

Al, Rotherham

No problem, Al. Rest assured that all subsequent free calendars in Viz will include the general, recycling and garden waste bin collection dates for the Rotherham area. And that's a promise.

STAR LETTER

WHEN the peasants were revolting during the French Revolution because they had no bread, surely the aristocrats could have given them all the crusts that they would likely have cut off their sandwiches. A little thought would have saved a lot of bloodshed, and may have changed the entire course of history.

Andrew Wordsworth, Sunderland

I FELT badly let down by Sir David Attenborough the other night, when he was marvelling at some species of insect that spits at its predator during an attack. Well, I don't know about him, but I've always found spitting to be a disgusting habit and nothing to be applauded. And my kids were watching too. Bad show, Sir David.

Sally Pokewhistle, Crewe

I DON'T want to rock the boat, but surely women should go through the womenopause, not the menopause. And I'm not sure what menstruation is all about either, as men have absolutely nothing to do with it.

Grovis Plumsack, Scarborough

LATE week, I came home to find my wife in tears, and visibly shaken. I asked her what was wrong, and she told me all about the climate crisis and humanity's impending doom. However, I explained to her that it won't directly impact us, but will instead devastate the society of our children. After that, she calmed down and we were able to laugh the whole thing off.

Chris Crumbs, Ballymena

ON page 8, Bertrum Hubris suggested that increasing the count from three to ten before lifting patients in medical dramas would add to the suspense, and I think he has inadvertently hit upon something. In the real world, the NHS could apply the opposite and lift on the count of two. This would potentially reduce treatment times by a third and therefore resolve the current NHS crisis without the need for an empty slogan on a bus.

Steve Cooper, Newmarket

IN *Carry on Up the Khyber*, when Sir Sydney Ruff Diamond (played by Sid James) dictates a letter to Queen Victoria, he refers to her as Empress of India, and then signs off by sending his best wishes to Prince Albert. Well, any twat knows that Albert died in 1861, and Victoria didn't become Empress of India until 1877. Come on, you can't fuck about with history like this.

Lucy Worsley, Hampton Court

IF Lord Sugar has a face like a ballbag, then I certainly don't want to see his actual ballbag. I can't even begin to imagine what it looks like, which is probably a very good thing.

James Wallace, Belper

I WAS watching a video the other day of a honey badger scrapping with a pride of lions. It then went on to tackle a python, then have a go at a couple of jackals. They're right little brick shit-houses, honey badgers are. Our piss poor normal badgers, on the other hand, never get in a dust-up with anything. In fact, they wait until everything else is in bed before coming out and getting squashed on the A55.

David Houghton, Wigan

THEY say that plastic takes millions of years to decompose, but I bought a cheap nylon canopy for my garden swing off Amazon last summer and the thing has already fallen to bits. Come on, boffins, which is it?

Odd Skodheim, Notts

I WAS relaxing to a jazz flick the other day, and as the male thespian launched his spendings all over an obliging young lady, for some reason he loudly groaned the phrase "Fandabidozi." Luckily, I had already shot my bolt, otherwise the incongruity of this exclamation and its setting would have ruined it for me.

S Arsecandle, Llareggub

Top Tips

CREATE your own thick-sliced bread by supergluing two pieces from a medium-sliced loaf together.
Michael Thompson, Wales

PILOTS. Eliminate the chances of birdstrike during take-off by attaching a scarecrow to your nosecone.
Desulphdaz, M'brough

DOCTORS. Coma patient still not responding to treatment? Try turning the life support machine off and then back on again.
John Mason, email

CONVINCE colleagues that you're David Tennant by doing a little grimace at moments of high drama at work.
Tilly Turner, Salford

POSTIES and couriers. When delivering a parcel, please give ample time for the recipient to wipe their arse and get down the stairs.
John Elton, email

ATTACH mesh bags of differently coloured flour to the buttocks of everyone at a social gathering. Then when someone farts without owning up, the colour of the pump cloud will identify who supplied it.
2Tone, Ipswich

GHOSTS. If you want to be believed in, stop hanging around ruined castles and only coming out at night. Try a Lidl or IKEA on a Saturday morning.
Maz, Peebles

INCREASE the fun at family gatherings by putting a whopee cushion on Grandma's chair. And a little gravy in the bag makes a convincing 'follow through'.
Martin, Tamworth

toptips@viz.co.uk

THE other day, I was in driving along listening to the news on the radio when I glanced at my odometer and saw the mileage was reading 2112. Just then, the newsreader announced the death of Rush drummer Neil Peart. My blood ran cold as I thought of the title of the band's 1976 seminal concept album *2112*. Had I been a great fan of the band, I might have thought this was some kind of message, but I never really liked them that much.

Edgar Cottonbobbin, Truro

ON police shows, I don't know why the chief always says, "You've got twenty-four hours to crack this case." Surely it would be more realistic if they told them to crack it by "a week on Tuesday" or "the weekend after next." When my lawnmower got nicked out of my shed recently, the fuckers didn't even show up for a fortnight.

Miles Perhour, Derby

WHY is it that whenever James Bond is in a casino he is always at a card table, playing for high stakes against his nemesis? Doesn't he ever fancy having a go on the slot machines for a change? For starters, he wouldn't have to get all dressed up, and he would be less likely to piss off some super-villain and get his bollocks burnt off with a laser beam. Unless Mr Blofeld or whoever had been shovelling money into the bandit all night, only for Bond to drop the jackpot on his first pull.

Hector Dolittle, Leeds

I LOVED it when Doug McClure used to make films where he battled crap monsters at the centre of the earth on a Sunday afternoon. Why doesn't he make them any more? I would definitely watch them, if it was raining or I was poorly.

Terry Farricker, Blackpool

I KNOW the late astronomer Sir Patrick Moore is credited with finding loads of stars. But with the eyebrows he had, I often wonder how many of those finds could be attributed to a speck of dandruff getting on the telescope lens?

Percival Lowell, Luton

I WAS looking over my wife's shoulder when she was logging in to her bank account, and her password was just a series of asterisks. I didn't count them, but I'm sure, after two or three attempts, I'll be in there. Stupid cow.

Brian Petrie, Carnoustie

I'D love to see an episode of *It's A Knockout* featuring our current shower of politicians as competitors, with the disgraced Stuart Hall as presenter, and the full complement of Pan's People performing risque dances between rounds. But it probably won't happen though.

Johnny T, Kirkcaldy

THE only animals I know of that are black and white are zebras, penguins and badgers. But surely that can't be it, there must be more. I didn't know who to write to about this, so I just thought I'd try here.

Willy Balls, Banbury

✳ *Well we're afraid you've come to the wrong place, Willy. Our readers may know of a few black and white animals, like magpies or those tropical fish, and could perhaps write in and tell us. But we think you'd probably do better writing to BBC Wildlife Magazine or Zookeeper Monthly.*

A LOT of the Netherlands is below sea-level, so pretty much everything there is lower than everything else around it. Consequently, there is no need for health and safety regulations on Dutch building sites, because it's possible to fall off a ladder and end-up higher than you were when you fell. That's just how negative numbers work.

Mark Glover, Coventry

WHEN I'm in the doctor's waiting room, I like to pretend I'm a contestant on *The Price is Right*. When my name is called out, I firstly look very surprised, then immediately jump up, waving my hands in the air and screaming enthusiastically as I trot off towards the surgery.

Tony Claassen, Nott'm

EVERY Christmas, I watch *The World's Strongest Man* on TV. I have to admit that these muscle-men's sphincter control never ceases to amaze me, especially after all those sprouts they've had over the festive period. In all my years of watching, I have yet to see a competitor follow through.

David Houghton, Wigan

I'M no ecologist, but rather than people moaning about the deforestation of the Amazon, perhaps if they started planting a few of those Leylandii trees to even up the balance, then there wouldn't be a problem. My neighbour put some in and those fuckers shoot up like a fucking rocket.

B Twelves, Hull

THEY say an iPhone has over 100,000 times the processing power of the Apollo 11 guidance computer. The thing is, my phone has barely enough power to last me a full day at work, let alone blast me off to the fucking moon. Come on, boffins. Check your sums.

Max Quayle, Isle of Man

ROAR FEAR!

IT SEEMS that *Viz* readers are terrified of being attacked by lions, and you've been writing in your hundreds to tell us all about it. Here are a few of the best letters we've received.

EVER since I saw the film *Born Free* as a little girl, I've been terrified of being ate off a lion. Consequently, I avoid all places where I might come into contact with them, such as zoos, safari parks and African savannahs.

Edith Creamhorn, Bude

I'VE been attacked by lions twice – once when one escaped from a zoo that I was visiting, and again when my car broke down in a safari park and I foolishly got out and started tinkering under the bonnet whilst eating a sausage sandwich.

Frank Underwear, Luton

ALTHOUGH extremely dangerous, lions are quite easy to escape from. If you encounter one, remain calm, turn slowly and start to run. If the lion begins to catch up with you, simply run a little faster.

Chester Zoolander, Hull

I DON'T know why they are referred to as the 'King of the Jungle'. If a lion got hold of you, it would rip you to shreds without a thought – hardly regal behaviour in my book. I can't imagine her Majesty the Queen tearing her subjects limb from limb when she meets them on her walkabouts.

Ingrid Sewerage, Deal

I CUT the grass at my local safari park, and I've been mauled by lions more times than I care to remember. Admittedly, it's terrifying the first time it happens, but you soon get used to it.

Hector Boardwalk, Hull

WHEN attacked by a lion, you will be perfectly safe if you kick it in the bollocks. If it's a lioness attacking you, however, she won't have any bollocks to kick her in, which makes the female of this species far more dangerous than the male.

D Attenborough, London

I'M absolutely terrified of lions… and I work as a zookeeper! Fortunately, however, I just take care of small mammals, like wallabies, capybaras and those stupid looking rat-like things from the adverts that sit on their hind legs. My colleague Stan does the lions as he's not scared of the fuckers.

Barry Turtle, London

37

HENRY VIII 2020 AD

We name 6 modern day wives for randy Tudor monarch

2020 marks the 500th anniversary of the twelfth year of the reign of King Henry VIII, the fiery Tudor monarch who changed the face of Britain forever. Although he was responsible for the Dissolution of the Monasteries, the 16th century religious schism that drove a wedge between the Holy Roman See and the Church of England, Henry is best known as a serial fanny rat who married 6 times. His wives were drawn from a fascinating variety of countries, cultures and backgrounds, and each one illuminates a different fascinating aspect of Tudor history. *But if Henry were on the throne today, who would he choose as his six wives?* It's time to take a look at the half dozen modern day celebrities to whom Henry VIII would plight his mercurial troth, if he hadn't been dead for 473 years.

Wife Number One

BACK in 1509, the young Henry married Catherine of Aragon, Spanish-born widow of his dead brother Arthur, and mother of "bloody" Mary, Queen of Scots. This was the Tudor monarch's longest marriage, lasting nearly 24 years until Henry divorced the staunchly religious Catherine just three weeks short of the couple's silver anniversary. So for the King's twenty-first century opening marriage, he will be looking for a family-orientated, aristocratic homemaker with whom to establish his modern Tudor dynasty.

Henry could do much worse than taking Channel 4 *Location, Location, Location* presenter **KIRSTY ALLSOPP** as his first bride. Daughter of a some Duke or other, Kirsty has the blue blood that a Tudor monarch like Henry is looking for, and her ability to craft household decorations on a shoestring – as seen in shows such as *Kirstie's Handmade Treasures, Kirstie's Handmade Christmas* and *Kirstie's Celebrity Craftmasters* – would prove an invaluable asset in Henry's royal household, meaning that the profligate monarch wouldn't have to raise taxes every time he wanted a war with the French or a new palace.

However, such a marriage of royal convenience may well begin to falter over the years, as Kirsty's TV commitments filming shows such as *Kirstie's Fill Your House for Free* tempt her to spend more and more time away from the marital four-poster, and Henry may well feel jealous of the time his consort spends with her on-screen partner Phil Spencer. Just as it did with his 16th century wife Catherine of Aragon, his marriage to TV's Queen of Crafting would inevitably hit the rocks and end in an acrimonious divorce.

Wife Number Two

IN 1533, following his divorce from Catherine of Aragon, Henry took his second bride Anne Boleyn. Anne's father, Sir Thomas Boleyn, was an ambitious social climber who did much to engineer the liaison, seeing his daughter's royal marriage as a way to enhance his standing in Tudor society. And in many ways, US president Donald Trump is a twenty-first century equivalent of Sir Thomas, a vain moron, keen to promote his dullard offspring to prestigious positions of power.

Once installed on the throne as the lovestruck King's consort, **QUEEN IVANKA** would attempt to meddle in politics, making political enemies just like her predecessor did in the sixteenth century when she attempted to undermine Henry's Lord Chamberlain Thomas Cromwell. Ivanka would sit in on meetings about subjects that were beyond her intelligence, and barge her way uncouthly to the front as diplomats and statesmen posed for photographs, a trick learned at her boorish and charmless father's knee.

Eventually, the narcissistic King would tire of playing second fiddle to such a shallow, attention-seeking consort and seek a divorce from Ivanka. Although she would fare slightly better than her beheaded 16th century predecessor, in the same way that Thomas Boleyn sided with Henry at his disgraced daughter's rigged trial for treason, the US president would similarly throw his own daughter under the bus. In a series of badly spelled, ungrammatical tweets, the small-handed POTUS would point out what an *"unbelievable guy"* the Tudor monarch is, and how he has been treated very badly by his *"no good loser Queen. SAD!"*

Hen picked: Who would be Henry's partners of choice if he had his pick from today's celebs?

Wife Number Three

HENRY'S third consort was Jane Seymour, who had caught his eye as lady-in-waiting to his two previous wives. Jane gave Henry the son and heir that he craved, and the King was thrown into despair when she tragically died just nine days after giving birth to his sickly heir, Prince Edward. And in an ironic twist of fate, the front runner to be the late Queen's 21st century counterpart as Henry's third wife shares exactly the same name… actress JANE SEYMOUR!

The glamorous star of 80s potboiler TV series *Dr Quinn Medicine Woman* is well known as the face of Max Factor cosmetics, and Henry is quite likely to demand that she gives up her showbiz career to become his full time Queen. In this situation, Seymour will be faced with an uncomfortable choice between a life as a cosseted monarch or one as a busy A-list star of top-rated shows like *Franklyn and Bash*, *The Kominsky Method* and *Here Come the Double Deckers*, and the King's Royal edict to his third wife may well lead to a full-blown constitutional crisis.

Not only that, over her career Seymour has posed for raunchy photoshoots in top-shelf grumble mag *Playboy* three times, and her X-rated centrefold antics could reflect badly on the House of Tudor. If a well-thumbed copy of the magazine were to fall into the hands of her famously jealous 16th century husband, he might erupt into a violent rage, casting her out of his royal court and into shame and disgrace.

Wife Number Four

IN 1540, after the death of his previous wife, Henry sauntered up the aisle for the fourth time with German princess Anne of Cleves. The King had never met his bride before the service, and he was reportedly so disappointed by her plain, horse-like appearance and bodily odours that the marriage remained unconsummated; indeed, it was annulled after just six months. Half a millennium later, Brexit Party MEP ANNE WIDDECOMBE is a shoe-in to become Anne Widdecombe of Cleves, modern-day Henry VIII's fourth wife.

On his wedding night, and indeed thereafter, the randy Tudor monarch would almost certainly be unable to rise to the occasion in the marital bed when faced with the musty, cobwebbed contents of Anne's no-nonsense dunghampers. And if, by some miracle of mind over matter, he did manage to summon half a royal teacake in his codpiece, the famously chaste Widdecombe would almost certainly reject his amorous advances, probably delivering him a withering whack on the lid with a wooden spoon just to be on the safe side.

It would be clear to all Henry's courtiers that his new marriage to the anti-European battleaxe was going nowhere, and the highly-sexed King would have no choice but to give up on his chaste new bride. His fourth marriage would be annulled by the Archbishop of Canterbury shortly afterwards, as surely as night follows day.

Wife Number Five

CATHERINE Howard was a busty and curvaceous teenage saucepot when she caught the eye of the now ailing and bloated King Henry. After their hurried marriage, the King found himself unable to keep up with her insatiable sexual demands, and she quickly took a string of younger, more virile lovers. The blow to Henry's pride proved too much, and Catherine and her string of randy paramours were sent to the block to pay the ultimate price for their impetuousness. Her place today could be filled by any of the plastic-titted women off LOVE ISLAND.

Any one of the low-rent show's randy, scantily-clad female competitors would surely catch the shallow, sex-starved monarch's eye and quickly accept his offer of marriage. However, on their wedding night, when faced with the wheezing, ague-riddled monarch's pustulated legs and weeping sores, their thoughts would wistfully turn back to the hunky fellas - male models, oilrig workers and failed *Hollyoaks* actors - that they had left behind in their tropical reality TV paradise.

The affairs would soon begin, and when Henry saw the humiliating stories plastered across the covers of *Chat, Heat* and *Take a Break*, perhaps whilst opening a newsagents shop, his famous Tudor temper would explode, just as it did with Catherine half a millennium before. And this time there would be no stay of execution – the King would use his influence with ITV2 management to take an axe to the entire series.

Wife Number Six

TWICE-WIDOWED Catherine Parr was not so much Henry's sixth wife as his nursemaid; the Queen's principal duties in his bedchamber extended little beyond applying ointment to the weeping sores on the King's legs and changing his dressings. Indeed, so grateful was His Majesty for his wife's gentle attentions that he only threatened to have her beheaded once or twice. And a modern day counterpart who could ably fill Parr's courtly shoes is *Coronation Street*'s AUDREY ROBERTS.

Like Catherine, Audrey, played by actress Sue Nicholls, is a widow, after her husband Alf tragically died in a chair at her grandson Nicky Tilsley's eighteenth birthday party. And with her years of experience caring for a fat husband in his autumn years, Audrey would make an excellent nursemaid for the ailing, overweight Tudor monarch. Indeed, back in 1984 Sue actually played the nursemaid in a TV production of *Aladdin* – alongside Johnny Morris and Terry Nutkins as Widow Twankey and Wishee Washee. This medical training should stand her in good stead when attending to her ailing royal husband, as open, pustulating sores will hold no horrors for her.

Audrey has appeared in *Corrie* on and off for the past 40 years, starring in nearly 3,000 episodes of the Weatherfield-based soap, so she's clearly the kind of person who sees a job through to the bitter end, and it's safe to assume that the same would be true of her Royal marriage. And when the King finally succumbs to his medical conditions brought on by years of over-indulgence, she would no doubt take the opportunity to hook up with a succession of elderly *Coronation Street* suitors, such as Nigel Havers, Johnny Briggs and Roy Hudd.

44

Let's Look at... The Intern

YOU CAN'T get a job without experience... and you can't get experience without a job. It's the Catch-22 situation that faces everyone looking for work these days. And it's the reason why *INTERNSHIPS* have become the norm in many spheres of our economy.

These non-paying positions allow new workers to gain valuable on-the-job experience, whilst giving employers the chance to see how potential recruits fit into the workplace before making the commitment of offering a full-time job; it's a win-win situation. So let's visit a typical London advertising agency and follow an excited young intern from his first day at work...

JULY 1980 Tom Golightly graduates from a top Humberside University with a degree in Media Studies. This is the first step on his dream journey to becoming a top advertising executive - the career he has always dreamed of. He knows that the advertising world is a notoriously competitive one, but with a first class honours degree in his pocket, he has a head start, and is confident his £57,000 student debt will quickly be paid off once he becomes a top earner in the lucrative world of advertising.

SEPTEMBER 1981 After a year of job-hunting, during which time Tom applies for over 1,800 positions, he finally catches a break. He gets an interview at Filch, Purloin and Steel, one of the most creative ad agencies in London, and is offered a 1-year internship. Of course it's an unpaid position, but that doesn't matter; it comes with a promise of possible permanent employment and perhaps - eventually - even a partnership at the company. Tom has taken his first step on the ultra-competitive ad-business ladder.

OCTOBER 1981 It's Tom's first day on the job, and he arrives bright and early at the ad company's swish Soho Square offices. His first task is to make the coffee for the high-powered account executives' meeting. He is then invited to sit in on the meeting to watch and learn. It is valuable experience that money simply could not buy, but the £10,000 his parents have given him from a cashed-in life insurance policy to cover his immediate living expenses will certainly help launch their son on his glittering career in the lucrative ad business.

DECEMBER 1981 For the last two months, Tom has been learning the craft of creating campaigns at the sharp end of the ad business. From reimagining the endings to films, reinterpreting jokes from magazines, and stealing plots from books by emerging authors, he is learning how to create powerful, persuasive advertising. His boss, Dan, notices that Tom has a talent for picking up on the latest trends and 'thinking outside the box'. He realises that his unpaid intern is shaping up to become a valuable asset to the company.

JANUARY 1982 Tom's initial 3-month internship is now at an end, and he is called in to see Dan. It's good news; everyone at the agency is so impressed with his performance, attitude and ability that they are offering to extend his internship for another 18 months. Tom jumps at the chance to develop his creative skillset even further. He knows that an extra year-and-a-half's experience at the sharp end of a top ad agency will give him a huge advantage when he eventually seeks paid employment in such a competitive field.

MARCH 1983 A position for a Junior Account Executive has opened at Filch, Purloin and Steel, offering a starting salary of £30k. With nearly 2 years' experience doing that same job at the agency already under his belt, Tom is hopeful that he will be the successful candidate, and he eagerly applies for the position. But it's an exceptionally competitive field, and after a 2-minute interview, the position is offered to Dan's son, Barnaby, who everyone feels will bring "a fresh perspective to the creative process".

JUNE 1990 Ten years in, and Tom's internship has been formally extended on a 'rolling basis'. Over the last decade, he has shown his worth to the company by creating a range of multi-million-pound ad campaigns. It's hard work, but with each year that passes Tom is making himself a more attractive prospect to future employers. His parents have now used all their savings to help him launch his career, an investment they feel will pay dividends when their son eventually lands his dream job.

OCTOBER 1996 Tom's boss Dan is taking early retirement and moving to a chateau in France, leaving the post of Senior Account Executive open. It's a high-flying role, but one in which Tom is confident he will shine. However, the board feel Tom lacks relevant management experience, and so the job goes to Dan's son, Barnaby. This leaves the Junior Account Executive post vacant. After 15 years at the agency, it will be a backward step, but at least Tom will be on the employment ladder. But the post goes to Barnaby's girlfriend.

FEBRUARY 2000 It's a new century, and Tom is feeling confident about the future. There have been rumours that the company is restructuring, and that he will soon be enjoying the fruits of his long internship. But then he is dealt a blow. He is called in to Barnaby's office and told that although the company is financially healthy, it's not quite yet in a position to offer him a permanent job. It's not all bad news; he is promoted to Senior Intern, a position which entitles him to a space in the company car park, not that he can afford to run a car.

APRIL 2006 Barnaby suffers an injury in a jet-skiing accident in the Maldives and is off work for 6 months. The board ask if Tom, as Senior Intern, will step in and cover for him while he recuperates. It's a golden opportunity for Tom to show the board at Filch, Purloin and Steel what he is made of. Under his stewardship, the agency wins high-profile contracts with, amongst others, a global drinks company and a Japanese car maker. As a result, Tom's boss Barnaby is given a prestigious advertising industry award at a plush dinner hosted by Jimmy Carr.

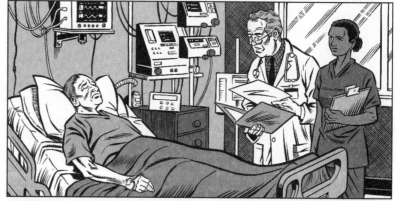

JUNE 2010 Tom recovers from a stress-induced heart attack, and his doctor advises him to take a break from work. However, his boss, Barnaby, foresees problems. Not being on the payroll, Tom is not entitled to statutory sick leave or any kind of benefit whatsoever. Moreover, although his boss is sympathetic, he is running a business, not a charity, and he tells Tom that there are many people out there looking to improve their chances in the job market, hungry for an internship like his. Tom stays at work.

JULY 2010 Barnaby also suffers a stress-induced heart attack, and his doctor advises him to take early retirement. Tom has recently completed an evening course and earned a Masters in Business Administration, and this, coupled with his 30 years' intern experience, makes him hopeful of stepping into his boss's shoes. But the company chief executive feels that some new blood is needed, and appoints Emma, a woman with a background in media and the arts, with whom he's been having an affair for the last 3 months.

JANUARY 2018 Tom requests a meeting with his new boss, Emma, to discuss his career prospects and a more permanent position. His parents have released the equity on their house in order to continue kick-starting his career, and he feels the time is right for him to be paid for the work he does. Emma explains that the market has been sluggish lately, and he must be patient. There are indications of an upturn in advertising spend amongst big companies, and she hints that another position may be available very shortly.

MARCH 2020 The big day has finally arrived, and Emma calls Tom into her office. She tells him that all the board are impressed with his work over the past decades, and they want to make him a permanent - and more importantly, a *paid* - member of staff! He will start as a tea boy - a very junior role on the minimum wage - but he is still jubilant. He finally has a foot on the first rung of the job ladder and the world at his feet. His employment contract is being drawn up and will be ready for him to sign the following week.

MARCH 2020 It's a day of double celebration for Tom, as it is both his 61st birthday and the day he finally becomes a paid employee of Filch, Purloin and Steel. But a phone call brings bad news. The Covid-19 epidemic has seen ad revenues plummet as firms tighten their financial belts, and an underling at the agency tells Tom he is being furloughed with immediate effect. Two months later, he receives a call saying the company has gone into receivership, and thanking him for all his work over the past 40 years.

20 GREAT WAYS TO KEEP YOUR SPIRITS UP DURING LOCKDOWN

WHILE we all try to avoid catching Covid-19, we're faced with the daunting prospect of spending an indeterminate amount of time holed up in our homes. Some experts fear we could all be stuck indoors with our families and away from our loved ones for up to a year, or even longer.

In an attempt to buoy up our spirits via social media, celebrities have posted jolly videos of themselves similarly self-isolating. But their houses are much nicer than ours, with expensive furniture, tasteful carpets and fresh paintwork. So their valiant efforts to cheer up the public have only left us feeling even more miserable about the long period of enforced quarantine that is presently stretching out in front of us.

But we must not despair. We should look upon this period stuck indoors as an opportunity to spend as much time as we want doing all the things we never normally have the time to do… the things that ordinary life and work get in the way of. So here's…

1 ...Read

WHEN we were young, we all spent endless hours reading, engrossed in swashbuckling tales of pirates on treasure islands, eccentric detectives hunting down ruthless criminals, or brave astronauts fighting aliens on faraway planets. But as we grew up, the opportunity to lose ourselves in the world of fiction was overtaken by the mundane, ordinary tasks of everyday life; shopping, taking out the rubbish, walking the dog. This new virus lockdown gives us a never-to-be-repeated opportunity to rediscover our love of literature and lose ourselves once again in the limitless world of our imaginations. Even better, if you're quick you can probably get a reasonably clean copy of James Herbert's *The Fog* and a box of tissues delivered to your door for about two quid.

2 ...Write

OR why not *write* a book? It's said that we all have at least one good book in us, although anyone who's ever read any of the shit that Jeffrey Archer has written will probably disagree.

3 ...Train your pets

TRAIN your pets to do tricks. It's a well known fact that animals need mental stimulation; a domestic pet stuck indoors with nothing to occupy its mind will quickly become destructive, chewing through table legs, slippers and electric cables out of sheer boredom. So, while you're stuck indoors, why not spend some time teaching your animals some of those tricks like that woman used to do on Cruft's every year. And if your pooch can already sit, lie down, beg and die for the Queen, teach it to ride a bicycle, juggle or smoke a pipe.

4 ...Learn an instrument

IT IS said that it takes a solid 12,000 hours of practice to play an instrument properly, and a year stuck in the house – in between trips to the supermarket to fight over bog roll – gives us all the ideal opportunity to put in that time and become a concert stage virtuoso. If you don't have a piano, trumpet or violin, make yourself a drum kit out of pans and wooden spoons, or wire up an old tennis racquet to make a Jimi Hendrix-style electric guitar.

5 ...Break a record

THERE are thousands of amazing achievements commemorated in the *Guinness Book of Records*, and twelve months of enforced leisure gives us all the opportunity to secure one of these coveted honours for ourselves. Obviously, during the lockdown period some records – for example, the ones for tap-dancing round the BBC Television Centre fountain, the world's longest Conga dance or the most people cramming themselves into a telephone box – will be out of our reach. But many will be possible to break in the comfort of your own home, such as the one for eating the most hard-boiled eggs in half an hour, the one for growing the longest toenails, or the one for going the longest without wiping your arse.

6 ...Exercise

MANY of us splash out hundreds of pounds each year on expensive gym memberships, but a year spent trapped in our own homes with no access to cross-trainers, leg presses and running machines will mean we will have to make other arrangements to keep ourselves fighting fit. Try weight-lifting with your furniture, or run on the spot until the bloke in the flat downstairs comes up for an ad hoc 'boxercise' sparring session.

7 ...Grow your hair

THE ENFORCED break from work will enable men to grow a giant beard in the style of Grizzly Adams or Terry Waite, whilst women will have the once-in-a-lifetime opportunity to cultivate a fanny that looks like Ken Dodd's tickling stick or Germaine Greer's fanny.

8 ...Cook

A YEAR stuck indoors will force us all to be much more creative in the kitchen, using the few ingredients we can find in the supermarket and the back of the cupboard to whip ourselves up something tasty and nutritious, *Ready Steady Cook*-style. Who fancies a tin of peaches, boiled into a casserole with Maxwell House coffee and dried onion gravy? Or how about a past-its-sell-by-date Christmas pudding topped with a swirl of Marmite and three crushed Foxes Glacier Mints out the bottom of a duffel coat pocket for dessert? Delicious!

9 ...Make models

PRISONERS OF WAR in Colditz were famed for fashioning elaborate architectural models from matchsticks, and whilst trapped in our houses due to Coronavirus, we could all do the same. Depending on how long the pandemic lasts, and whether it's still possible to get matches a fortnight from now, we could find ourselves building anything from a fiftieth-scale model of Anne Hathaway's House in Stratford upon Avon to a detailed, life-size copy of the Petronas Towers in Kuala Lumpur.

10 ...Fix things

WE'VE ALL got a few broken appliances lying around that we were once planning to repair. Maybe you have an old toaster that's blown a fuse, a hoover with a snapped drive belt, or a wireless set that went on the fritz back in the 90s. With a whole year to kill, there's never been a better opportunity to get out your toolbox and have a tinker. Just remember not to let the red and the brown wires touch each other, and have fun.

11 ...Learn a new language

INTERVIEWED by Andrew Marr at the start of the Covid-19 crisis, Stephen Fry said that he intended to spend the enforced lockdown period learning the international language of Esperanto. So why not do the same as the famously erudite *Jeeves & Wooster* star? By the time the all-clear is sounded, you and Stephen will be able to hold a halting, stilted conversation about Esperanto with a handful of other linguists scattered around the world. Or, to put that another way, *"Vi kaj Stephen povos teni emfaza konversacio pri Esperanto kun kelkaj mil aliaj Weirdos tutmonde."*

12 ...Do impressions

SITTING in the house with the same two or three people to talk to for the thick end of a year is enough to drive anyone up the wall, so why not keep yourself sane by pretending to be someone else? Spend a day being your favourite movie characters, such as practically perfect Mary Poppins, hilariously nutty Mrs Doubtfire, or eccentric caretaker Jack out of *The Shining.*

13 ...Throw a ball

THROW a ball against the wall and catch it in a big glove. Just like Steve McQueen in *The Great Escape,* this is a fantastic way to keep yourself entertained during a long period of enforced isolation. If you haven't got any baseball equipment in the house, use an old onion and an oven glove.

14 ...Learn to tattoo

WHY NOT take this enforced break as an opportunity to teach yourself tattooing? When we all emerge from quarantine, the economy will have collapsed and there won't be any jobs anyway, so re-training yourself as a gonzo-punk tattooist might be a great career move. If you buy yourself a machine off the internet and practise doodling skulls, bloody daggers and mermaids with big tits on your own legs and those of your family, you'll find yourself in great demand in the dystopian, *Mad Max*-style future that is waiting just around the corner.

15 ...Listen to Popmaster

LISTEN to 'Popmaster' on the Ken Bruce show. It's on Radio 2 for about a quarter of an hour at half-past ten, five days a week; so that's 0.7% of your quarantine time taken care of, although a good five minutes or more of that is a record and that interminable bit where the contestants say hello to a big list of all their fucking friends and families, and everyone out the fucking darts team at their fucking local.

16 ...Blow glass

IF YOU have a furnace, some sand, and a length of pipe, you could teach yourself to blow glass. There are plenty of informative instructional videos available on the web, and after a year indoors you'll end up with countless beautiful, translucent vases for your mantelpiece.

17 ...Paint

IF YOU have oil paints and some brushes, you could exercise your artistic skills. Pick a topic, such as 'Man's Inhumanity to Man' or 'The Spanish Civil War' and paint yourself a colourful mural across the living room wall. Really let yourself go and express your innermost emotions; don't be afraid to slap the paint about with wild abandon. If you don't like what you've created once you've finished, simply paint something else over it, for example a load of soldiers charging into battle on horseback in the Boer War or the Last Supper. If you can't do horses' legs or hands, make it a Jackson Pollock-style abstract.

18 ...Solve maths problems

EVERYONE'S heard of the famous conjecture Fermat's Last Theorem, but someone's already worked that one out. Luckily, there are many other abstruse mathematical theories that still require proofs, and with so much time on your hands, it's the best opportunity you'll ever get to throw your hat into the mathematical ring and have a go. If you concentrate really hard, you might come up with a copper-bottomed proof for the Four Exponentials Conjecture, the Invariant Subspace Problem, or solve Lyapunov's Second Method for Stability in Dynamical Systems. And you never know, thinking so hard about sums might even take your mind off your itchy ringpiece.

19 ...Cut your own hair

BARBER'S SHOPS and hairdressers will be out of bounds for the foreseeable future, so we'll all simply have to knuckle down and cut our own hair. Nobody's going to see, so it's a great time to experiment with exotic styles. Ever wondered what you'd look like with Phil Oakey's asymmetric eighties fringe, a Kevin Keegan bubble-perm or a BBC Arts correspondent Will Gompertz's ventriloquist doll-style head-curtain? Coronavirus has provided you with a great chance to reach for the wallpaper scissors and find out!

20 ...Keep a diary

FINALLY, keep a diary. In years to come you'll be fascinated as you look back at all the adventures you got up to whilst sat in your fucking house for a year, watching Challenge TV between wanks with no food and nothing to wipe your arse on.

NEXT WEEK: 20 Ways to Celebrate in the short window between this lockdown and the next one.

LEAMINGTON SPACE

LEAMINGTON SPA Councillors this week unveiled plans to rocket into the record books as the first town in Britain to journey into space. And the town's planning committee have set an ambitious date of 2021 to get it done.

"It's time to put Leamington Spa on the map, and the way we've decided to do that is by sending everyone who lives here into space," said local councillor, Rilkie Balbatross. "Leamington has a population of 55,733, so getting everyone up there at the same time sadly won't be possible. We're currently in talks with NASA discussing the logistics of doing it in shifts," he added.

bylaws

The council plans to use the 2011 census to work through the various wards, allocating time slots to each household instructing them when to arrive at the Kennedy Space Station in Florida for their 90-minute flight into the thermosphere. And a loophole in local bylaws means that not going won't be an option, with anyone failing

EXCLUSIVE!

to make the journey facing a hefty fine, court summons or a visit from the bailiffs.

in-laws

At £250,000 per person, the ambitious project will set the town back over £13 billion, and councillors have warned that a hike in council tax rates of 4000% is on the cards. And the council's head of planning, Frank Margerine, confessed that all spending on urban development, maintenance and public services will have to be put on ice for at least 100 years.

"Everyone will have to feel the pinch," he told the *Leamington Spa Clarion and Trumpet*. "We'll have to shut down libraries, a few care homes and end school meals. But when we become the first town to take that one small

Warwickshire Spa town to bodly go where no Spa town has gone before

step, it will all have been worth it," he added.

Despite the massive financial implications, many residents were excited about the prospect of their town leaving the earth's atmosphere.

outlaws

"I'm really looking forward to it," said local resident Eric Fisticuffs. "As someone who left school at 14 to work in the local abattoir, I was honestly starting to think that my chances of becoming an astronaut and boldly going where no-one has gone before were almost over."

"So I'm over the moon," he quipped.

But not all were as excited about the venture, and there has been angry opposition to the idea from some residents.

"I'll be ruddy livid if they send me into space," said local florist Bunty Horsebasket, one of many embittered locals, who thought that being projected out of the Earth's orbit at 2485mph against her will was a step too far for a local council.

shake it all about laws

"I'm terrified of flying, and I can't say I'm relishing the prospect of being blasted 62 miles into the sky and forced to experience the sensation of weightlessness," she added. "I've got a shop to run."

And school crossing lady Edna Grumble, whose job is likely to fall under the axe, was equally unimpressed.

"They don't know what to waste their money on next," she told reporters. "Last year there was talk of building a 25-mile circumference Hadron Collider under the town and stretching as far as Kenilworth. Now this."

"If they've got money to send us all into space, they've got money to collect our bins weekly instead of fortnightly," Mrs Grumble added.

Town control to Major Tom: Spa residents to visit final frontier.

THE BROON WINDSORS

Viz Comic, P.O. Box 841 Whitley Bay, NE26 9EQ ∙ letters@viz.co.uk

I RECENTLY took an empty, unattended pushchair from outside a supermarket and I wheeled it into the canal. I think toddlers should be taught that they live in a cruel world, and a long walk home on barely developed little legs should help them to realise this fact.

Stuart Achilles, Wigan

COULD I introduce your readers to a wonderful game called Dungraiders, which is best enjoyed in a large office environment? It is played by two opposing teams from different departments, and the aim is for each side to stink out the other side's toilets. The current world champion is an anonymous solo-player who targets the gents' loos next to the staff canteen at a large research-oriented botanic garden.

Prof. Arthur Fflange-Cunnox, email

DURING my divorce hearing, my wife accused me of visiting prostitutes. Alright, she has me bang to rights on that one, but just because I paid them a visit doesn't prove anything. She regularly visits her Aunt Jackie, but do you see me throwing accusations around willy-nilly?

Torbjorn Golightly, Crewe

I DON'T know why everyone is always so complimentary about that Ghandi bloke. All I've ever seen him do is walk about in his underpants.

A. Cheesemonger, Hull

PEOPLE tell me that *Citizen Kane* is the best film ever made. But is it really? It doesn't have any CGI dinosaurs in it. Or any spaceships. And to make matters worse it's not even in colour! I think that's checkmate, film buffs.

Mark Wolstenholme, email

NOT that I know much about basketball or netball, but it seems to me that you have to be well over six feet tall to stand a chance of winning. Why don't they just make the hoops a bit lower, then we could all join in?

Toby Teitelbaum, email

THE LATE haute couture designer Alexander McQueen made his reputation as the creator of low-hanging 'bumster' jeans. But back in the early 1980s, we had a 20-stone bloke deliver some filing cabinets to our office, and his jeans were hanging down a good four inches below his sweaty arsecrack. I suspect that, unlike McQueen, he never got an OBE for services to UK fashion.

Brett Winnfield, Newcastle

LAST night I had a dream in which I fitted a dimmer switch, but it didn't work because we have fluorescent tubes in the kitchen. Could any reader who is a qualified electrician tell me if I was in any danger by doing this, and if it's possible I could have been electrocuted or started a fire?

Vincent Wallace, Tooting

FOLLOWING on from Mr Wallace's letter at the bottom of the column to the left of this, I read somewhere that if you die in a dream, you die in real life. This got me wondering if any *Viz* readers have ever died in a dream, and then woken up to find that they'd actually died in their sleep as a result.

Marcellus Vega, Boston

✱ *Have you ever died in a dream, and if so, did you also die in real life, or did you somehow manage to survive the experience? Write in and let us know if you survived, or if you died, get in touch by moving the glass on a Ouija board.*

TV channels are always saying that they "know their audience". Yet when I called the BBC Duty Office to complain about an episode of *Homes Under the Hammer*, they had absolutely no idea who I was.

Ian Dunkley, Stanmore

WATCHING the survival program *Naked and Afraid* has really opened my eyes to the level of determination and willpower some men have. If I'd just had a grandstand view of a naked woman with a lovely arse climbing a palm tree, I'd be straight behind the nearest bush for a quick J Arthur. The last thing on my mind would be building a fire.

Grovis Plumsack, Scarborough

BEES! Bees! Bees! That's all these so-called environmentalists bang on about. I honestly don't see why, as they are just fat wasps, and what's so special about that? Wasps are cunts, but at least they watch their weight. So bees are just fat cunts. And what's more, if they sting you, their arse falls off.

Paddy O'Furniture, Orkney

I HAVE to say, I was more than a little miffed when we left the EU at the end of January. Forty-seven years we were in it, and they didn't even throw us a bit of a leaving do. I was a welder for thirty-five years and when I retired, my mates gave me a set of golf clubs and threw me a proper piss-up. But we never even had so much as a card from Brussels. Good riddance to the fucking lot of them, I say.

Nigel Garage, Wells

I HAVE just discovered a great new bit of the nuts to be tickled – right at the back and top. Actually, I might have already known this and just forgotten. Either way, it's terrific.

Fang, Swansea

WEEBLE KNIEVEL

BBRRRM!

★ VIVA WE

★ VIVA WEEBLE KNIEVEL! ★

/A WEEBLE KNIEVEL! ★

CRASH!

YAY! WHOOP! YAHOO!

DON'T TELL ANYONE BUT HE'S ACTUALLY BEEN DEAD FOR TWO YEARS.

IF aliens from outer space have technology which allows them to travel millions of light years across different universes and to other dimensions, how come they always have lights on their spacecraft? Surely, travelling at such speeds and through time would make the ability to see the road ahead purely academic.

T.O'Neill, Glasgow

WITH reference to Mr O'Neill's letter (above). Surely, if these spaceships were travelling at the speed of light, then the light from their headlamps would never leave the bulb, as the spaceship would simply 'catch up' with the light as it was emitted. So it is utterly pointless fitting them. It's good to see that garage mechanics on other planets take the piss out of their customers too.

Hampton Crumbs, Deal

HI Hi. How is your mood? Nowadays, the pace of life is incredibly high. People do not set aside the right time in their life to relax. Our lovely female conglomerate intends to eliminate this injustice. We have many girls eager to meet esteemed gentlemen readers of your famous magazine. The girl you have chosen, on the first date, will not take anything from you except a glass of wine and a good mood. This is beginning of a beautiful collaboration. We also offer many ladyboy.

Crystal Aho Agency, Bangkok

I CAME across this cheeky chappy in Madeira. Unfortunately, I totally misinterpreted the service that was being offered and, needless to say, I'm now barred from that restaurant.

Ivan Edwards, email

I AM sick and tired of ticking the "I am not a robot" box on internet sites. It should be changed to "I am a robot", so that only robots need to bother with it, saving humans valuable time. It's why we built the bloody things, after all.

Toby, Swindon

WHILST getting ready in the morning, I find that Paul Simon's hit *Slip Slidin' Away* provides the perfect melody for singing "Shit, shower & shave."

Gav H, Hebden Bridge

FOOTBALL commentators often say "the shot was difficult because it was an acute angle." But the majority of shots are taken at an acute angle. In fact, the only time that a shot taken is taken at an obtuse angle is when the ball is within a minimum of 12 feet of the goalposts. Simple trigonometry of isosceles triangles will prove that these so-called 'experts' are idiots.

Mr Bowen – Maths tutor supremo – Worcester

✻ We think Mr Bowen means a maximum of 12 feet from the posts. If you are one of his pupils, perhaps you would like to point this 'schoolboy error' out to him. You may also like to give him some kind of nickname as a result of his mistake, and follow him down the corridors doing an impression of him whilst your mates all laugh.

I DON'T envy anyone living in any of the other houses on Downing Street. What with all those baying mobs of reporters and flashbulbs going off all day, it must be a right bastard trying to get a bit of kip if you're a shift worker. And you couldn't even drive home after a few pints because the Old Bill are always loitering about.

Barney Rubblesworth, Hull

WE'RE now all being encouraged to reduce our carbon footprints by cutting our consumption of red meat and dairy by 20%. It's hard to see how vegans are going to help much with this goal. Perhaps that might help wipe the smug, holier-than-thou smiles off their faces as they leave the real heavy lifting to us carnivores.

Phil Kitching, Isle of Jura

I'M not surprised that actresses in porn films always let jizz dribble out their mouths after performing a blowjob. I tried some of mine just now and, quite frankly, it's vile.

Dave Edwards, Bridport

IF Doctor Doolittle could really talk to the animals, as he claimed, why didn't he have a quiet word with them about not shitting and pissing all over the place?

Tex Harrison, Derby

I APPLAUD the lengths to which the marketing departments of motorway service brands, such as Roadchef and Moto, go to lure me in, with such varied shopping options as M&S, Gregg's, Waitrose and Burger King. Notwithstanding, I find that my choice of service station is usually based on needing a really urgent shit.

Adrian Newth, Stratford upon Avon

COULD your readers please advise me on the time of the day when you switch from being "still in pjs" to "already in pjs". It's been nine months since I lost my job, and I never know which excuses to make to the shopkeeper when I'm buying my whisky.

Anne Claire, Liverpool

WHEN I was at school, we made electricity by putting wires into potatoes, so why don't we just do that instead of building nuclear power plants? Completely renewable, plus I've never seen a spud have a meltdown.

Peter Queef, Braintree

PRIVATE *Eye* has been going since 1961, and its success has been due to its mix of highbrow humour and investigative journalism. If you want *Viz* to be as long-lasting, may I suggest dropping the fart jokes and replacing them with articles about corrupt council bin collection contracts?

Nick Haskell, Adelaide

WHY do people always talk about solar energy as a 'renewable fuel'? Our sun will go supernova and subsequently die in five billion years time at which point all the solar panels will stop working.

Ben Nunn, Caterham

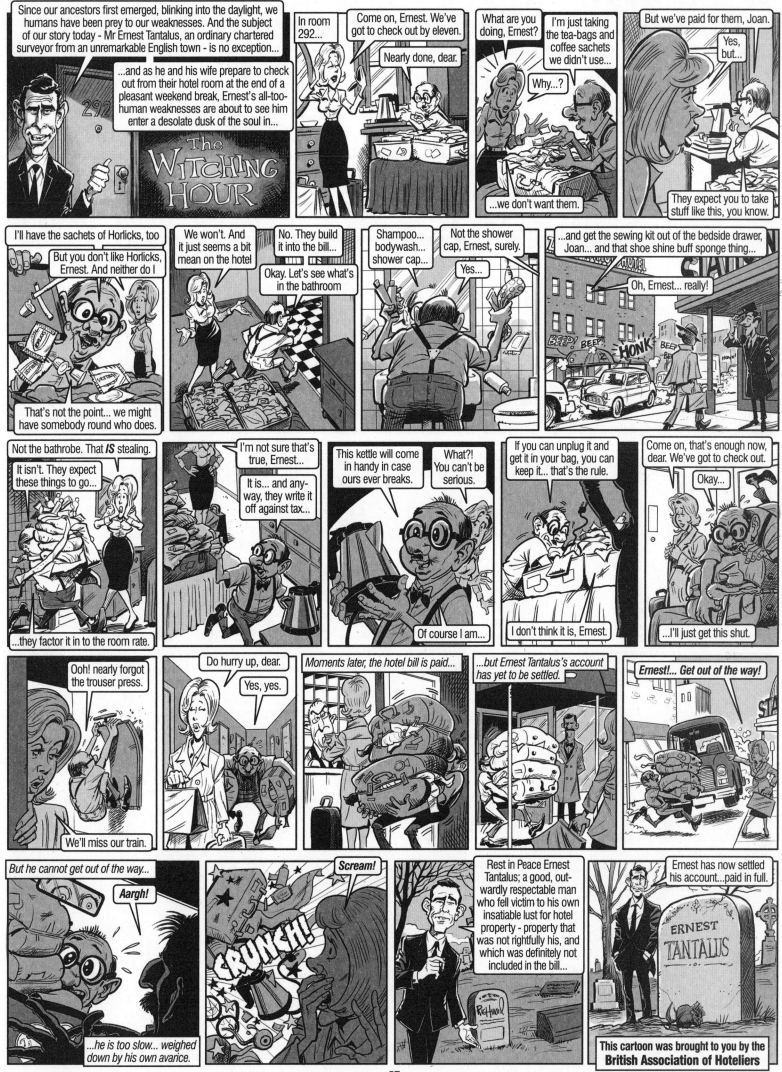

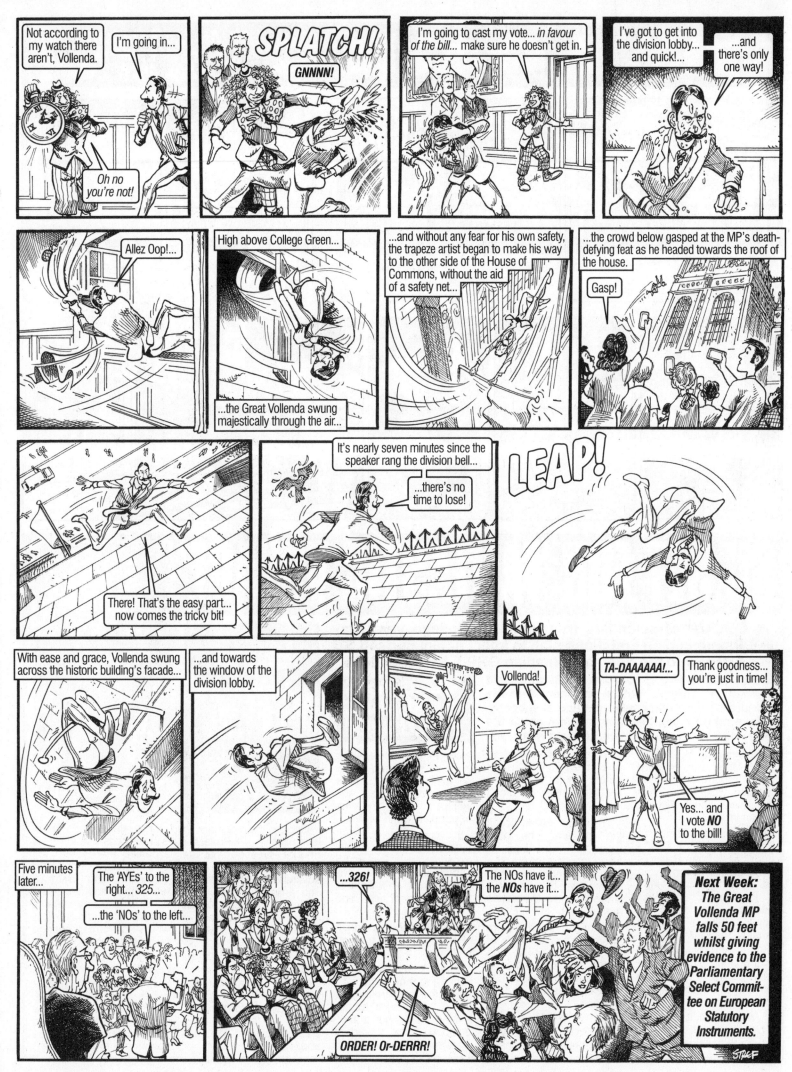

SU SET FOR 'FANTASTIC VOYAGE'

A GROUP of scientists from Imperial College yesterday announced an ambitious plan to inject a miniaturised SU POLLARD into the body of comedian GRIFF RHYS-JONES.

Group leader Professor Dinesh Bhugra said it would be difficult, but he was confident the venture stood a reasonable chance of success. "Make no mistake, this is an experiment at the very edge of our capabilities," he told reporters.

VIZ IS TOPS FOR SCIENCE EXCLUSIVES

"Miniaturising Su Pollard off *Hi-Di-Hi!* will be hard enough, but then injecting her into Griff Rhys Jones increases the difficulty exponentially."

When asked what ailment Rhys Jones was suffering from, and how Pollard's minuscule presence in his body might counteract it, Professor Bhugra was adamant. "As far as we know, Griff is perfectly healthy," he said.

"And with the best will in the world, I'm not sure what Su would be able to do even if he were ill," he added.

"We just think it might be a bit of a laugh."

The *Alas Smith And Jones* funnyman, 64, said that when the scientists asked if he'd like to take part in the experiment, he didn't think twice.

"I'm really excited about the project," he told reporters. "Su's been a friend for years, so I'm very much looking forward to seeing what adventures she gets up as she travels around my body."

"Perhaps she'll swim around in the contents of my stomach, or use one of the tiny bones in my ear to play my eardrum as if it were a real drum," he quipped.

waste

And Pollard, who played scatter-brained chalet maid Peggy Ollerenshaw in the hit 80s comedy show set at the fictional Maplin's holiday camp, said she wouldn't be letting the opportunity go to waste.

"I can't believe it! First I'll go in a special experimental electron compressor which will shrink me down to smaller than a grain of rice," she told reporters.

"Me! Smaller than a grain of rice!" she added, doing that face.

"Then I'll be dropped into Griff's ear, from where I'll make my way around his body. I can't wait to get a look inside his brain!" quipped the *Starting Together* hitmaker.

This little Peggy: Tiny Su (left) to make pioneering journey into Rhys-Jones (above).

Although it is a pioneering technique, Professor Bhugra stressed that he had no interest in how the advances in miniaturisation and insight into the workings of the human body might eventually have useful medical applications.

insyde leg

"I really cannot emphasise strongly enough that we are undertaking this project purely for the sake of it," he told reporters. "We're doing it for shits and giggles."

Since the human body is two-thirds liquid, it is expected that Pollard will be doing a lot of underwater swimming, and Bhugra's team have spent months developing a tiny wetsuit, flippers and snorkel into which Pollard can change once miniaturised.

When asked why she couldn't simply put on a normal-sized wetsuit before being miniaturised, Bhugra was silent for a few seconds, before getting up and calling the press conference to an end.

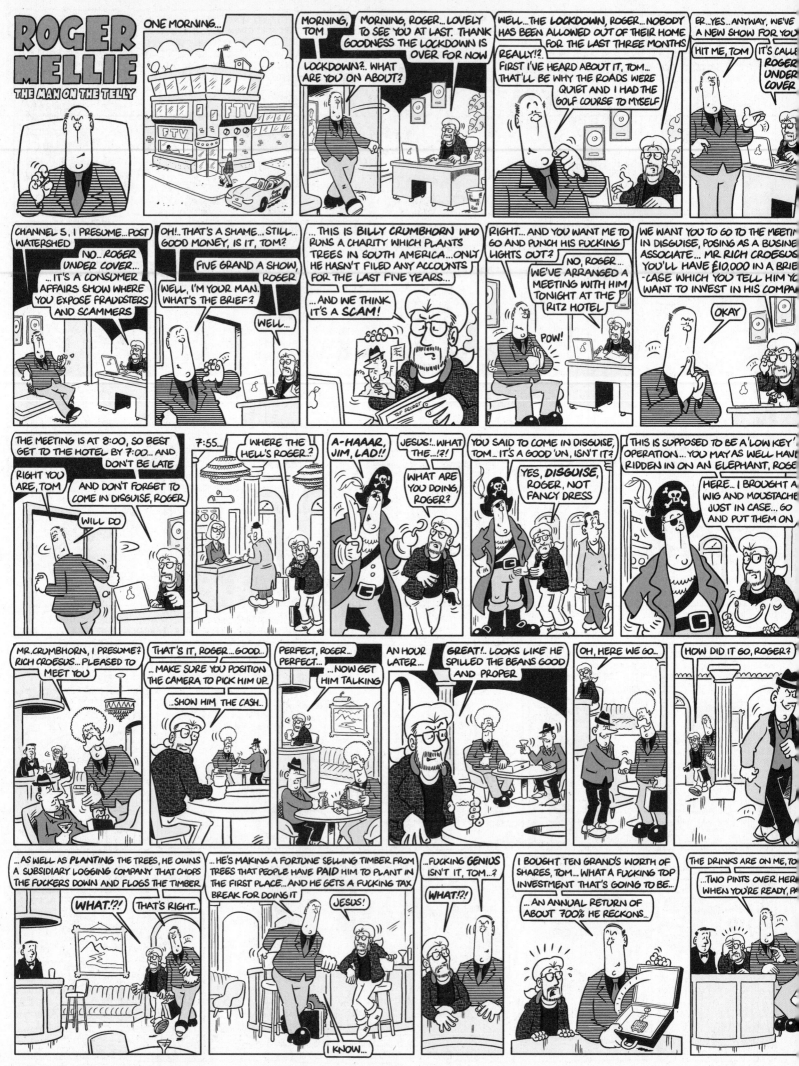

BULLSHIT CORNER

ON 25TH MAY, Downing Street advisor Dominic Cummings held a press conference in the garden of Number 10 to explain the misunderstanding around his breaking the Covid-19 lockdown rules. All was cleared up when reporters were told that what at first glance appeared to be a family jaunt to a local beauty spot on his wife's birthday, was in fact an essential eye test, permitted under the 'medical emergency' clause of the regulations.

Unfortunately, not everyone in Westminster is as truthful as Mr Cummings. We asked a selection of MPs if they had ever come up with an enormous pile of bullshit to cover their tracks when caught doing something they shouldn't.

Keir Starmer, *Leader of the Opposition*

WHEN I was shadow Brexit minister, one of my under-secretaries brought in a massive chocolate cake for all the staff in my parliamentary office to have at our morning coffee break. However, it looked so delicious that when no-one was looking, I sneaked into the stationery cupboard and scoffed the lot.

When it was discovered missing, I initially denied knowledge of it, but I had all chocolate round my mouth. Then somebody played the CCTV footage of me taking it from the kitchen area. I told everyone that I had a weird disease that meant I had to eat about 4lb of sugar mid-morning or else I could die. I told them I usually bring 4 bags of Tate & Lyle to work with me, but that particular day I had left them in my ministerial car. I said all this in a calm, measured, almost forensic manner, and although a few of my staff saw through the bullshit, most of them fell for it.

Liz Truss, *Foreign Secretary*

I WAS fed up with my neighbour playing his radio in the garden, so one night I poured some petrol on his shed and set it alight. It went up like a rocket! Unfortunately, he filmed me doing all of this on his mobile phone and went to the police.

When I was interviewed under caution, I told them that there was some bird shit on his shed roof and I was throwing some water over it to clean it off, only I had inadvertently picked up a petrol can instead of a watering can. I then said I lit a match to have a cigarette, but remembered that I didn't smoke and so threw the match over the fence. I don't think they believed me, but I reminded them that my friend was Home Secretary Priti Patel who could make life very difficult for them, and they took no action.

Hilary Benn, *Labour MP, Leeds Central*

I WAS clocked by the tit-heads doing 196mph up the M1 on my way back to my constituency. I told them that I had a pain in my right side which I thought might have been appendicitis, and I was trying to get to hospital before it ruptured.

The copper told me that I should have called an ambulance, but I said that I used my judgement and decided that stopping on the hard shoulder to make the call would have put myself and other road users in more danger than if I just floored it. He agreed and offered to escort me to the hospital with his blue lights flashing, but I told him that I was feeling much better now. They fell for it hook, line and sinker, and let me go, the stupid fuckers.

Jacob Rees-Mogg, *Con. MP, NE Somerset*

I ONCE stole a pornographic magazine from a newsagents in Claverton. I was looking for a copy of Country Life when I spotted the latest Razzle, drawn to it as my eye was by the naked ladies cavorting on the cover. I waited until the owner was preoccupied, selling a scratchcard to an old lady, before quickly slipping its glossy pages under my top hat.

However, as I approached the shop door, I was apprehended by a security guard who searched my hat and found the magazine. I explained that it was not for me, but for one of my constituents who was on his deathbed and wanted to flick through a grumble mag one last time before meeting his maker. Furthermore, I said that I was unable to purchase it like normal people because, being almost royalty, I never carried money upon my person. I don't think this excuse would work for anyone else, but I said it all in Latin, and he just called me a fucking halfwit and let me go.

ISLE OF MAN *FARCE*-TIVAL

Sound of silence: Festival revellers were outraged when The Quacks' frontman Gastap (left) apparently refused to sing chorus of hit song.

Festivalgoers demand refund as band frontman "stops singing"

MUSIC fans who attended the Isle of Man Festival have been left fuming and demanding their money back after Bernie Gastap, lead singer of rock band The Quacks, consistently went quiet during the chorus of the band's hit song.

The silence meant that festivalgoers, some of whom had paid hundreds of pounds for tickets, were forced to sing the chorus themselves whilst Gastap watched, smirking and holding his microphone out to the audience. Pop fan Danielle Harp, 22, who stumped up £350 for her weekend ticket plus hundreds more to travel from London to see the band, was left unimpressed.

"I stood through an hour of them playing dross from their new album before they finally got to their one hit single from 1977, Onion Lady," she told *NME*.

"The verse went as expected, but as the chorus came up, the lead singer suddenly stopped singing, held the microphone out and put his hand behind his ear."

Harp continued: "Everyone was a bit confused, but some quick-thinking members of the audience started singing the chorus themselves, and soon everyone else did too."

EXCLUSIVE!

"I thought it was odd that he could have forgotten the words after all the times he must have sung Onion Lady," said Craig Galbani, who had paid over the odds for black market tickets. "But we all make mistakes and I gave him the benefit of the doubt."

"But then the chorus came round a second time and Gastap shouted *'Everybody!'* which isn't even in the original lyrics, before going quiet again," he added.

"The worst thing is, when we were all doing his job for him and singing the song, he had the gall to shout *'I can't hear you!'* Galbani fumed.

"Talk about a brass neck."

onion

Alma Gumshoe, who travelled from John O'Groats to see The Quacks, was disappointed, but had no complaints about the other band members.

"The lads kept on playing throughout the song," she told *Mojo* magazine. "But I felt insulted when Gastap asked the crowd to do what he's paid to do. It's no way to treat loyal fans."

The band was eventually booed off the stage, and festival organisers were inundated with demands for refunds from disgruntled fans.

Many other fans took to Twitter to express their disgust, vowing never to buy a Quacks record again, not that many people have done since 1977.

And some said they would be taking legal action against the band under the Sales of Goods Act 1973, claiming that the service they had paid for had not been provided.

responsibility

Isle of Man Festival organisers released a statement, saying: "We apologise for any disappointment caused during The Quacks' performance. We have reminded all performing artists of their contractual responsibilities at the Festival."

But consumer champion Martin Lewis says fans should demand their money back anyway. "If you pay a brickie to build you a wall, you wouldn't expect to have to mix the mortar for them," he told us. "Clearly, fans paid good money to see The Quacks singing their hit song, and this service was not provided."

"The good news is that fans who bought tickets using credit cards can claim their money back from their card provider under Section 75 of the Consumer Credit Act," he added.

IT'S THE incendiary festive debate guaranteed to rent families in twain at every Yuletide dinner table: *Which is the Best Eve?* For some people, the only sensible answer is jobbing telly actor *TREVOR EVE*, who's kept us glued to the small screen since the late seventies with his thrilling performance as down-at-heel private eye, Eddie Shoestring. Others will vouchsafe that the real candidate for 'Best Eve' is *CHRISTMAS EVE*, the 24th of December on which families across the globe gather to sing carols, wrap presents and hang up stockings for Santa. Others still will violently insist that Trevor and Christmas cannot hold a candle to *ADAM AND EVE* - the apple-chomping Biblical nudists whose shameful expulsion from the Garden of Eden left mankind cursed with Original Sin.

But let's not have another festive season of bloodshed, with friends and families fighting tooth and nail over this age-old question. The year 2020 has brought nothing but chaos and despair thus far, and it would be a tragedy if it ended with a ruined Christmas. That's why we're settling the debate right here, right now: pitting these three evergreen Eves against one another in a six-round fight to the death to find out once and for all...

TREVOR WH

TREVOR

ROUND 1
Global Popularity
SUTTON Coldfield-born Trevor has enjoyed a long, varied and successful career on stage and screen. From 1979 to 1980 he won the hearts and minds of the nation by playing the titular dishevelled PI in much-loved TV series *Shoestring*. What's more, London Theatre Critics have twice garlanded Trevor with a Laurence Olivier Award for his West End stage performances. But this round explicitly states its focus is on *global* popularity - ask anyone if they've heard of Trevor Eve on the streets of Santiago in Chile, or Ashgabat in Turkmenistan, and you'll be met with a blank stare. Trevor's recognition has come almost exclusively from the UK, meaning the moustachioed thespian gets off to a bad start. **Score 1**

ROUND 2
Nudity
While we can assume that Birmingham-reared Trevor was born naked - and still regularly removes his clothes to bathe or fornicate - there is scant evidence of him appearing 'au naturel' in the public eye. The *Shoestring* fave's lengthy filmography features absolutely no full nudity, and while he did perform a sex scene in the 2010 ITV drama *Bouquet of Barbed Wire*, strict Ofcom regulations meant that you could see neither his cock, balls, arse nor perineum. It's another disappointing score for the mostly-clothed board treader. **Score 1**

ROUND 3
Apple Consumption
A cursory Google search for the query, *'How many apples has Trevor Eve eaten in his life?'* drums up precisely ZERO results. While some might argue that this is simply because it's a ludicrous question that no one would ever ask, others might see it as part of a sinister cover-up that goes all the way to the top of the British fruit industry. Let's be clear: we are not saying that Trevor Eve is chronically addicted to apples and he is bribing Google to muzzle this shameful secret - but we are also not NOT saying that, either. It's only fair to award half marks here to the potentially-apple-infatuated actor. **Score 5**

ROUND 4
Angering God
 **With guest judge AB of C Justin Welby** "As far as I know, God has no problem whatsoever with Trevor Eve. In all my years conversing with the Almighty, I've literally never heard Him mention the guy. This could mean that God likes Trevor Eve, He is ambivalent about him, or He has never watched *Shoestring* and so doesn't know who Trevor Eve is. Either way, He's certainly not angry with Trevor. Trust me, when God's angry about something His wrath is so mighty as to maketh the mountains shake and the seas to boileth. It's another low scoring round, then, for the moustachioed *Death Comes To Pemberley* ace." **Score 0**

ROUND 5
Mentions in Bible
Having not read The Bible from cover to cover, we cannot say for sure whether Trevor Eve features at any point or not. However, even the most recent books of the New Testament were written sometime around the first Century AD, which is almost two millennia before the *Waking The Dead* star was born. Of course, we cannot rule out the possibility that of one of the gospels predicted the coming of a moustachioed journeyman thespian whose filmography mirrors Trevor's, but it does seem incredibly unlikely. **Score 1**

ROUND 6
Appearances on *Shoestring*
Between 30 September 1979 and 21 December 1980, Trevor Eve starred as detective Eddie Shoestring in the popular BBC crime drama, *Shoestring*. He appeared in every single one of the series's 21 episodes, for which he receives a point apiece. And we are also obliged to award him a TEN POINT bonus for playing the lead role - private investigator Eddie Shoestring himself! It's a stellar round for the Brum-born entertainer. **Score 31**

HOW DID THEY DO?

TREVOR · · · · · · · · · · ·
CLEVER TREVOR! The Artist Formerly Known as Eddie Shoestring has defied critics to overcome both of his famous namesakes in this fearsome six-round battle to the death. Birmingham's favourite son can hold his head high this Yuletide season, safe in the knowledge that he's the Greatest Eve Ever!

39

CHRIS

Global Popularity
FROM Land's End to Honolulu and from John O'Groats to Pyongyang, we all love the night before Our Lord's birthday, even if we don't believe in Him. Whether we spend it huddled up by a roaring fire, roasting chestnuts before taking a bite of one and throwing them away, or belting out *Good King Wenceslas* on the doorstep of an irritated

Nudity
Unlike other more saucy days of the year - such as Valentine's day or International Oral Sex Day - the night before Christmas is not a day traditionally associated with nakedness. Of course, many of us will still find ourselves momentarily in the buff at

...e Consumption
There are plenty of foods we associate with the 24th of December - Satsumas, Quality Streets, roasted chestnuts, Terry's Chocolate Oranges - but apples are probably not one of them. That said, mulled apple cider is a festive favourite at Christmas street markets the world over, and children will often

Angering God
With guest judge AB of C Justin Welby "God is a huge fan of Christmas Eve. It's the day when people around the globe celebrate His son's birth by singing carols about Him and generally praising His good works. That said, God also looks upon December 24th with a degree of wistful sadness. You see, Christmas Eve in the

Mentions in Bible
We all know that The Bible dedicates a large chunk of its narrative to the 25th of December - the day Christ was born in a lowly stable. However, every good story requires a build-up, and in The Bible that build-up happens... on Christmas Eve! Yes, the much-loved 24-hour-period pops up time and again in the Good Book's pages, whether it's Mary

Appearances on *Shoestring*
THE IMDb summary for *Shoestring* series 2, episode 10: 'The Dangerous Game' reads: *"When Santa gets toys off the back of a lorry, Shoestring*

CHRISTMAS
HOLY NIGHT? Wholly *Shite*, more like! The 24th of December may be a favourite with the kids, but it has been given a thoroughly festive thumping in this three-

...TMAS

...neighbour, Christmas Eve is a day that is treasured by quite literally every single person on Planet Earth. As such, it's a stonking opening round for everyone's favourite 24 hour-period.

Score 10

...some point during the 24 hours that make up Christmas Eve, but for the most part we spend the day wrapping pressies, hanging stockings, or sprinting to the all-night garage to frantically purchase last-minute gifts - activities that are all habitually performed with clothes on.

Score 3

...leave out a freshly buffed Braeburn or two for Santa's reindeer. So, despite not having any data to back it up, we can say with absolute certainty that the global consumption of apples sees some sort of spike on Christmas Eve.

Score 6

Year 0 BC was God's last day of freedom before He had His first kid. From that day forward, He had to assume parental responsibility, and could no longer go out on the piss at short notice. So while Christmas Eve doesn't make God angry as such, it still fills Him with a sense of melancholic nostalgia for His carefree bachelor days."

Score 2

...and Joseph riding their donkey into Bethlehem on December the 24th, or the Three Wise Men making last-minute purchases of gold, frankincense and myrrh from an all-night market around the same time.

Score 7

...endures a less than merry Christmas." This certainly suggests at least one appearance of Christmas Eve on the show. But since the episode is not available on YouTube, we cannot say for sure. We have no choice but to dish out a low mark here.

Score 1

...way clash of the Eves. Forget about hanging your stockings - this 24-hour period has been hung out to dry.

29

ADAM AND

Global Popularity

THE first human beings to walk the Earth, Adam and Eve are a bit like Marmite - you either love them or hate them. Some people respect the couple's headstrong determination to eat whatever sort of fruit they want and talk to whichever snakes they please. Others find it difficult to forgive them for introducing the concepts of guilt, evil, shame and death to all mankind. Just as they divide critics across the globe, these iconic original sinners have divided their score in this first round 'Eve-aluation'.

Score 5 — ROUND 1

Nudity

Cheeky forbidden-fruit-fans Adam and Eve were the world's first nudists - cavorting merrily through the Garden of Eden in nothing but their birthday suits. What's more, even after eating from the Tree of Knowledge and comprehending the shame of being in the Billy Bollocks, they still only donned skimpy fig leaves to cover their naughty bits, rather than opting for bulkier, more concealing clothing, such as Duffel coats, jumpsuits or onesies. It's a bountiful round for the lusty lapsarians.

Score 9 — ROUND 2

Apple Consumption

Adam and Eve only ate ONE apple in their lives - a fact you think would make them a shoo-in for a low-scoring round here. However, that apple was the single most famous apple in history, even more famous than the one that hit Sir Isaac Newton on the head - the iconic 'Forbidden Fruit'. Scoffing this supernatural apple transformed the pair from obedient, immortal simpletons to sex-obsessed sinners who were condemned to suffer thanklessly until death. Thus, if we weigh up the biblical duo's apple consumption in terms of 'quality not quantity', we can see they fully deserve the impressive score bestowed upon them here.

Score 7 — ROUND 3

Angering God

With guest judge AB of C Justin Welby "Adam and Eve famously fell into God's bad books when they disobeyed His orders about eating fruit from the Tree of Knowledge, and He was fucking livid. In fact, to this day, if you want to send the big man's blood pressure sky rocketing, just mention the words 'Adam and Eve' - and then run for cover! Only joking, but The Almighty did make those two with His own holy hands out of all dust and ribs and that, so when they mugged Him off, He really took it personally, and furiously casteth humanity for evermore into a pit of guilt and despair. Not surprisingly, it's a high scoring round for the deity-displeasing double act."

Score 9 — ROUND 4

Mentions in Bible

As we learned in the previous round, for someone who wasn't massively keen on Adam and Eve, God certainly liked to write about them. His debut book, The Bible, is chock-a-block with irate references to the scantily clad snake-botherers. In fact, if you were to flick through the Good Book and stop at any page at random, you'd be almost certain to find some mention of the Fall-Of-Man-initiating fruit-scoffers.

Score 8 — ROUND 5

Appearances on *Shoestring*

At no point during any of *Shoestring*'s 21 50-minute episodes does gumshoe Eddie meet, discuss, mention or even think about the first man and woman in creation, Adam and Eve. The mud-moulded man and wife have romped through the early rounds here, but in failing to be mentioned in the BBC TV detective drama they have slipped up at the final hurdle. Like eating the forbidden fruit, this slip may cost them dearly.

Score 0 — ROUND 6

ADAM AND

WOULD you Adam and Eve it?! They put in a Biblical performance, but the naked truth is that these apple-scrumping God-infuriators were pipped (like an apple pip) at the post by a bearded Brummie thespian. They may be the first man and woman - but they're only the second best Eve!

38

NEXT WEEK: South Sea v Westminster v Off of Big Brother 2: **Which is the Best Bubble?**

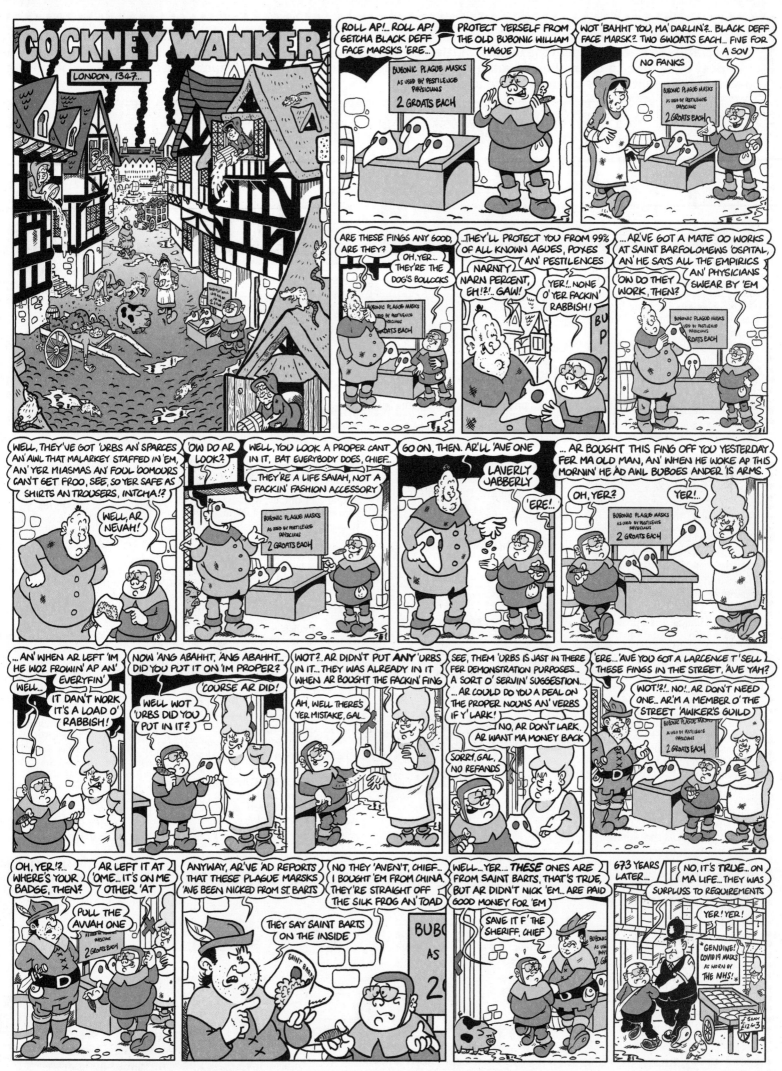

THEY can be big, they can be small, they can be round and they can be square... but they're no use when they're flat. They're *batteries*, and these handy little tins of electricity have been making our lives easier for longer than most of us care to remember. We take them for granted every day, but how much do we really know about these oh-so-handy pocket power stations? Here are ...

21 THINGS YOU NEVER KNEW ABOUT BATTERIES

1 ON DECEMBER 25th 1836, 8-year-old Denis Daniell opened a Christmas present from his uncle – a remote control monster truck. Unfortunately, there were no batteries to operate the toy. And that's not surprising, because they hadn't been invented yet!

JF Daniell: Battery boffin.

Luckily, Denis's dad, John Frederick Daniell, was a professor of Chemistry, and when he saw his disappointed son's tears, he immediately popped into his laboratory and invented the world's first "voltaic cell". This primitive battery, which consisted of an earthenware and copper pot filled with sulphuric acid, copper sulphate and a zinc electrode, powered the monster truck perfectly well. Unfortunately, Dennis tried to drive it along the back of the sofa and it tipped over, spilling the corrosive acid onto his mam's best cushions. As a result, the truck and its revolutionary power source were put in the back of the garage and forgotten about for the next hundred years.

2 THE ELECTRIC EEL (*Electrophorus electricus*) is a fish that can deliver a powerful shock to any angler unfortunate enough to land one. Each 6-foot eel contains enough electricity to start 300 Ford Fiesta 1300E cars, or power every transistor radio in Lincolnshire for the entire duration of Ken Bruce's *Popmaster* every day for a whole year.

3 THE ELECTRICITY in batteries comes in two forms – *Volts* and *Amps*. In a normal household plug, the electricity is about 13 Amps and 240 Volts, making it suitable for running televisions and vacuum cleaners etc. But batteries only contain about 9 volts and fractions of an amp, which scientists refer to as a "milliamp". This means they are ideal for torches, mobile phones and ladies' neck massagers.

4 AND WATTS, so that makes three.

5 IN CLASSIC 70S sitcom *Fawlty Towers*, health inspector Mr Carnegie is offered a tin of crackers in the dining room, only for Manuel's pet rat 'Basil' to poke its head out and look left and right. The realistic animatronic rat, built by the BBC's special effects department, was designed to run on a 9V PP3 battery, but during recording it was discovered that the battery was flat. Thinking quickly, actress **CONNIE BOOTH** turned the electrical motor that operated the rat by hand, and the hysterical studio audience was none the wiser. The episode went on to win a BAFTA for Best Animatronic Rodent in a TV Situation Comedy, with the award presented by former UN Secretary General Kofi Annan.

6 THE SMALLEST batteries in the world are the ones used to power the digital watch of the world's smallest man Calvin Phillips. These are so tiny that they only contain enough power to run the tiny watch for 20 minutes, meaning that Phillips has to go to Timpsons in the precinct to get a new one fitted dozens of times every day.

7 MODERN CARS run on clean batteries that can be recharged at one or two motorway service stations dotted around the country. By contrast, the old-fashioned tow trucks that come out to take these eco-friendly cars to the next charging point run on outdated and polluting diesel fuel.

8 CHANCES ARE your TV remote control runs off two AA or AAA batteries, and there's nothing more frustrating than them running out of juice just as *Mrs Brown's Boys* is about to start. But don't throw those flat batteries away – simply take them out and warm them up by rolling them in the palms of your hands and they'll work for a few more minutes, long enough to turn the telly off.

9 BATTERIES are an important tool in the fight against crime. The ones in a policeman's walkie talkie allow him to call in reinforcements if he happens upon a 'blag' taking place, and they also power the tazer that he uses to bring a heavily armed assailant to his knees. Whats more, the batteries in his torch let him peer into vehicles parked in unlit lay-bys to see what the couples inside are getting up to, and the ones in his phone allow him to take pictures of the action and show them to all his colleagues back at the station.

10 NOT ALL BATTERIES are made of metal and electron-liberating chemicals. Battery hens, for example, are made out of live chickens and a few scruffy feathers.

Lineker: Scared of batteries.

certain how many batteries there actually are in the Land of the Rising Sun. "There could be millions, or even billions of them. The truth is, we just don't know," he told his fellow scientist **PROFESSOR JIM AL-KHALILI**, who also didn't know.

11 THE PSYCHOLOGICAL condition termed *navitasnavisphobia* is an irrational fear of batteries. Upon seeing a battery, sufferers typically display a variety of symptoms including sweating, shaking, shortness of breath, panic attacks and knocking knees. Well known navitasnavisphobes include crisps pundit **GARY LINEKER**, crime writer **IAN RANKIN**, and soul singer **GLADYS KNIGHT** and two of the Pips.

12 IN CONTRAST, people who exhibit a pronounced love of batteries are known as *navitasnavisphiles*. Upon seeing a battery, these people experience a sudden, heightened sense of euphoria, possibly including sexual arousal and, in severe cases, spontaneous ejaculation. Well- known navitasnavisphiles include newsreader **HUW EDWARDS**, mock schoolboy **JEANETTE KRANKIE**, Hungarian premier **VIKTOR ORBAN**, and Human League frontman **PHIL OAKEY** and one of the girls.

13 WHEN he was a guest on Radio 4's *Desert Island Discs*, former Prime Minister **SIR JOHN MAJOR** chose as his luxury item "four eternal batteries that never ran out" so he could listen to *Test Match Special* when castaway on his island. Unfortunately, Major forgot to include a radio in his request, so the batteries were never used.

14 WITH COUNTLESS mobile telephones, Gameboys and transistor radios, Japan is truly the home of the hand-held electronic gadget. But according to D:Ream's **PROFESSOR BRIAN COX**, nobody knows for

15 IF YOUR mobile phone goes flat while you're in a fruit shop, don't panic. Simply buy a lemon, stick two wires in it, *and voila!*

16 CONVERSELY, if you're at a party and there are no lemons for your gin and tonic, simply take the battery out of your phone, drop it in your glass, *and voila!*

17 GET A PAIR of 1.5V batteries and connect them together in series, and you'll end up with 3V. However, wire them up in *parallel* and the voltage will remain the same, 1.5V. "It's probably something to do with the way they're connected together, or they might of got the wires the wrong way round or something. The truth is, we simply don't know," admits the late Nobel Prize-winning quantum physicist **PROFESSOR RICHARD FEYNMAN**, speaking via former footballer and TVs *Most Haunted* psychic **DEREK ACORAH**.

18 ACCORDING to physicists, when a battery is connected in a circuit, current flows out of the tit-ended (or 'positive') end and back into the flat (or 'negative') end. "Or it might be the other way round. The truth is, I just don't know and I can't be arsed to look it up," says American TV boffin **NEIL DEGRASSE TYSON**.

19 AS WELL as the famous electric eel, several other animals also generate electrical current, including the Black Ghost Knifefish, the Torpedo fish and the Electric Ray. However, out of the estimated 400,000 types of plants on the earth, not a single species is able to generate a volt of electricity, including the Red Oak, the Bee Orchid and the Blue Barrel Cactus.

20 CUMULONIMBUS storm clouds are effectively giant, floating batteries that charge themselves up by rubbing against the sky. During storms, electricity comes out of them in the form of lightning and thunder, and it doesn't stop until they go flat.

21 PROFESSOR Brian Cox's Large Hadron Collider experiment at CERN consumes 1000 Gigawatt Hours of electricity during an average year. If it was powered using ordinary AA batteries – each providing 1.2 Watt Hours, it would require 8.3×10^{11} batteries to function. "That's enough batteries to fill 37 Albert Halls," said the former D:Ream synth-stabber. "And checking that we'd put them all in pointing the right way round would take fucking ages, so we just plug it in the mains instead."

NEXT WEEK: 20 Things You Never Knew About Magnets and Sausage Rolls

Letterbocks

Viz Comic, P.O. Box 841 Whitley Bay, NE26 9EQ : letters@viz.co.uk

IF someone asked me what is my favourite film from the nineties, I'm really not sure what I'd say. Fortunately however, nobody has yet asked me, so that will buy me time to give it some thought.

Dominic Twose, Leamington Spa

PEOPLE hard pressed to sum up a situation in a few words should consider using the phrase 'in an egg shell' rather than 'in a nutshell,' thus allowing a greater freedom of expression. This would also have the added bonus of not offending anyone with a nut allergy.

Chuddy Way and Half Pint Andy, Ely

THE press is making a big deal out of Priti Patel's so-called 'bullying', but I reckon she went to a good school so it would probably be a different class of bullying – perhaps being made to toast crumpets for her, or warm her lavatory seat. I doubt her bullying has left any civil servants walking around Whitehall with their pants pulled halfway up their arse crack.

Gideon Kerplunk-Smythe, Uncheval

I HAVE to disagree with the writers of the previous letter. Nuts come in many different sizes, so the phrase 'in a nutshell' allows them to sum something up briefly, eg. a pistachio, or at greater length, eg. a coconut. Also, many people are allergic to eggs.

Bjorn Toblorone, Malmo

ARE any of your readers missing pages 63 and 64 of the June 1987 issue of *Men Only*? Only I found them on the way home from school in July of that year and I'm nearly finished with them.

D Williams, Donegal

IF the word 'gnaw' was spelt with a silent 'k', as in 'know', as opposed a silent 'g' it would spell 'wank' backwards. Do I win a fiver or something?

Mr S Andrews, Bristol

THE other day, I was driving my son home to the complex where he lives, which has large, automatic gates. As I approached them, they slowly and majestically swung open as the theme music to *The Big Country* played on the car stereo. Once they were fully opened, I drove through as the tune reached its rousing crescendo. It was perfect.

Tarquin Balls, Cheam

FOLLOWING on from Mr Balls's letter *(above)*, the first time I drove a car on my own after passing my test, the theme from *The Big Country* came on the radio, and really stirred my spirit as I kangarooed past Mrs Etherington's house up the street in my dad's Peugeot. In the 30-odd years since, it's been indelibly linked in my mind with that sense of freedom and the adventure of the open road.

Spud, Luton

Has a momentous event in your life ever been fortuitously accompanied by Jerome Moross's iconic theme music from The Big Country? Perhaps it came on the radio the moment your first child was born, or it was playing on a jukebox at the moment you first laid eyes on your future partner. Or perhaps it's indelibly linked in your mind with an experience you'd rather forget. Did an ice-cream van playing the tune run down your grandfather and leave him critically injured in the road when you were 7; or did you go to see the film at the cinema, only to fart and follow through during the opening titles, meaning you had to sit in your own filth for the movie's duration while your date repeatedly checked the soles of her shoes? Write in and let us know at the usual address.

I'M not sure why something easy is described as being "like taking candy off a baby" because that's anything but easy. They've got a surprisingly strong grip and I had to run for at least half a mile before I'd shaken the brat's angry father off my tail. And then the sweets were covered in baby spit anyway.

H. Chromium, London

THE Romans were said to have put spiced toast in their punch bowls, but I'm pretty sure they didn't have toasters back then, so I'm calling bullshit on it.

Mark Dixon, Failsworth

SOMETHING happened to me in the bathroom the other morning, something so unspeakably vile and embarrassing that I can barely bring myself to share it. I wonder if any other readers have wiped their arse after a catastrophic shite, thrown the discarded paper and missed the bowl, then bent down to retrieve it and left a giant skidmark on their wife's white dressing gown that was hanging on the door behind them?

Palmer Vjorhend, Portstewart

THANKS to my guitar-tuning app, I now know that my arse is naturally in the key of B-flat.

Shunter, Edinburgh

DO any readers know of a convenient method of measuring the volume of gas expelled from the arse during a fart? I would like to stress that I'm asking for a friend.

Swan Vestarse, Cardiff

Unless Viz readers know otherwise, the most obvious way would be to take an empty pop bottle, add 10ml of water and mark the level on the side with a Sharpie. Then add a further 10ml and make another mark on the side. Repeat this until you have marked 1000ml up the side in 10ml

CUNT DRACULA

CHECKOUTS

I'M SORRY, SIR - IT'S ONE PACK PER CUSTOMER ON LOO ROLL RIGHT NOW...

YOU VILL LET ME BUY ALL THE LOO ROLLS I VANT.

I WILL LET YOU BUY ALL THE LOO ROLLS YOU WANT.

OI!

EXIT

—Taylor

Jellyfish Fact File
with Dwayne 'The Rock' Johnson

THE HARDEST man in the World brings you the *hardest facts* about the world's *softest animals!*

Jellyfish have probably been around for thousands of years. But scientists don't know exactly *how* long because they are *made from jelly*, so they don't turn into fossils like dinosaurs.

The most toxic jellyfish in the world *has enough poison in it to kill 500 animals the size of a rhinoceros*, such as 500 hippopotamuses.

Jellyfish have no bones, brain, eyes, blood, gut or nervous system. Yet according to scientists, *they are still animals!* You couldn't make it up!

The Portuguese Man o' War, a floating jellyfish that looks like a Tesco's 5p carrier bag, *has legs 165ft long* – that's equivalent to 28.41 Adam Sandlers, or 27.48 Eric Stoltzes who played drug dealer Lance in Quentin Tarantino's *Pulp Fiction*, lying end to end.

Or 27.18 Quentin Tarantinos standing one on top of the other.

The Icelandic word for jellyfish is *marglytta*. You couldn't make it up!

Till next time, jellyfish fans!
The **Rock** X

---

increments. Then cut the top of the bottle off. Next, run a bath, get into it and place the bottle under the water, open side up, until it fills. Then, keeping the cut end under the water, turn the bottle upside down and position it between your legs. Then pass wind, allowing the flatus to bubble up into the bottle, displacing the water. The volume of carbon dibaxide expelled can then be read off on the scale on the side of the bottle to an accuracy of + or - 10ml (about the volume of a Tommy squeaker). If you produce more than a litre of gas, either use a larger pop bottle, or go and see a doctor.

I WOKE up this morning with stomach cramps, cold sweats and a headache, so I decided to go on Google. What a mistake that was. I've spent the last four hours masturbating to Anal Creampie Teens on Pornhub and I still don't know what's wrong with me.
Michael Thompson, North Wales

HOW absurd to claim that a room can be so quiet that you could hear a pin drop. I tested this idea and, admittedly, there was a faint metallic ring when it hit the floor, but whilst it was dropping there was utter silence. These so-called 'experts' must take us for idiots.
Phil Kitching, Isle of Jura

I SAW this in a local supermarket, I think it's wasted on cats.
Bob Pitt, Kendal

"THERE'S nothing new under the sun," my grandmother always says. Well, recently I told her about the advances in robotic sex dolls powered by artificial intelligence. You should have seen the old bat's face.
H. Proctor, Tullibody

IT'S much easier to explain suddenly slamming shut a laptop when your wife walks in the room if it's nearing her birthday. How you explain your trousers being round your ankles is up to you.
Guy Venables, Chilgrove

THE nanny statists tell us that making ourselves out of breath a few times a day is good for our health. But I find smoking 40 or more tabs a day is a great way to get out of breath, yet we're told that's bad for us. These so-called 'health experts' haven't thought it through.
Mark Starling, Norwich

I LEARNED recently that William Shakespeare first coined the word 'wig' in his 1589 play *Two Gentlemen of Verona*. However, looking at pictures of Shakespeare, we see that he himself was bald as a coot. Since he went to the trouble of inventing wigs, you have to wonder why the slap-headed dramatist didn't wear one of the ruddy things?
Felicity Shortshrift, Ludlow

HATS off to the late President John F Kennedy for his vision of space travel which ultimately saw man land on the moon. But let's not forget President Donald Trump's comb-over. The planning and sheer mind-blowing complexity of organising and actually executing such an operation is a thing of wonder.
Hymen Prepuce, New York

I DON'T know why people need colanders. If you don't like boiling water on your potatoes, then don't put them in there in the first place.
D. Fishbones, Oban

MY husband has always been sensitive about losing his locks, so a few years back I hit upon a rather ingenious solution. Every night, I hoover up the hairs that our three cats have shed over the course of the day and then glue them over my hubby's bald spots while he's asleep. I've been adding to this makeshift wig for thirty-five years now and the daft ha'porth still hasn't twigged, despite the fact that the colour of his 'hair' has changed from blonde to ginger to tortoise shell.
Drusilla Deranged, Herts

I DON'T know why guide dogs need all that money they keep asking us to donate. They are perfectly happy with a few tins of dog food and a stick to fetch.
Jane Hoole Garner, St. Ives

IF there really is an Abominable Snowman, then how come there aren't loads of them? Surely he must breed. Unless of course, being a snowman his dick really is just a carrot, which would explain the whole thing.
Archie Spelks, Goole

IT'S not often that the wife pays me a compliment, but the other day she said I reminded her of Elvis Presley. So imagine my disappointment when she explained that when she was passing the bathroom door while I was having a shit, it sounded like I was having a heart attack.
Harpo Bradwurst, Kensington

DRIVERS always speed up after they pass speed cameras. If the powers that be moved the cameras back 100m, they would catch all these lawbreakers who think they're too clever to be caught.
Prufrock Stubbs, Kent

ROGER MELLIE THE MAN ON THE TELLY

Panel 1: ...NOW IT'S TIME FOR 'GOOD MORNING BRITAIN' WITH REGULAR HOSTS PIERS MORGAN, SUSANNA REID, AND ROGER MELLIE...

Panel 2: GOOD MORNING, AND WELCOME TO THIS SLIGHTLY UNUSUAL EDITION OF GMB DURING WHICH, FOLLOWING GOVERNMENT ADVICE, WE'LL BE WORKING FROM HOME.

Panel 3: THANKS TO THE WONDERS OF TECHNOLOGY WE'LL BE PRESENTING THE SHOW TOGETHER IN SELF-ISOLATION, AS IT WERE...I'M HERE IN THE KITCHEN AT MORGAN TOWERS...HA-HA...! ...WHERE ARE YOU, SUSANNA..?

Panel 4: WELL I'M HERE IN MY SITTING ROOM, PIERS, WITH A NICE CUP OF TEA...I TELL YOU WHAT, I COULD GET USED TO THIS WORKING FROM HOME! HA-HA! SO WHAT HAVE WE GOT COMING UP ON THE SHOW THIS MORNING?

Panel 5: WELL, I'LL BE CHATTING TO DANNY DYER - REMOTELY, OF COURSE - TO ASK HIM HOW THE CORONAVIRUS IS DISRUPTING THE FILMING OF EASTENDERS...AND TO TALK ABOUT THE EFFECT IT HAS HAD ON THE ACTING PROFESSION IN GENERAL...

Panel 6: ...THEN I'M GOING TO HAVE A VIDEO-LINK CHAT WITH SOME HOSPITAL STAFF TO SEE HOW THEY ARE COPING UNDER THESE EXCEPTIONALLY STRESSFUL CIRCUMSTANCES.

Panel 7: YES, THE HEROES OF OUR TIME... ...WHAT ABOUT YOU, ROGER? WHAT HAVE YOU GOT FOR US...?

Panel 8: WELL, PIERS...I'LL BE FINDING OUT ABOUT A NEW SCHEME THAT'S BEEN SET UP TO ENSURE THAT BRITAIN'S PET OWNERS CAN STILL GET THE VETERINARY CARE THEY NEED FOR THEIR PAMPERED POOCHES AND MOGGIES...

Panel 9: ...THEN I'M GOING TO CHAT LIVE OVER THE WEB WITH ALAN TITCHMARSH, WHO HAS SOME EXCELLENT ADVICE FOR... HEY! YOU'RE SUPPOSED TO BE POINTING THAT FUCKING CAMERA AT ME!

Panel 10: HELLO! GIGGLE I'M NOT PISSING ABOUT HERE, LOVE. COME ON...YOU'RE MAKING ME LOOK A RIGHT TWAT.

ALL THE CELEBRITY NEWS & GOSSIP

PIERCE DORGAN

Vegans - Get off your High Horses (and eat them!)

LAST year, when Greggs launched their vegan sausage roll, I ate one of them on my extremely popular TVAM show, and I vomited on air. That's how bad it was to not be eating meat.

But it now it seems that Greggs are not content with making me throw up once. They are determined to do it again, and to do so they have launched a "steak bake" with no steak in it!

As I said to **Mats Wilander** (the famous tennis professional who won seven Grand Slams in the Singles, and a Doubles Grand Slam with **Joakim Nystrom** - who isn't very well known so I don't count him amongst my close, personal friends) the other night at the Noma restaurant in Copenhagen (where I can get a seat any time I want, even though anybody else couldn't get a reservation for years- that's how fancy it is. And most of you reading this article couldn't imagine how expensive it is, and that's if you don't have a starter or a pudding. And the portions are really small), "When are people going to realise that

humans are carnivorous animals?"

"Yes, Piers," said my close friend **Scarlet Johannsen**, who was dining with us, sitting between two of my other very close friends **Phil "The Power" Taylor** and **Martin Amis**. "We have canine teeth, designed for chewing and tearing flesh. So you're right, Piers, and vegetarians are wrong."

A round of applause for me broke out from my close friends around the table, including **Barry White, Sandi Toksvig, George Clooney, Warwick Davies, Richard E Grant, Emerson Fittipaldi, Thieri Henry, Werner Fassbender, Richard Dawkins, Felicity Kendal** and **Idris Elba**. Of course, I knew I was right, but it was nice to have my brilliance acknowledged by so many of my dear, famous and rich, close, personal friends who I do know.

I tried to hush them, but one by

one they rose from their seats to give me a rousing standing ovation. However, one member of the party was not joining in with the applause, which by this time had turned into wild, cheering support for my outspoken, anti-vegan-pastie stance. I looked across at the still, silent figure, who was sitting between **William Shatner** and US President **Donald Trump** (on the other side of the table from **Robbie Williams, Joan Bakewell, Sir Ian McKellen** and **Mick McManus**).

"You're forgetting that human jaws go side to side like a herbivore or a ruminant," she lied. Immediately, the cheering stopped and all eyes - including those of **Julie Goodyear,** Funkadelic's **George Clinton** and **Professor Sir John Curtice** - turned to see who was speaking.

It was my former close friend **Meghan Markle**, the so-called Duchess of Sussex, who had broken the hearts of my close friend

A few of my friends who I could phone up anytime and just say "Hi, it's Piers" and they'd know who I was.

Her Majesty the Queen, together with those of the British public, and - worse of all - myself with her two-faced duplicitousness.

I summoned the Maitre d', who immediately escorted Meghan from the premises, and everybody started chanting my name, including **Fred Dinenage, Mo Salah, Mo Farah, Michael Fish, Buzz Aldrin** and Ted Rogers's 3-2-1 sidekick **Dusty Bin**.

© Pierce Dorgan 2020

81

MERRY BONSAI XMAS

2020 Christmas trees are smallest on record

THERE is no more festive a sight than a Christmas tree standing tall in the corner of the room, trimmed with tinsel, baubles and twinkling lights. But it's a sight that may not be quite so impressive in years to come, as research shows that Christmas trees are getting smaller.

And festive season experts believe that this year's trees could be the smallest on record.

"The days of having an 8-foot tree standing in your hallway are gone," said Bartram Twochips, leader of the National Festive Tree Vendors' Union.

"Traditionally, a 6-footer has been exactly 72 inches high ever since Christmas trees first became popular back in Victorian times. They stayed at that height throughout both world wars and until the end of the twentieth century. But since the year 2000, they have been dropping in size," Mr Twochips revealed.

average

"The average size of a 6-foot tree these days is about 5 foot 2 inches. And I've seen some 6-footers on sale that are around the 4 foot 10 mark," he said.

And Twochips had this advice for anyone looking for a 6-foot tree. "You should go for one around the 8-foot mark and you'll be in the right ballpark."

jolly

And the reduced size phenomenon of these traditional festive decorations is not just confined to real trees – artificial Christmas trees have also been getting noticeably smaller since 2010.

Retired Tyldesley piano teacher Doreen Newton bought a 5-foot Frosted Emerald Fir from John Lewis in Bolton, only to discover it was much smaller than she expected.

"When we got it out the box and put it up, we couldn't believe how small it was," she said. "My husband measured it with his woodwork tape and it was only 3 foot 11," she added. "He said he thought it was a metric one that had been re-packaged."

"When he put it up, and I saw it sat there in the corner of the room, I wept," she added.

Tree-mendous: With Christmas tree sizes on the decline, might trees like this be a thing of the past?

Derren Brown's How to make your Christmas tree look BIGGER

THE size of a Christmas tree is a fixed parameter. A 6-footer is the same size wherever you are in time and space. So if your 6-foot tree is only 4-feet tall, there's little you can do about it… *or is there?* According to TV mentalist **DERREN BROWN**, the size of your Christmas tree is all in your mind, and it is easy to fool your brain into believing your tree is bigger than it actually is. Here, Derren shares a few of his mind techniques to help you increase the size of *your* tree.

🎄 **WHEN** we get our tree in December, most of us plonk it in the furthest corner of the room where perspective will make it appear small. So set it up in the centre of the room instead. That way you will be much closer to it at all times, making it appear much larger than when it is further away.

🎄 **WHEN** we look at something, we look at only part of it and our consciousness 'fills in the gaps'. So place your tree on a table or sideboard. When you look at the bottom, you will indeed see a small tree on a table, but when you look up at the top, your brain will simply see the top of a very tall tree.

🎄 **OUR BRAINS** are very poor at judging the size of things, and when we look at something, we compare it with something else – think how the moon looks much larger when it is close to the horizon than when it is high up in the sky. So, when you trim your tree, use very small baubles and thin tinsel with a tiny star on the top. Your brain will be fooled into thinking that the tree is large, rather than the decorations are small.

🎄 **AS WITH** the baubles, put smaller presents round the base of the tree to heighten the discrepancy and make the tree look larger. Similarly, don't invite any tall relatives for Christmas dinner, just the smaller ones, such as grandmas and children. And if you are friends with the Harlem Globetrotters, invite Jonte "Too Tall" Hall (5' 2") round rather than 7' 7" Paul "Tiny" Sturgess.

🎄 **THINK** about celebrating Christmas in a smaller room in your house, such as the kitchen or toilet. A 5-foot tree in the living room could easily appear 8-feet tall in your bathroom.

🎄 **USING** a pocket watch on a chain, hypnotise yourself into thinking your tree is twice as tall as it is. You can test if you are fully hypnotised by eating a raw onion and seeing if it tastes like an apple.

🎄 **WE TEND** to judge the height of Christmas trees by how far they are off the ceiling rather than how far from the floor. So suspend your tree on a wire a couple of inches from the ceiling and only ever look at the top. To make the illusion even more effective, wear a surgical collar so you can't look down.

SLEEPY-BYE BRITAIN!

How a fatigued UK will look post-Covid

THE COVID-19 pandemic has had a profound impact around the world. And as the infection rate steadily declines, recovered victims report suffering intense fatigue long after the symptoms of the illness are gone.

Extreme exhaustion mid-way through the day seems to be one of the long term effects of this virulent virus, and many sufferers are only able to get through their regular routine with a rest.

Covid-19 has affected people from every walk of life, leaving them tired, listless and debilitated. And with such a high number of cases in the country, post-Covid Britain will prove to be a very different place from the one the virus initially infected.

Viz scientific correspondent, Prof Stanley Jordan takes a look at how every aspect of life in Britain will look as we all battle post-viral fatigue.

with Viz's Scientific Correspodent
PROF. STANLEY JORDAN

Travel

TODAY we take non-stop travel for granted and think nothing of jumping on a plane, train or bus, settling back and enjoying the journey to our destination.

Before the virus hit, the average train journey from Newcastle to London took around 3 hours, but future travellers will have to add another 90 minutes on top of that because, half way through the journey, the driver will become drowsy.

The soporific rhythm of the train on the tracks will not help matters and around Northallerton, he or she will have no choice but to pull in at a siding and get their head down for an hour or so.

Of course, an aeroplane can't pull over mid-flight, so when the pilot and co-pilot need their post-Covid afternoon cat-nap, a replacement crew, who have just woken up refreshed, will take over. This essential doubling of pilot numbers will have an inevitable effect on ticket prices, making air travel unaffordable to all but the richest.

Sex

SEX with a partner is one of the most intimate moments we share with the person we love – a minute-and-a-half of intense pleasure in which we give ourselves completely to each other.

Nothing would spoil the mutual feeling of trust and respect that goes with the physical expression of love more than one of us nodding off whilst on the job.

The upset caused to a person when their partner begins to snore halfway through a scuttle is not difficult to imagine, but it is a scenario that couples are going to have to get used to.

Many people will find it hard to deal with the hurt of their partner going to the land of nod whilst in the vinegar strokes, and marriages will inevitably suffer. Indeed, Marriage Guidance will be one of the few professions that will boom in 2021, as post-Covid couples try to salvage their faltering relationships.

Shopping

THE DAYS when shops all closed for lunch between 12:00 and 1:00 seem to belong to a bygone age.

But in post-Covid Britain, we will once again be greeted at the shops with a 'CLOSED' sign half way through the day. But the staff won't be having a sandwich and a cup of tea in the back room – they'll all be curled up on sofas and camp-beds, fast asleep.

Some of the larger stores may be able to arrange sleeping rotas, with some staff manning the shop floor while their colleagues are giving it some Zs in the staff room. Customers will probably be unaware, except for those in B&Q, where finding a member of staff is difficult at the best of times, and will now be all but impossible.

Entertainment

IT IS good news that cinemas and theatres are once again opening their doors as Britain gets used to the 'new normal' after Covid-19.

But once inside, audience members will not find things quite as they remember them.

At the flicks, there will be little point in starting the film on time, as everyone will be fast asleep almost as soon as they sit down. After the adverts and trailers are finished, staff will dim the lights further and let the audience sleep for an hour or so, before waking them all gently and starting the main feature.

In the theatre, the phrase 'The Show Must Go On' will still apply, but actors will be required to deliver their lines in a stage whisper so as not to wake any audience members who simply couldn't keep their eyes open.

Sport

BRITAIN loves to watch people playing games, but when our sporting venues open for spectators once more, we may find more than a few changes.

Football matches will still be played over ninety minutes, but the half-time break will be just as long again, giving the players and match officials time to grab a much-needed forty winks before coming out for the second half.

And test cricket, slow-paced and drawn out as it is, is set to get even longer as a 'nip-nap' break is introduced between the lunch and tea intervals.

Meanwhile, in the fast-paced world of Formula 1, power-nap pit-stops will be introduced so that heavy-eyed drivers can pull over and have a little doze if they feel that they are in danger of falling asleep at the wheel.

Law

ENFORCING the law is a 24-hour-a-day job, but our boys and girls in blue need their Covid-19 shut-eye just like the rest of us. So, mid-afternoon, the entire police force on duty will be down in the cells getting their cop kip.

You might think that this would leave the streets vulnerable and at the mercy of every villain and underworld low-life. But don't forget that criminals are people, too, and they are likely to be at home at the same time having their own viral-induced siesta.

At the other end of the legal system, when a criminal is found guilty in court, the judge will adjourn the session, not for sentencing, or to await reports, but so that everyone – the convict included – can have a nice little snooze.

War

ALTHOUGH humankind realises that we are all better off when we cooperate and share our knowledge, possessions and culture with each other for a common good, we still cannot seem to stop coming into conflict.

And it's a tragic fact that although we worked together as one to combat the common enemy that was Covid-19, we will resume fighting each other in wars across the globe once that virus has been defeated. But not in the afternoons.

The Geneva Convention will be re-written to include a clause that no hostile action can be taken between half-past one and three o'clock every day, when soldiers will be conked out in their bunks catching flies. Any combatant breaking this rule, or indeed making any loud noises, could be charged with committing a war crime and sent for trial in The Hague.

NEXT WEEK: *How the post-Covid-19 loss of smell will shape Britain in the future.*

DESPOT SUFFERS COVID SETBACK

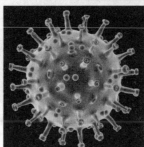

Flu only live twice: Ernst Stavro Blofeld, supreme commander of SPECTRE, yesterday.

AMULTI-BILLIONAIRE autocrat has become the biggest economic victim so far of the Covid-19 pandemic, after announcing that he is temporarily suspending plans to take over the world.

Evil criminal mastermind *Ernst Blofeld* spoke on a live YouTube stream yesterday, telling the world that a global pandemic is not the best time to seize control of the planet.

lap

Badly positioned so viewers could only see the Persian cat he was stroking on his lap, the 72-year-old tyrant assured viewers that he would be back to assert his ultimate authority over humanity once it was safe to do so.

"I had spent years preparing a litany of evil plans to hold the world to ransom which I was about to abstractedly explain in excruciating detail to world leaders," he told the earth's 7.8 billion inhabitants.

Megalomaniac's domination plans on hold

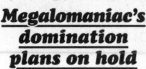

"Then this virus comes along and I've had to put it all on ice. It's very disappointing."

rain

And the head of global criminal organisation SPEC-TRE admitted to being disheartened that nations were 'pulling together' to control the virus.

"My modus operandi has always been to act as puppet master to individual governments, fostering discord and suspicion and pulling the strings of power to fulfil my own evil machinations," he told a spellbound planet.

"I have to say, when governments work together, it makes my job much more difficult."

safety

The sinister autocrat, who earns more in one second than many people earn in their lives, has been locked down on his superyacht since March, unable to go about his business of using billions of people as pawns in his evil, power-hungry and maniacal plans. And he told his online audience that it had been a very difficult period.

"I've spent most of my time binge-watching boxsets on Netflix, listening to podcasts and making sourdough bread," he announced to the entire human race. "It was good fun at first, but now I can't wait to get back to my usual routine of threatening to wipe entire countries from the map at the flick of a switch."

football

But top MI6 officials were upbeat about the setback to Blofeld's plans. "The Covid-19 outbreak has been a terrible thing, but it's an ill wind that blows no good," said 006 Terry Golightly, a triple-agent currently working undercover in Moscow.

"There might be the thick end of a million Covid deaths worldwide, but you could times that by ten if Blofeld gets his way," he said from his secret hideout opposite the Tretyakov Gallery in Lavrushinsky Lane.

MANY BUSINESSES are struggling to keep afloat during the Covid-19 pandemic, and those in the field of totalitarian oppression are no different. Here's how a few evil geniuses have survived through lockdown and how they plan to adapt to the 'new normal.'

Ah! Covid-19... I've been expecting you

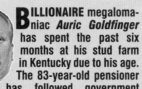

ASSASSIN-for-hire *Francisco Scaramanga* has not shot any public figure dead in an attempt to de-stabilise the United Nations since February. "I have mild asthma, so I've been shielding," he explained on a crackly, untraceable phone line. "I've been quite anxious about going out, but luckily I have a private island patrolled by 300 henchmen trained in the martial arts," he added.

But coronavirus has put the 65-year-old's assassination duties on hold. "Nobody wants anybody killed during this plague," he said. "Anyway, I've ran out of gold bullets since my source in China has been shut down."

And the tri-pappilate hitman was not optimistic about prospects for his homicide business when lockdown restrictions eventually end.

"During this pandemic I've certainly taken a hit, if you'll pardon the pun," he joked. "I'm already the highest paid assassin in the world, but even so, I reckon I'll have to put my fees up when all this has blown over."

EVIL mastermind *Sir Hugo Drax* was preparing to send satellites armed with chemical weapons into space when the lockdown began. "I was all set to destroy the entire human race, save for a small group of carefully selected astronauts to breed a future master race when all this kicked off," said Sir Hugo, who was knighted in 1997 for services to charity.

"I had 500 henchmen ready to unquestioningly do my bidding, and they've all been furloughed."

"What's more, I've had to mothball all my rockets. And I'm even having to feed all the piranhas in the tank below that trapdoor myself," he grumbled from his atomic-bomb-proof bunker two kilometres below the surface of the earth.

BILLIONAIRE megalomaniac *Auric Goldfinger* has spent the past six months at his stud farm in Kentucky due to his age. The 83-year-old pensioner has followed government advice and self-isolated, spending his time admiring his own ingot collection and caressing his custom-made laser spy-cutting gun.

"I was planning to steal the entire U.S. gold reserve from Fort Knox this year, but I really can't take the risk of bumping into anyone who might be infected," he told us via a video link.

"I had my own private army ready, a sinister matt black helicopter on standby, a bomb primed, the lot. I was good to go, but then the virus struck and I was confined to the house."

"My friend Pussy Galore has been doing my shopping for me and leaving it at the door," he said.

The former SMERSH treasurer admitted that it had been a lonely lockdown, but said he had spent the six months wisely, learning to speak Swedish and taking crumbhorn lessons over the web.

"I could order a pint of beer in Sweden now. It's just a pity I can't afford to," he quipped.

"No, seriously, have you seen the fucking prices out there?"

FORMER British agent turned cyber-terrorist *Raoul Silva* was prevented from implementing his plan to get revenge on his former MI6 boss M during lockdown.

"M allowed the Chinese government to take me prisoner in return for six British agents, the rotten cow," he told reporters via an encrypted email, sent using a series of proxy servers. "I was planning to piggy-back social media to reveal the identities of loads of British spies to get my own back, and then my computer went tits up."

The disfigured former secret service agent, whose real name is *Tiago Rodrigues*, was unable to get an IT expert to come out to his Shanghai hideaway to sort out his 4-year-old iMac.

"IT engineers were not deemed 'essential workers' so they couldn't come out and take a look," the sinister villain said.

"My usual engineer, Clive, was working from home and offered to have a look remotely via TeamViewer, but that relies on you having a working computer, so I was in a Catch-22 situation," he added.

With the necessary files unobtainable, the cyberterrorist has postponed his plans of seeking revenge until 2021.

"I'll wait until I'm fully up and running computer-wise, so I can do it properly," he said. "Until then, I'll just get my PC laptop and piss about with a few cyber-attacks on elections across the world, and launching the odd nuclear strike here and there," he told us.

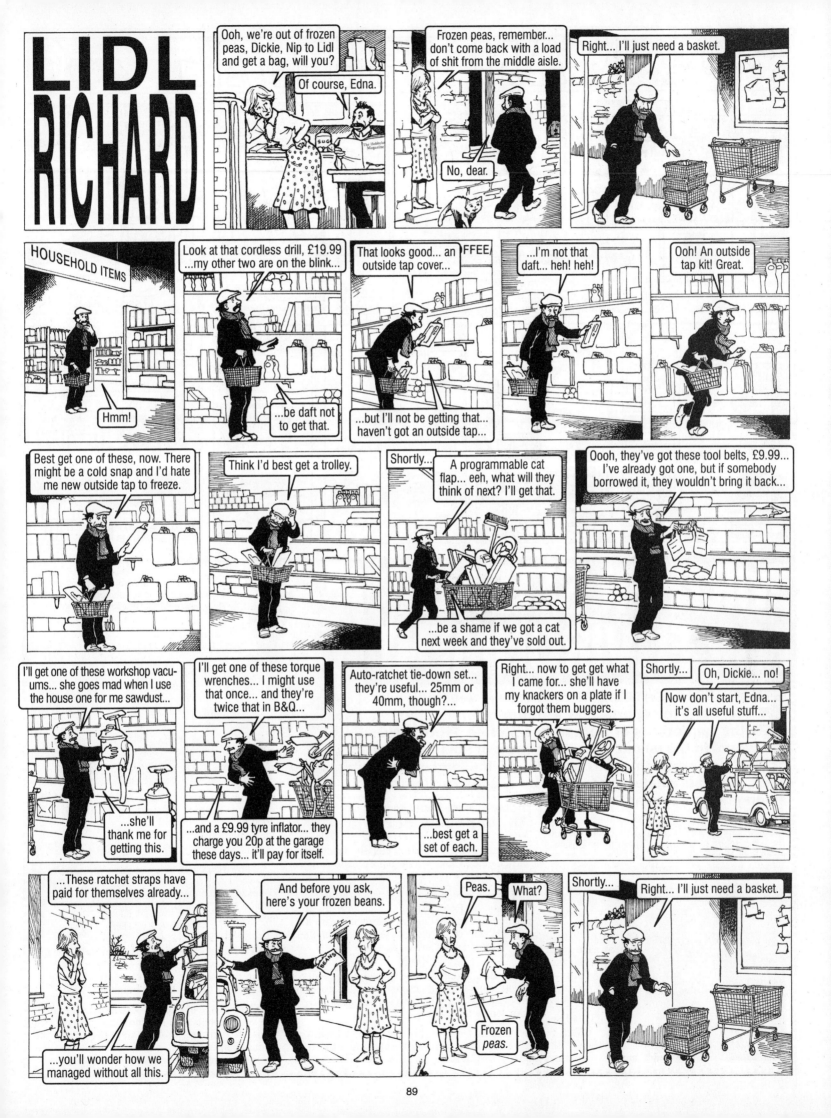

IVAN JELICAL

FURTHER SETBACK FOR ENVIRONMENT

ENVIRONMENTALISTS yesterday reacted with concern to reports that a group of orangutans in the rainforests of Borneo has started **FRACKING**. Residents in the island's southern town of Pelaihari, one of the last remaining strongholds of the endangered apes, noticed what appeared to be a construction site among trees early last week.

Locals reported seeing the orange-coloured simians felling large trees and stripping them of their branches in order use them as beams in a primitive drilling rig.

plant

"It happened so quickly," said local farmer Eric Chia. "One minute the apes were lounging round in the canopy, masturbating and throwing their shit at each other as usual, the next they'd built a working shale gas extraction plant."

Mobile phone footage taken by Chia shows the hairy primates

Frac-king of the swingers: A young orangutan, yesterday.

By our Science Correspondent
Dr. Ingledew Botterill

releasing a high pressure mix of water, sand and chemicals into a hole before capturing the emerging gas in a palm leaf gasometer.

"I can't pretend this isn't a setback," said Greenpeace President Jonathan Porritt. "Just when we were starting to realise the extent of the challenge posed by climate breakdown, these bloody monkeys go and do this."

page

But BBC naturalist and national treasure Sir David Attenborough thought that discovering the orang-utans could learn to frack added to our knowledge of them.

"At first I thought this must be the mimicking behaviour for which the great apes are renowned," he told *BBC Wildlife* magazine. "But it seems that fracking has never taken place in Borneo, so they must have come up with the idea themselves. So that's great," he added.

Energy suppliers around the world wasted no time in contacting the simian frackers, hoping to cut a deal on any newly-extracted gas.

bonham

"It's a total no-brainer," said Texan billionaire Hyram T Funkbucket. "This is a whole new front in the energy market and we want in, big time. We're going to pay them in bananas."

"Shale gas, extracted by endangered animals, the very animals who live in the rainforest? Hot dang! It don't get more ethical than that," he added, whilst wearing an enormous Stetson hat and chomping down on a fat Cuban cigar.

Forest dump: Simian fracking is stripping the Bornean rainforest of its vegetation, but Attenborough (below) is excited by the development.

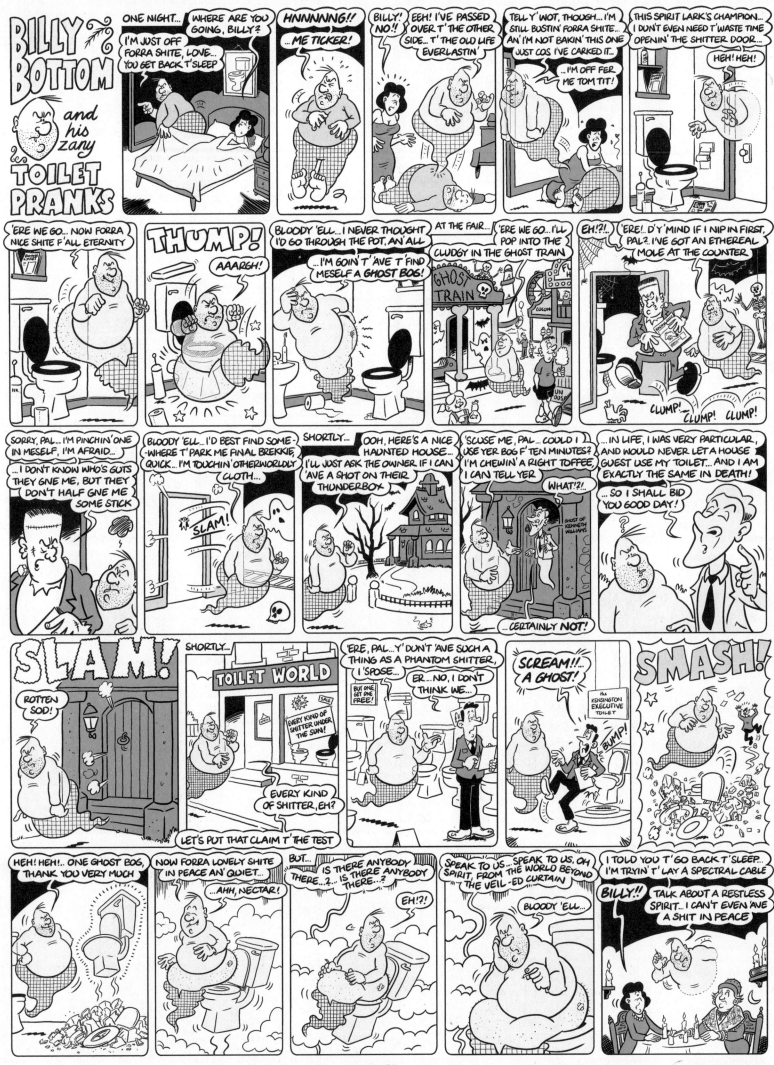

How Our Government Works

This Week:

The COBRA MEETING

THERE'S to be a **COBRA** meeting. The announcement strikes concern into the heart of the British people, for these highly secretive conferences are called only in times of national crisis, when the country faces a natural disaster, or a man-made threat from home or abroad.

The secretive nature of these meetings means nobody except those involved know what is going on. Indeed, only a few people actually know what **COBRA** stands for, and we're not one of them.

So let's take a look at the timeline of a hypothetical crisis and take a speculative look at what goes on in the top secret **COBRA** meeting that ensues…

1 THURSDAY: 15:15
REPORTS come in that a Russian dissident has been assassinated on the streets of Fulchester using a powerful neurotoxin. It is feared that the town could be contaminated with the deadly chemical and that the loss of life is potentially huge. It's time for the COBRA machine to roll swiftly into action.

6 TUESDAY: 10:06 am.
EVERYONE has their coffee, but before the meeting begins in earnest, the Secretary for Business, Energy and Industrial Strategy suggests that whilst everyone is assembled, they take the opportunity to quickly discuss a series of potential venues for the upcoming Cabinet Christmas party. It is agreed that after the COBRA meeting, he will make a few phone calls and get some quotes for prices.

7 TUESDAY: 11:31
AFTER a 15 minute toilet break, the meeting begins in earnest. The chair explains the urgent nature of the crisis and outlines a series of factors which need to be considered before any decisions on the correct course of action are taken. Suddenly, The Cabinet Secretary's phone rings. All other members of the COBRA Committee have, under order, put their phones on mute. But there may be fast-paced developments in the situation that are pertinent to the meeting, and the Cabinet Secretary is the designated 'contact.' The meeting holds its breath, eager to know if and how this new information will change the circumstances. But it's just the CS's wife asking him to pick up a bag of salad on his way home. Everyone breathes a sigh of relief.

13 TUESDAY: 15:12
AN IT technician arrives and, since he does not have the necessary security clearance, all talk of the situation must once again stop whilst he tries to get Powerpoint working.

14 TUESDAY: 15:42
AFTER half an hour, he is still unable to fix the problem without a different lead and the presentation looks at risk of being abandoned. The Chief Scientific Officer suggests passing his laptop round the table.

12 TUESDAY: 14:59
THE government's Chief Scientific Officer explains the seriousness of the situation and outlines the options open to the Committee in a Powerpoint presentation. Unfortunately, he cannot get it to show on the big screen in the briefing room, and someone from the IT department is summoned.

NO INPUT SIGNAL

15 TUESDAY: 15:45
IT'S time for afternoon tea and biscuits, and all talk ceases as the catering manager comes in. But once she vacates the room, the intense discussions begin immediately. In a normal cabinet meeting, the attendees would relax over their refreshments, but there is no time to spare in this dynamic, fast-paced COBRA meeting. Time is of the essence and tea and biscuits must be consumed 'on the hoof.'

16 TUESDAY: 15:52
EAGER to ensure that no decisions are rushed in a matter of such vital importance, and aware that the traffic will start to get busy soon, the Chair decides to call the meeting to an end. He sums up the situation, saying that it is of such gravity, that further discussion is essential, and it is agreed that another COBRA meeting must be called as soon as is practicable.

2 THURSDAY: 15:22

SEVEN minutes after the first report comes in, the Home Secretary is informed and immediately calls to update the Prime Minister. She suggests that the PM chairs a COBRA meeting that evening to organise the response to the crisis. Unfortunately the PM is booked to do an after dinner speech at 8 o'clock and he's got other stuff on for Friday, including driving round the *Top Gear* test track. Then it's the weekend and Monday is a bank holiday, so the meeting is given top priority and scheduled to start first thing at 9:00 sharp on Tuesday morning.

3 TUESDAY: 09:23

AFTER coffee and Danish pastries in Starbucks, members of the Cabinet, the government's Chief Scientific Officer and some senior figures from the armed forces and intelligence services amble over to Whitehall to get the emergency COBRA meeting started. There is no time to lose.

5 TUESDAY: 09:51

WITH attendees and absentees noted and a Chair appointed, it's time for coffee, and a member of the Whitehall catering team brings in refreshments. Catering staff have only the basic level of security clearance, and anything discussed in the meeting would be way above their pay grade. So all discussion of the situation must stop until the coffee has been poured and the room cleared of non-essential personnel.

4 TUESDAY: 09:45

THE COBRA committee members are seated around the big oak desk in Cabinet Office Briefing Room A, ready to discuss the best way to tackle this fast-moving crisis. After a little smalltalk, the meeting begins with the Cabinet Secretary reading out the Apologies for Absence, including the Home Secretary, the Foreign Secretary, the Chancellor of the Exchequer, the Health Secretary, the Attorney General and the Prime Minister. As the most senior ranking minister present, the Parliamentary Under Secretary of State for Environment, Food and Rural Affairs assumes the chair.

8 TUESDAY: 11:55

THE committee members are now in full possession of all the facts and are fully briefed about the situation on the ground. They next have to discuss which of a series of proposed courses of action is the best to take. Not wanting to make any rushed decisions, the Chair decides to adjourn for lunch and orders the committee to reconvene at 1:30 pm.

9 TUESDAY: 14:08 pm.

ALL the members are back from lunch, refreshed and ready to get to work. But before the meeting re-starts in earnest, the Under Secretary of State for International Trade asks everyone to sign a "Sorry You're Leaving" card for a Junior Cabinet Minister who has been selected as the scapegoat for an incident and forced to resign.

11 TUESDAY: 14:52

THE Cabinet Secretary's phone rings again, and once more the committee holds its breath. It is the Russian ambassador, who has learned about the situation from the Kremlin. Concerned about relations between the two countries deteriorating, he is calling to ask whether the Foreign Office is still going to take him to their corporate hospitality suite at the next Arsenal match. The committee members relax again.

10 TUESDAY: 14:49

AFTER 20 minutes of pleasantries, including the Secretary of State for Local Government showing everyone pictures of her cat, the Chair calls the meeting to order and recaps the main points of the morning session of the meeting.

17 TUES: 16:05

THE members of the Committee exit Whitehall and nip for a quick drink in one of their exclusive clubs before going home.

18 TUESDAY: 18:01

THE nature of the situation is such that the press can be told nothing. Consequently, the evening news will feature reporters standing outside Number 10, speculating on what might or might not have been discussed in the meeting until Larry the cat comes out and starts licking his arse.

Next Week: How Government Works -

The Cross Party Select Committee Briefing

I MUST BE THE UNLUCK[...]

"That's Life!" – Yorkshireman Gary remains philosophical over lost millions

WINNING a life-changing fortune on the lottery is everyone's dream. But to lose the magic ticket before even cashing it in is surely the stuff of nightmares. And it's a nightmare that former West Yorkshire binman GARY EGGPIPER knows all too well, after he came into unbelievable fortunes on several occasions, only to have his riches cruelly snatched from his hands by the fickle finger of fate.

"I sometimes feel like the world is playing a sick joke on me," Eggpiper, 57, told his local paper the *Choddington Chronicle*. "To see my winnings go up in smoke once is rotten luck, but going through the same experience on multiple occasions makes me think it just isn't supposed to happen."

And Gary' isn't the only victim of his bad luck. It has also cost his friends and family the chance of living the high life.

"I wouldn't mind so much if it was just my money, because I'd only have myself to blame," he told us. "But unfortunately, my winnings have always been part of a syndicate. That means that my losses have robbed my loved ones of their fair share as well."

"I feel pig sick about it."

He told us: "Money shouldn't be the most important thing in the world, but sadly my lousy luck has resulted in bad blood between me and the people I care about most."

Rollover and Out

Eggpiper, who enjoys racing exotic sports cars at the weekend, explained how, about 10 years ago, he came to both win and lose his first mammoth windfall.

" Me and my family had been paying into a little syndicate since the National Lottery first started. Me, my mum, my sister and my two brothers each chose a line made up of birthdays and dates that were significant to the family. My older brother, Alan, kept it in his wallet and we'd all give him the money so that each week he could buy the ticket when he went to pick up his fish and chips on a Friday night.

EXCLUSIVE!

Over the years we'd won the odd tenner for three numbers here and there, but nothing to write home about. Then one evening I got a call from Alan. I could barely understand what he was saying through the excitement, but it didn't take me long to realise that we'd hit the motherlode.

That night had been a double rollover and the jackpot was a whopping £24 million!

I was so excited that I actually felt dizzy; winning the lottery really is a feeling like no other. Me and the family all met up at the local pub and we celebrated like we'd never celebrated before. This money would be life-changing for all of us, and not least for my dear old mum who needed an operation on her legs. And it meant my sister Pat, who'd been off work with depression, could finally give up her job at the chicken chlorination plant.

I told Alan that I'd take the winning ticket to Camelot and sort out all of the boring paperwork.

What happened next still sends a shiver down my spine."

detached

The binman, who lives in a 9-bedroom detached house in a private road near Ilkley, explained how he came to LOSE the lotto ticket which would have seen his mother, and each of his siblings, receive almost £5 million each.

> ## It didn't take me long to realise that we'd hit the motherlode

"I was walking to the bus stop with the prizewinning piece of paper firmly wedged in the pocket of my jeans. The burden of responsibility weighed so heavy on me that I remember my brow dripping with sweat.

Suddenly, out of nowhere, a fox ran out of the woods and knocked me over. As I fell, my jeans must have torn on a fence post or something, and I remember watching as the lottery ticket fluttered out of my pocket and into the road.

With no thought for my own safety I sprinted into the path of oncoming traffic to retrieve the prized coupon, but alas I was too late. I watched in horror as a peregrine falcon swooped down, picked it up in its beak, and flew away into the distance with everything we'd ever dreamed of."

Gary, who owns a boat in the Dordogne, now had to tell his family the bad news and pray that they could find it in their hearts to forgive him.

"The next few weeks were all a bit of a blur. I remember there was a lot of shouting and tears as tension in the family ran high.

I frantically tried to find a way to sort it out, but there was nothing I could do and the money was gone. Unfortunately, the bird must have dropped the ticket which somebody then found and handed in, because Camelot said that the prize had been claimed. We tried to tell them it was rightfully ours, but we couldn't prove it. Tragically, my brother Alan had bought it from a shop that didn't have CCTV.

I tried to explain to my family that in many ways it was Alan's fault, but things turned ugly and I decided it might be best if I moved out of the family home that we all lived in and into a new house that had a bit more room."

Road to ruin: Gary's dreams of a Lotto win were thwarted when a peregrine falcon (inset) flew off with his winning ticket.

Eggpiper, whose mansion contains an underground swimming pool and bowling alley, was confused by his family's reaction.

"I appreciate that my family don't want to see me any more, but I sometimes feel like they don't understand that I've lost out as well. I also had things I'd have loved to have done with that money.

I sometimes think they forget that I'm a bin man. They say that time heals all wounds so I'm hopeful that they'll forgive me one day for my momentary lapse of concentration."

Coining It In

32-stone Gary who is currently dating a 22-year-old Ukranian underwear model, thought that he'd seen enough drama for one lifetime, but in an unbelievable turn of events, he was about to go through it all again.

After the lottery debacle I started spending a bit more time with the lads that I worked with on the bins. I hadn't been turning up to work much because I was studying for my helicopter pilot's licence, but I was still seeing the boys at weekends.

We used to go metal detecting around the Yorkshire Dales and then spend the evening in the pub studying the bits and bobs that we'd dug up. Our plunder was usually just old bottle tops and the odd rusty key, but we had a laugh.

But one day, while we were detecting in a field in Norfolk, our detectors started beeping and flashing away like Billy-o. We began digging and what we found absolutely blew us away. *We'd just unearthed a treasure hunter's dream – thousands of gold Anglo-Saxon coins dating back over 1000 years and worth a king's ransom.*

We had it valued at almost £15 million and the British Museum immediately offered to buy it.

The next day, after an interview with the local rag, I agreed to take the life-changing hoard down to London and sort out all of the tedious museum paperwork. What happened to me on my way still makes me wake in the night in a cold sweat."

terraced

Eggpiper, who was last week photographed at one of Elton John's after-show parties, described how he lost his second opportunity to become filthy rich in another bizarre and unfortunate turn of events.

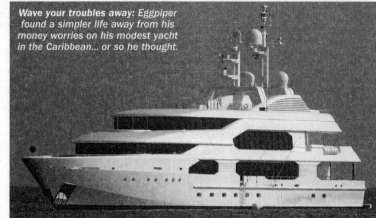

Wave your troubles away: Eggpiper found a simpler life away from his money worries on his modest yacht in the Caribbean... or so he thought.

"I was on the train with a case full of the extremely valuable coins, thinking about what had happened the previous year with the lottery ticket. I was determined to take extra special care of what I was carrying this time, and also looking forward to being able to have the opportunity to give my share of the cash to my family as a way to start building bridges.

Suddenly, out of nowhere, the train door opened, probably as a result of a fault with the electronics. I went over to try and fix it, but the train must have gone over some points or something, because as it jolted I fell out and rolled down a hill into the woods.

Dazed and confused, yet only concerned with my colleagues' money, I frantically darted around the undergrowth trying to find the case. But just as I spotted it lodged in a nearby bush, a fox appeared from nowhere and grabbed it. I could only watch helplessly as it ran away into the undergrowth, never to be seen again, with the case containing the treasure in its mouth."

Fox on the run: Eggpiper watched while wily creature stole valuable case.

Gary, who owns a Tuscan vineyard and was recently featured in Forbes Magazine, now had to tell his workmates that they wouldn't be jumping off the bin lorry just yet.

"I felt absolutely awful. I simply couldn't believe it was happening again. None of the lads were as understanding as I'd hoped and the whole thing put a deep fracture in our friendship. At that point I decided it was time to quit my job and get away from it all for a while.

Don't Bet On It

Eggpiper decided to go and spend some time on the Caribbean islands of St. Kitts and Nevis whilst he let things cool down back in Yorkshire.

I was sat on my yacht thinking how lonely I was and actually feeling a bit annoyed with my friends and family. They simply didn't appreciate that missing out on the chance to become a multimillionaire was something that I'd have to live with for the rest of my life too.

I buddied up with some rich fellas whilst I was on holiday. They were nothing like me and we had very little in common, but we seemed to rub along okay. One evening we all had a skinful in a Champagne bar and decided to all go in on buying a thoroughbred racehorse.

It all seemed a like a bit of a mad thing to do for a penniless binman like me, but you only live once and I was on holiday.

brick shit

A few weeks later our horse, *King Croesus*, was running in a race at Cheltenham and we all pooled a bit of money for a little flutter. We each threw a million into the pot and stuck it on our horse at 50/1. Unbelievably, the bloody thing won, and as we stood watching on the telly, we realised we were holding a betting slip worth almost £250 million. I've never drunk as much as I did that night, I can tell you. I couldn't believe I was going to get my third shot at a fortune."

Gary, who owns the publishing rights to over 30 tracks by The Beatles, couldn't wait to get hold of the money and make amends with his friends and family back in Yorkshire.

"With my share of the £250 million, I'd be able to pay back my family and my bin colleagues and still have enough left to live out my days in luxury. The next morning, I offered to take the betting slip to the bookies on the main island and deal with all the faffing about.

Surely, I thought, it couldn't happen again and this time I'd be extra, extra careful.

bob's full

I hired a small motorboat and headed towards the island with the betting slip safely stowed in the gusset of my underpants. I wasn't taking any chances this time. I was about halfway across the choppy Caribbean waters that separated the two archipelagos when something, possibly some kind of jumping fish, hit me hard in the side of the head, knocking me into the sea.

I spluttered to the surface with no consideration for my own well-being, and spotted the invaluable slip of paper floating away from me. But then, as I thrashed towards it, some sort of exotic tropical swordfish leapt out of the water and speared the betting slip on its razor-sharp beak. I could only watch in despair as the fish dived into the inky-blue depths of the

> ## We each threw a million into the pot and stuck it on our horse at 50/1

Caribbean Sea, vanishing forever with our quarter of a billion pound fortune.

At the mainland, I decided to get on the first plane back to West Yorkshire, where I resolved to stay at home with only a team of armed security guards and my supermodel girlfriend for company.

And that's exactly what I did. I don't gamble or put bets on anything any more, as I'm terrified of what might happen if I ever try and collect the winnings. Cruel fate has already cost me my family and friends.

I sometimes think about how different my life would be today if Lady Luck hadn't dealt me such a series of cruel blows, and I still had all of that money. I suppose it just wasn't meant to be.

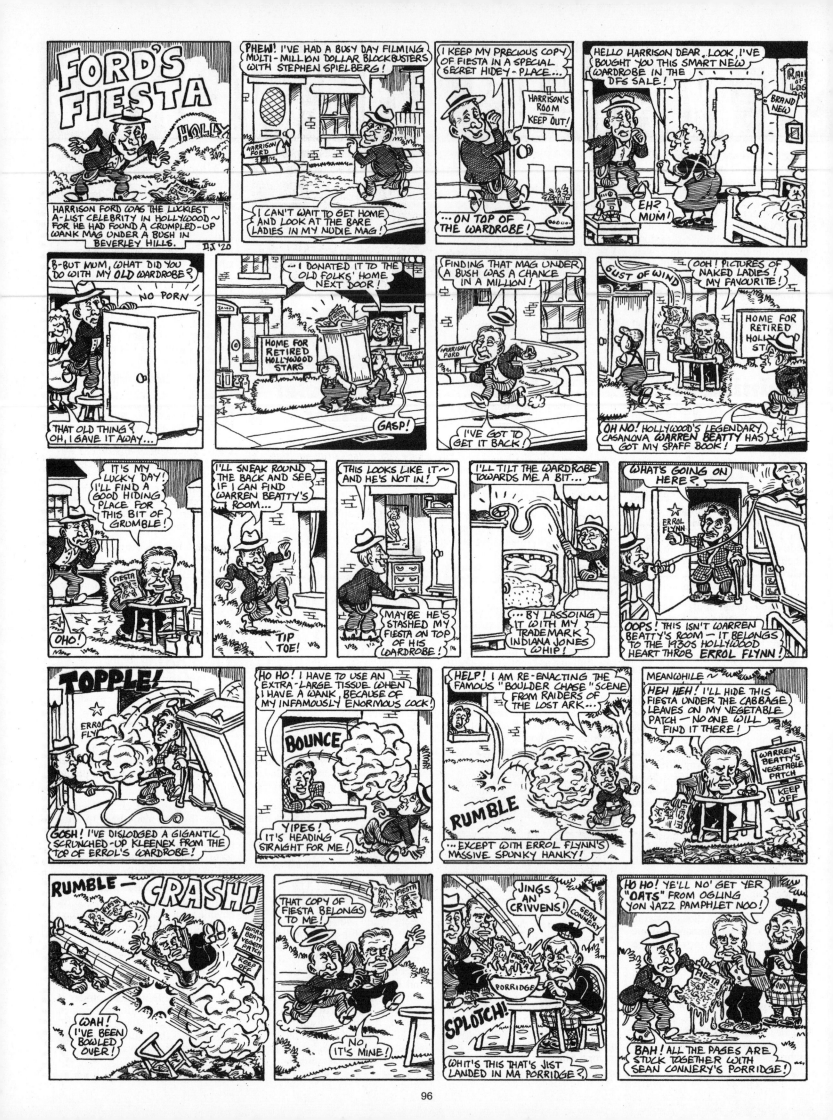

FARMER PALMER

FAN-CRAGGY -DOZI!

CELEBRATIONS were underway in Glasgow last night after the announcement that Ian Krankie has been named 'Britain's Craggiest Ian 2020,' knocking long-time champion Ian McShane off the top spot that he has occupied for the past 25 years.

Crinkled Krankies: Ian (left) 'deighted' after claiming craggy crown from Lovejoy heart-throb.

Fold-faced Krankie said he was delighted with the award, and said that he and his wife and son James 'Wee Jimmy' Krankie would be celebrating at a private get-together of close friends and internet contacts in a layby off the A74 near Bridgeton.

absurd

The BBC's absurdly-coiffed arts correspondent Will Gompertz dubbed Krankie's win *"a victory for the people."* He told us: *"For a long time now people have felt that Ian McShane's craggy face hasn't been what it used to be in his early-1990s heyday."*

McShane: Significantly smoother.

Following an unexpected late-career resurgence in American TV and film, many commentators have felt that the former *Lovejoy* actor has enjoyed a relaxed, stress-free Hollywood lifestyle, complete with all manner of creams, unguents and new-age skin treatments, which has inevitably led to a significant smoothing and softening of his previously rugged, careworn and irregular visage.

"In the meantime," Gompertz continued, fiddling with his glasses and wobbling his head to ensure that stray strands of hair flailed around eccentrically, *"the Krankies have continued to plough a solid furrow in unglamorous, low-end showbiz work such as provincial pantomimes and occasional ironic guest appearances."*

gruelling

"This gruelling lifestyle, coupled with the effects of being an ageing Scotsman, have added countless lines, ridges and bumps to Ian's already jowly countenance," he added.

McShane himself took the top spot in 1993, at the height of his popularity in the British fictional antiques dealer-cum-sleuth field, when it was revealed that the previous title holder, *Star Wars* actor Ian 'Evil Emperor' McDiarmid, wore prosthetic make-up to achieve his rough and pitted facial appearance in *Return of the Jedi.*

LETTERBOCKS

Viz Comic, P.O. Box 841 Whitley Bay, NE26 9EQ ★ letters@viz.co.uk

ST★R LETTER

WHILST watching the film *V For Vendetta*, I couldn't help thinking that actually V was for Viennetta, the delicious frozen dessert.

Richard Devereux, Hereford

WHY is it that in the shops now you can get sandwiches filled with avocados or hummus or salad, but never sandwiches filled with jam or crisps like real people eat? It's probably something to do with offending the minorities, no doubt. It's political correctness gone mad.

Shenkin Arsecandle, Llareggub

TO kill time, I was trying to come up with a witty – albeit unoriginal – Profanisaurus post, and I was leaning towards a twist on "wetter than an otter's pocket" by putting the otter in a Jacuzzi. This got me thinking about otters enjoying a Jacuzzi, and I couldn't think of a more joyful, happy scene, especially in contrast to the original smut intended. For all your readers' morale in these trouble times, could you print this picture?

Darren Quinney, Witney

* *Of course, Darren. Here's some lovely otters in a Jacuzzi to cheer our readers.*

WHY do we say elephants never forget? Surely it should be wives. I've yet to hear an elephant give me earache over something I said or did 15 fucking years ago.

Eldon Furse, email

BIG game hunters unfairly get a lot of bad press these days. I think they should follow the lead of the angling community and release the elephants back into the wild after they shoot them and chop off their tusks and feet.

John Moynes, Dublin

I DON'T know why people on the telly report big stuff in terms of Olympic swimming pools, Nelson's Columns and distances to the Moon. I've been to school and I've got a pretty good grasp of feet, inches, metres and kilometres. On the other hand I've never been to the moon or swam in an Olympic swimming pool.

Bren, Middlesbrough

I DON'T consider myself to be a conspiracy theorist, but I've just noticed that *Coronation Street* starts with the word Corona. I'm just working on the next bit.

Dominic Twose, Leamington Spa

I READ on the internet that pineapple juice improves the taste of your jizz. I tried it on my wife, but she reckoned it just ruined the pineapple juice.

Granty T, Australia

I CAN'T help but think that the people involved in Chicken Marketing in Britain are missing a trick with the male 18-30 demographic. By simply renaming 'Chicken Breasts' as 'Chicken Tits', they would surely increase their sales tenfold. Tender Chicken Tits would go down a treat in my eyes.

Tim Buktu, Timbuktu

THE Rock might be the hardest man but his Jellyfish Fact File *(page 77)* shows his knowledge of these creatures leaves a lot to be desired. I was always taught that a Portuguese man o' war is a species of siphonophore – hundreds of little animals that come together to make a single colony. Jellyfish, on the other hand, are one single animal. Maybe it's pedantic but fuck it. My degree might be useless but this might be the only time I use the fucker.

Pedantic zoologist Chris Jordan, email

IMAGINE if you had to toast potatoes. Just think how wide your toaster would have to be. Utterly ridiculous.

Ian Baker, Weston-s-Mare

I HAVE recently purchased a yearly subscription for Viz magazine on the App Store. However, I didn't realise that it was a different Viz. I wanted to get the Japanese manga Viz subscription and not this comic. Is it possible to get a refund? I have not used the app nor the prescription benefit. You can surely check that. If not, are you the same company with the Japanese comic Viz? If so, would you be able to transfer my subscription.

Lia, Western Australia

* *That is very unfortunate, Lia, and you have all our sympathy. But we're afraid that this particular Viz comic operates a strict "No Refunds" policy. There is literally nothing we can – or indeed are going to – do. However, as a gesture of goodwill in future issues, we will draw some of our cartoon characters with enormous eyes and wearing Japanese schoolgirl uniforms.*

WHY is it that bullshitters all have a fixation with the SAS?

Alan Bleach, Hereford

TO alleviate boredom I decided to stack up every issue of *Viz* (apart from 1-12 which I haven't got) in a big pile. To my disappointment, the stack barely came up to half my own height. I thought these sorts of things were supposed to go half way around the earth, or to the moon and back three times or something? Come on *Viz*, pull your finger out. Maybe if you were to publish several times a day and make each issue 1000 pages long, the pile would look a bit more impressive.

Ben Nunn, Caterham

WHY is it that high profile Germans, such as chancellor Angela Merkel and national football coach Joachim Low, still sport the 'German Helmet' hair style? The war finished 75 years ago. Let's move on for heaven's sake.

Dick Foreskinsythe, Skye

THAT say that you never know what's around the corner. What bollocks. Where I live there is a bus stop and a shop.

Morsey, Swindon

I JUST learned that orangutans share 97% of their DNA with humans, but I'm willing to bet we selfish humans don't share any of our DNA with them. We could all learn some lessons from the wise and noble orangutan, especially in these dark times.

Nikko Elliott, USA

I NEVER ever negotiate with terrorists. It's not that I take a particularly firm line with violent criminals, rather I just don't ever seem to find myself in the position of needing to do so.

Micky Bullock, London

UP THE ARSE CORNER

2231

Sender: Joanne, *email*

MARY, MUNGO AND MIDGE URE

1 A.M.

♫ IT MEANS NOTHING TO MEEEE... 7

♫...THIS MEANS NOTHING TO MEEEE... 7

THUD! THUD!

JOE DOLCE!

AH, SHADDAP-A YOU FACE!

♫ OHHHH VIENNAAA!

IS THAT THE DOOR?

I'M-A TRYING TO FUCKING SLEEP!

AS I'm now confined to working from home due to the Coronavirus lockdown, I'm unable to entertain my works colleagues with my prolific farting. However, I now record my farts on my phone and send them to everyone via WhatsApp. Remember, not all superheroes wear capes!

David Whiston, Shepherds Bush

SHRÖDINGER stated that in his box, the cat was neither dead nor alive. In that case, wouldn't it have been useful if he'd made his box from glass? He could have clearly seen in and given us a definitive answer instead of confusing us for years, the stupid bastard.

Lewis, Bristol

WHY IS it considered worse to be shat on 'from a great height'? If anything, you'd have time to move out the way. If the arse cheeks were hovering two inches above your bonce, you'd have no chance.

Dr P Granola, K'minster

IT seems terribly unfair that one person should get all the cash in the National Lottery Jackpot. Surely the best approach would be to take that enormous sum of money and divide it out equally between everyone who bought a ticket.

George Breakfast, Bordeaux

WHY is it that we take a shit but we do a poo? Doing a poo makes sense, but surely we leave a shit, not take it? Yet we also speak of being sick or having a piss. I'm just saying some consistency would be nice, that's all.

D Cooper, Malta

WHY DO I need a birth certificate? I'm here. Isn't that sufficient proof I was born?

Crevice Wetshaft, Bristol

I'D never use the toilet on a train. I don't trust that automatic door that opens up like it's revealing you as a prize on a game show. I'll bake it for a bit, thank you very much.

David Wardle, Manchester

WHEN I was a lad, my mum used to cut my hair by placing a pudding bowl on top of my head and snipping around the edge. One day, she couldn't find the pudding bowl, so she used a colander instead. She couldn't do round the sides, because the colander's handles were in the way, and she also chopped off all the hair that stuck out through the holes. As a result I ended up with a ridiculous short blunt fringe, long sideburns and all stupid sticky-up bits on top. Rather than being annoyed, however, I liked this unusual look so much that I've stuck with it all my life!

Paul Weller, London

I HAVE been furloughed from my job as a museum curator. I've always meant to write to *Viz* and now I find myself with the time on my hands to write to you, so I am writing to you.

Harold Abrahams, email

∗ Thank you for your letter, Harold, but our correspondents usually have a theme of some sort. Writing to us simply to say that you are writing to us seems self evident and pointless. Why don't you try again, but this time make your letter about how you think that garden birds are less colourful than they used to be, or that there are too many types of cheese for sale in supermarkets, or something interesting like that? Or, if you can't think of an interesting subject for correspondence, you could always request that we print that picture of that bloke kissing that bird's arse.

WHAT is the point of arse-crack hair? All it seems good for is making clagnuts. Porn stars seem to get by perfectly well without it. I wondered if any of your readers are arse-crack hair specialists and could tell us what it's for.

Mark Starling, Norwich

I'M reading *Wolf Hall* by Hilary Mantel. It's alright, but most of the male characters are called Tom. Surely a Booker Prize winner should have a bit more imagination than that? What's wrong with Keith or Barry?

Iain Forbes, Falun

NOW that we all have to keep social-distancing from each other, please spare a thought for milkmen, posties, pizza delivery men, plumbers and the like. If they succumb to the charms of négligée-clad MILFs, whose numbers must have increased exponentially due to home working and who must be bored out of their minds, then they risk contracting COVID-19. There's never been so much opportunity, yet they can't take advantage of it.

Trevor de Payen, Lahndn

SPARTANIC PARK

CREATING a theme park featuring real-life dinosaurs from the Jurassic era has long been the stuff of Hollywood fiction. But a similar park containing actual **SPARTANS from 500BC is set to become reality, according to one Icelandic scientist.**

Archaeologist Professor Ingibjorg Magnusmagnusson from Reykjavic University says that a drinking vessel from classical Sparta could yield human DNA, which in turn could be used to clone the individual who drank from it two-and-a-half millennia ago.

Sparta cup: Could human DNA taken from drinking vessel clone ancient race?

EXCLUSIVE!

"It would be the first Spartan seen by human eyes since they became extinct in 192 BC," said Dr Magnusmagnusson.

"There are lots of Spartan artifacts in museums around the world – forks, spoons, swords – from which DNA could be extracted, and then it would be possible to clone a whole community of the ancient civilisation," he told *New Scientist* magazine.

"There would be warriors, free citizens and slaves, men and women, the lot," he continued.

"In a museum in Crete, there's a helmet that belonged to the ruling Spartan monarch from 486BC. We can easily get some DNA from the inside of that and clone a King Leonidas I to rule over the park. It's going to be fantastic."

plot

Magnusmagnusson plans to open his Spartanic Park early next year on a 40-acre plot of land north of Reykjavic. Visitors will be able to drive around and observe a real-life Spartan civilisation in action as the people go about their everyday life.

The archaeologist admitted he is yet to obtain any actual Spartan DNA and is uncertain about how Spartans could be cloned when he gets it, but he was certain that it could be done.

"I'm sure the museums will lend me things, then I'll just hand them to the

Greekjavik: Magnusmagnusson hopes to recreate ancient Sparta (above) with his 40-acre Spartan theme park north of Reykjavic in early 2021.

biologists and genetic engineers and let them do their stuff," he told the magazine.

Meanwhile, Magnusmagnusson, who has been suffering depression following a conviction for shoplifting, after which his wife left him, said that the park would rival the Blue Lagoon as Iceland's number one tourist attraction.

fortunes

And he claimed that Spartanic Park would boast a state-of-the-art gift shop larger than any others on the island, selling mugs, posters and small models of cats dressed in Spartan gear.

"I've had 100,000 pencils made with *'I've Been to Spartanic Park'* written on the side, and half a million rubbers in

the shape of a Spartan helmet," he said.

But he cautioned that visiting the park would not be entirely risk free, and guests would have to follow strict rules. "As anyone who has watched the film 300 will know, the Spartans aren't afraid of a punch-up," he said. "So all visitors will be asked to stay in their cars and keep their windows up at all times."

values

And he said that visitors from the middle east would, regretfully, be barred from entry at all times. "It's nothing racist," he insisted. "It's just that there's a lot of bad blood between the Spartans and the Persians, and I wouldn't want anything kicking off."

300 BLOOPERS

THE 2006 film *300* told the epic Spartan tale of the Battle of Thermopylae. And the movie well and truly earned the epithet "Blockbuster" after grossing $456 million at the box office. But it could have taken much, much more had it not been riddled with gaffs, goofs and bloopers. Here are a few howlers that held it back…

● In the gory fight sequences, the Spartans approach their enemies swinging their swords, with the film going into slow motion as the blade delivers the fatal blow, then speeding up again. But according to historians, Spartan warriors killed their enemies at the same pace without slowing down in the middle.

● The night before the 300 set off for Thermopylae, King Leonidas, played by **GERARD BUTLER**, spends a night of passion with his love, Queen Gorgo. The scene is tasteful and romantic, but eagle-eyed viewers will notice that Butler has a Glasgow Celtic FC tattoo on his arse. A lifelong fan of the Bhoys, Butler had the crest tattooed on his buttocks on his 16th birthday. Special effects technicians were meant to remove it digitally in post-production, but forgot.

● In the same scene, eagle-eyed viewers will notice that Queen Gorgo, played by **LENA HEADEY**, has 'Accrington Stanley 2003' tattooed on her left knocker. A lifelong fan of the Lancashire club,

Headey had the tattoo done to celebrate the Accys' victory in the Northern Premier League Challenge Shield. The tattoo was removed digitally in post-production, but special effects technicians submitted the wrong files to the film processing unit.

● The film begins with Dilios, a one-eyed Spartan soldier and survivor of Thermopylae, recounting the story of the battle to his men gathered round the campfire. The film then continues in flashback, and Dilios's eye has miraculously grown back! Later in the film, he loses it again… *in the same battle that he was recounting at the start of the film.*

● In one scene, King Xerxes – played by **RODRIGO SANTORO** – commands Leonidas to kneel at his feet. Eagle-eyed viewers will notice that the time on Xerxes' digital watch reads 15:22. The camera then cuts to Leonidas' defiant face for 3 seconds, before cutting back to Xerxes… *whose watch now reads 15:38!*

BRINGING THAT SPARTAN SPARKLE INTO MODERN LIFE

THE SPARTAN civilisation lasted for seven centuries, and was built on the cornerstones of bravery, honour, fairness and democracy. But despite being one of the most successful city states of ancient times, Sparta eventually came to an end in 192 BC. Although it was a tough and brutal culture, it arguably had many qualities which we in 2020 would do well to emulate. Let's look at how we could learn from the past and bring the best of Ancient Sparta into our own day-to-day lives.

Children

THE SPARTANS were notoriously strict with the upbringing of their children, treating them harshly, pointing out their faults and instilling a rigid code of honour in them. The result was that adult Spartans were strong and focused and able to deal with whatever life threw at them. Whilst not going quite so far as whipping our children with leather straps on their seventh birthday, we modern parents could benefit from toughening up our namby-pamby children in a Spartan manner. When dropping your kids off at school, don't give them a hug, but hold them firmly by the shoulders and tell them to *"Come home with a gold star, or don't come home at all."* Also let your young Spartan know that there is no shame, but rather honour, in taking crayons from weaker children, and fighting anyone who tries to take anything from them.

Religion

LIKE ALL ancient Greeks, the Spartans were polytheistic in their beliefs – Zeus, Aphrodite, Poseidon and Hera were just a few of the many Gods they worshipped. And anyone wanting to bring that Ancient Spartan variety into their faith should consider ditching the single God they follow at the moment and instead worshipping the lot. As a modern day Spartan, you should be popping into churches, mosques, gurdwaras and synagogues on a regular basis, and praying to each of the top men. Just remember which are the ones you must or must not wear hats in and you'll be keeping the traditions of ancient Sparta alive.

Exercise

SPARTANS WERE perhaps the fittest civilisation the world has seen due to their daily routine of vigorous exercise and regular bouts of competitive sport. And the modern Spartan should similarly train hard and long in the gym, spending as much time on the toning tables and spin machines as possible every day. If you're going to do this properly, you will probably need to upgrade from Off-Peak to Platinum membership. Furthermore, Sparta was the first city in Greece to practise athletic nudity – exercising, training and engaging in sport in the altogether. With this in mind, try doing your gym routine and pilates classes completely Billy Bollocks, remembering of course to wipe the seats of the machines after use. And if confronted by other gym users, simply challenge them to a wrestling bout.

Sparta fresh: What lessons could we learn from the Spartans?

Food

SPARTANS ATE meagre rations of food as a way to avoid becoming sluggish, but also to give them a taste of what it is like to not have enough; a feeling which gave them the incentive to defend what was theirs and fight for what was not. Anyone working on a zero hours contract or at Sports Direct will already be following this Spartan diet out of necessity, but anyone with a larger disposable income could do the same. When you cook a meal, put the amount you want to eat on the plate and then scrape half of it into the bin before sitting down and tucking into the remainder. If you fancy going out to eat, avoid belly-busting pizza restaurants or all-you-can-eat buffets and, instead, go for Michelin-starred restaurants that offer microscopic portions, or a McDonald's Happy Meal.

Work

ALL SPARTAN MEN were full-time soldiers in the city-state army. Everything they did was for the honour of their nation, and all duties were performed without complaint or question, and with zeal and enthusiasm. And the modern Spartan should take this work ethic with them to their place of employment. If your boss asks for a volunteer, perhaps to descale the coffee machine or fetch some paperclips from the stockroom, don't hide in the toilet or pretend to be engrossed in another task like the rest of your workmates. Step forward and proclaim in a loud, clear voice that it would be an honour to perform the task. Remember to keep an stern, impassive look on your face as you carry out orders and you're sure to win promotion.

Marriage

A MOST UNUSUAL custom took place on a couple's wedding night in Sparta. After the ceremony, the newly married bride was taken up to her husband's bedroom where her head was shaved to the scalp by a bridesmaid. She was then dressed in a man's cloak and sandals and left on the bed. After finishing his dinner downstairs, the bridegroom would go up to his room and consummate the marriage with his wife. It would be unthinkable to recreate this bizarre ritual today, but we need not throw it out completely. A newly married couple wanting to add a little saucy Spartan zest to their marriage could get the best man to shave the groom's head, put him in a dress and women's shoes and lay him on the bed to await his wife's arrival. It is the 21st century after all.

WOULD THE CELEBS HAVE CUT THE MUSTARD AT THE BATTLE OF THERMOPYLAE?

IT'S ONE of the most iconic battles of the Ancient World. An army of 300 Spartans led by King Leonidas taking on the might of Xerxes I and his 250,000 troops at Thermopylae – the Hot Gates. The odds were against Leonidas and his men, but the fierceness with which this tiny Spartan army fought – and the courage they showed in the face of such adversity – has gone down in history. The Battle of Thermopylae has become a byword for bravery and honour. But would that be the case if some of today's stars had been amongst that army of 300? Let's take a look at a few top A-listers and speculate on how they would have behaved at the Battle of the Hot Gates.

Lulu

ON THE FACE OF IT, you would imagine Scottish singer Lulu to be a little out of place amongst an army of warriors hell bent on destroying their Persian invaders. But being brought up in Glasgow, the *To Sir With Love* favourite probably spent many hours scrapping and brawling in pubs, so would be well used to the combative environment of the battlefield. And don't think her diminutive size would count against her, either. Two thousand years ago, people were much smaller than they are today, so Lulu - at 5 foot 2 - would be of fairly average Spartan height. And her booming voice, which she used to great effect at the start of her 1964 hit single *Shout,* could be put to good use to rally the troops to arms if the man with the trumpet were to fall in battle.

The only problem Lulu would face at Thermopylae would be one she could do little about… her *gender*. Whilst Spartans gave women equal rights in many areas of life, military service was not one of them, and no matter how hard she pleaded, King Leonidas would have insisted that the *Boom Bang-a-Bang* Eurovision joint winner stayed behind with the rest of the women.

SPARTAN RATING 120/300

Dan Snow

THERE IS LITTLE that historian Dan Snow does not know about war. With dozens of TV documentaries and books on the subject under his belt, he is surely Britain's foremost expert on military history and strategy. As such, he would be a huge asset to the 300 Spartans facing down the might of a Persian army a thousand times their size. What's more, with his expert knowledge of two centuries of fighting tactics, he could advise his commanders shrewdly and perhaps turn the tide of battle.

But perhaps not. Snow's knowledge is purely theoretical, and no amount of book learning or BBC training could prepare him for the horrors of what lay ahead. Looking up to see a million arrows blotting out the sun, he would most likely soil his armour. And if he survived that rain of death, at six-and-a-half foot tall, he would stand head and shoulders above his comrades, making him an easy target for a Persian lanceman.

SPARTAN RATING 172/300

Vinnie Jones

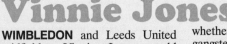

WIMBLEDON and Leeds United midfielder Vinnie Jones would certainly have been one of the fiercest opponents the Persians would have faced at Thermopylae. During his playing career, he earned his reputation as a tough nut on the field and even presented the now infamous *Soccer's Hard Men* video. And Jones's post football acting career is similarly peppered with hard roles, whether he is playing an East End gangster, a mob enforcer, or an elite assassin. So Jones would certainly have been welcomed into Leonidas's army of 300.

Or would he? Spartan warriors put great store by fighting with dignity and honour on the battlefield. But on the football field, Jones fouled his way to twelve red cards during his career – not to mention countless yellows, one of which was awarded just three seconds into a game. This lamentable record of ungentlemanly conduct would doubtless be frowned upon by his fellow Spartan warriors.

SPARTAN RATING 220/300

Benny Hill

THE LATE KING of bawdy comedy Benny Hill, with his rotund figure and round glasses, would look out of place amongst the ripped, bronzed bodies of his comrades in arms. In fact, had Hill been born a Spartan, the fat, short-sighted baby would have been cast into the Chasm of Mount Taygetos, a fate that awaited all newborns who didn't match the Spartan ideal. But it would have been their loss, for the comedian and *Ernie, the Fastest Milkman in the West* singer served as a mechanic in WWII and could have been put to good use on the battlefield at Thermopylae, mending spears, shields and helmets. And if for any reason King Leonidas called a tactical retreat, Hill could show his 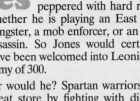 comrades how to run away at twice the normal speed whilst taking tiny little steps.

But it's not all positive. In many ways, Spartan society was ahead of its time, affording women rights, power and respect that they found nowhere else in the ancient world. For this reason, the Spartan warriors may have been offended by Hill's old-fashioned, sexist brand of comedy, with its heavy reliance on women's clothes being accidentally ripped off, and old men who are a foot-and-a-half shorter than their much younger, large-breasted wives.

SPARTAN RATING 260/300

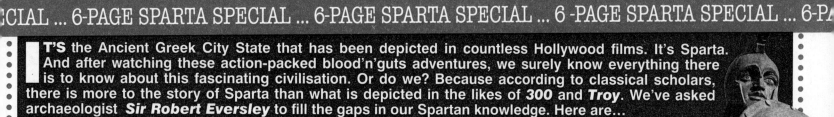

IT'S the Ancient Greek City State that has been depicted in countless Hollywood films. It's Sparta. And after watching these action-packed blood'n'guts adventures, we surely know everything there is to know about this fascinating civilisation. Or do we? Because according to classical scholars, there is more to the story of Sparta than what is depicted in the likes of *300* and *Troy*. We've asked archaeologist *Sir Robert Eversley* to fill the gaps in our Spartan knowledge. Here are...

300 20 THINGS YOU NEVER KNEW ABOUT SPARTA

1 **PACK** a suitcase and set off to visit Sparta today, and you're in for a disappointment. Because the city state was closed down for good in 192 BC by the Achaean League. And you can't visit that, either, because that was shut down by the Roman Empire 46 years later.

2 **SPARTA** was unusual because it was ruled by two monarchs... *at the same time!* The Agiad and Eurypontid families both provided kings who ruled in tandem with shared duties. One, for instance, would deliver a Christmas Day message to the Spartan people whilst the other opened the Spartan parliament. When chatting to a member of the public, the Agiad king would ask what they did for a living, whilst the Eurypontid would ask if they had travelled very far to be there.

3 **FASHION-CONSCIOUS** King Agis II came up with the idea of the Mohican-style crest on top of the famous Spartan helmet. He premiered the now-famous titfer accessory in his 492BC Spring collection, saying he wanted something hard-wearing that would stand up to the rigours of battle, but which was stylish and snazzy, and had that Wow! factor. The crest caught on, taking ancient Greece and the entire Roman Empire by storm.

4 **SPARTAN** shields were decorated with the Greek letter lambda. That's because according to the daft inhabitants of the city state, Sparta was actually spelled Lacedaemon – *you couldn't make it up!*

5 **RECORDS** of Spartan civilisation are patchy, and while archaeologists know a lot about their kings and warriors, little is known about the ordinary people. Indeed, no records at all exist as to who the smallest ever Spartan was. But with an ancient Spartan population much smaller in stature than modern humans, it is likely that the smallest Spartan ever was even shorter than Calvin Phillips, the smallest human being to have ever lived.

6 **MANY** sports teams incorporate Spartans in their name, including Blyth Spartans AFC, Leeming Spartan Cricket Club and Manchester Village Spartans RUFC. And if you put *'List of Sports Teams Named Spartans – Wiki''* into Google, you'll get many more.

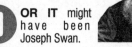

7 **ALL BABIES** in Sparta faced an ordeal from the moment they were born. Minutes old, they would be dunked in wine to see if they were hard enough to take it, then inspected and thrown off a cliff into a chasm if they were anything less than perfect. This ensured that the Spartans were the strongest race in all of Ancient Greece. Fortunately, the practice of dunking babies in wine and throwing them off cliffs was outlawed by Greek authorities when Sparta fell in 192BC.

8 **SPARTANS** lit their homes with oil burners and candles, a practice they shared with everyone up until the year 1880, when the incandescent electric light was invented by Thomas Edison.

9 **OR IT** might have been Joseph Swan.

10 **THE ACCELERATION** of an object due to gravity on the earth is 9.81ms^{-2}, whereas it is only 1.622m/s^{-2} on the moon. These two values were exactly the same in 500BC, meaning that a Spartan warrior weighing 80kg in full armour in the ancient City State two millennia ago would weigh just 13.23kg on the lunar surface today.

11 **OF COURSE,** in order to survive on the lunar surface, he would also require a spacesuit. The version worn by astronaut Neil Armstrong on the Apollo 11 moonshot weighed in at a whopping 200 lbs – the same weight as former US Secretary of State Henry Kissinger!

12 **WHAT'S** more, if, whilst on the moon, the warrior simultaneously dropped his heavy metal sword and a feather from the cresting of his helmet, they would both hit the lunar surface at the same time – a phenomenon that physicists and archaeologists alike cannot explain.

13 **SPARTAN** society was particularly liberal, and 'wife-sharing' was widespread. Many scholars believe the practice was so prevalent that Spartan relationships were to all intents and purposes polygamous and polyandrous. This concept has yet to be exploited by scud artist Ben Dover, who has failed to release such titles as *Spartan Wife Swappers*, *Spartan Housewife Fuckfest* and *Fuck My Spartan Wife While I Watch vol.7*.

14 **AS WELL** as being an ancient civilisation, Sparta also gave its name to a range of modern day car batteries. The Sparta BT065S, for example, offers motorists consistent starting performance even at low temperatures due to its special wrought-lead calcium grids and low resitance envelope separator – a fitting tribute to the noble fighting men from which it takes its name.

15 **THE SOLDIERS** who defended Sparta aren't the only heroic 300-strong fighting force in history. In the Old Testament book *Judges*, God commands Gideon to take 300 of his men and launch a sneaky night-time attack on the Midianites, who are encamped "as thick as locusts" in a nearby valley. Even though Gideon's men are only armed with trumpets, they are so bad at playing that when they launch their one-man-band-style attack, the Midianites run away as far as Beth-shittah.

16 **THE NAME** "Spartan" was also taken by a Derbyshire-based motor manufacturer, who made ugly, badly-proportioned kit cars based on the Triumph Herald or Wolseley 1500, that went tits-up in 1995.

17 **A PERSON** who loves Sparta and the Spartan civilisation - particularly with reference to its people's valour and success in war, their austerity and self-restraint, and their tripartite constitution - is known as a "laconophile".

18 **FAMOUS** laconophiles include Naked Chef Jamie Oliver, *Live & Kicking* presenter Jamie Theakston, *Halloween Kills* actress Jamie Lee Curtis, and Sky Sports TV pundit Jamie Carragher.

19 **DURING** his football career Jamie Carragher made 735 appearances for Liverpool, and retired with honours including 2 FA Cups, 3 League Cups, 2 Community Shields, a Champions League and 2 Super Cups.

20 **THE WORD** 'spartan' today means harsh, frugal and uncomfortable, reflecting the austere lives the people of the city state lived. But the term was not in use in Sparta itself, being coined long after the demise of the civilisation. Instead, ancient Spartans would have described their lifestyles as harsh, frugal and uncomfortable. But they wouldn't have said it in English, as English hadn't been invented then.

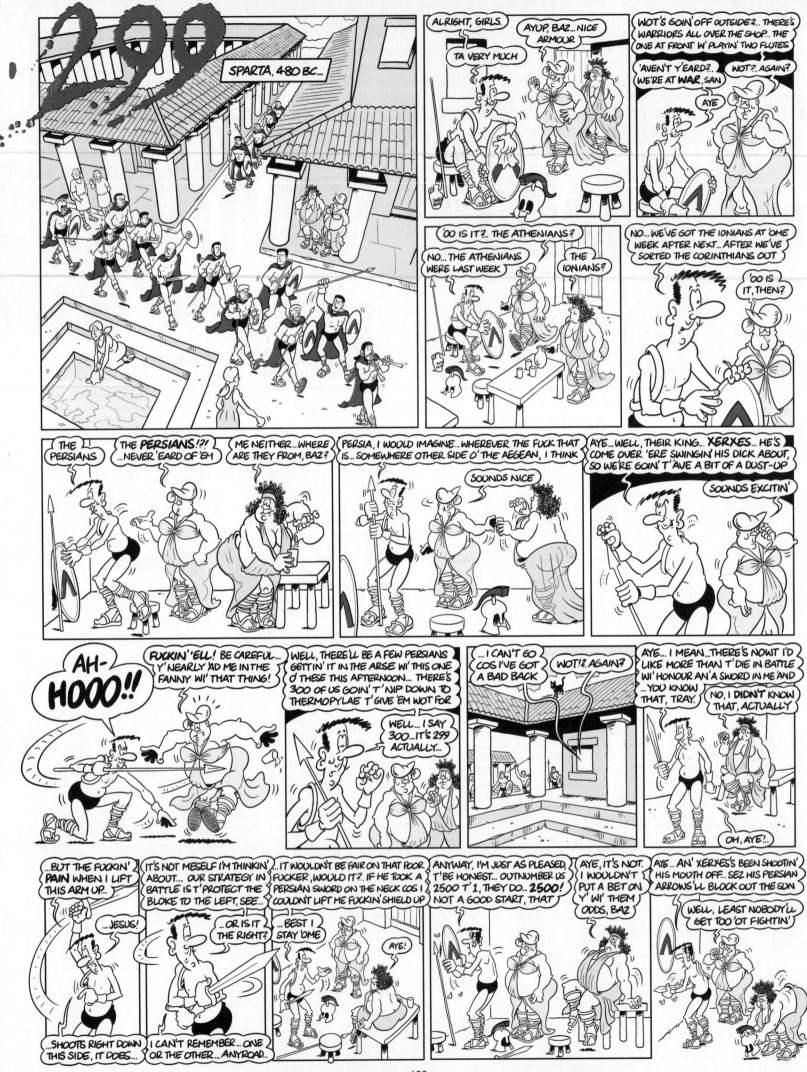

Roger's PROFANISAURUS

A Menagerie of Entries from Britain's Favourite Lexicon of Profanity

profanisaurus@viz.co.uk

apeshit 1. n. That which is flung at your granny in a zoo. 2. adj. In a state of mental perturbation. *Fucking radgy. 'Born on this day: Evel Knievel, human crash test dummy, 1938; Peter Stringfellow, fanny magnate, 1940; Gregg Wallace, apeshit greengrocer, 1966.'*

assquatch n. An abominable cryptozoological monster that is occasionally spotted emerging from its dark cave with a great deal of moaning. A post-constipation *Meat Loaf's daughter.*

babooning n. In *dogging* circles, inadvertently breaking the windscreen wipers off a car while engaging in vigorous sexual congress across the bonnet. Also known as *doing a Whipsnade.*

Bengal tiger n. An Indian beast that growls ominously in one's guts. *'Fuck me, what the fucking fuck was that?' 'Pardon me, your holiness. My Bengal tiger appears to have awoken.'*

bog ostrich n. A person who spends the latter part of an evening of drink and merriment with their head buried in the lavatory.

brown admiral n. zoo. The common and far from beautiful butterfly that can be found in the pants of someone who has failed to *draw an ace.* A *gusset moth, tiger's face* or *wind sketch.*

brown eagle has landed, the exclam. Something to say whilst trotting back from the *crapper* with a satisfied grin on your face. *'You look pleased with yourself, Mother Teresa of Calcutta.' 'And so I should, my child, for the brown eagle has landed.'*

brown panther, the n. Mythical anti-hero who strikes in staff toilets, leaving them in a disgraceful mess, with bits of *shite* on the seats & occasionally full *turds* on cistern tops or the floor. *'Remember Cato, the brown panther always leaves his calling card.'*

bush babies 1. n. zool. Cute, nocturnal, tree-dwelling primates. 2. n. Leftover blobs of *jizz* left in the *ladygarden undergrowth* following a hasty withdrawal.

camel tongue n. The outline of a man's *Johnson* in an overly tight pair of *strides. 'Nice camel tongue, Mr Plant. Big smile for the Cambrian News.'*

camel's foot n. *Twix lips, beetle bonnet, monkey's forehead.* The pediments of the *toblerone tunnel.*

charm the snake 1. v. To perform a public entertainment act whereby a king cobra is encouraged to rise and dance mesmerically before eventually spitting its venom. 2. v. To perform a personal entertainment act whereby a *membrum virile* is encouraged to rise and dance mesmerically before eventually spitting its venom.

clapping sea lion n. The sound that a woman's *jugs* make when they slap against each other during vigorous physical activity, eg. Cutting through a cast iron drainpipe with a hack saw, playing the congas, clubbing a seal, spanking a POTUS with a rolled-up copy of *Forbes* magazine.

couldn't pull a greasy stick out of a dead dingo's arse phr. A disparaging reference to a fellow's perceived merits. *'Fuck me, what are we going to do with him? He's utterly useless. He couldn't pull a greasy stick out of a dead dingo's arse.' 'I know. let's make him Health Secretary.'*

darted animal n. A *heavily refreshed* fellow who is reeling along and staggering from side to side, just prior to falling over in the gutter in a style strongly reminiscent of a rogue rhinoceros which has just been shot with a tranquiliser gun.

dingo's breakfast n. Aus. A *piss* and a bit of a look around.

faunacate v. To commit consensual lascivious behaviour with a saucy member of another species that's been giving you a come-hither look, eg. A sheep, dolphin, hamster etc.

feed the beavers v. To *drop a log* into the *yellow river.*

flamingo's flip-flops, wetter than a sim. Comical description of something, or rather someone, who is is a high state of sexual arousal.

giraffe piss n. The standard method of urination when in possession of a *panhandle,* ie. To stand with one's legs wide apart and angle the *tent pole* down towards the bowl in the manner of a long-necked cameleopard drinking at a water hole. *Full throttle for take-off.*

giraffe shit n. Any passed stool which causes one to stretch one's neck to get away from the smell.

giraffe's neck, cock like a sim. A description of an impressive *male member.* See also *baby's arm* clutching a *Jaffa or Pringles* tube with a sheep's heart on top. *'Goodness gracious, Mr Pound MP. You've got a cock like a giraffe's neck.'*

gorilla salad n. Ladies' pubic hair. *Twat thatch, roughage.*

gorilla salad days n. Fond *tosstalgia* for the time before bikini line management became de rigeur.

gorilla's armpit n. A *snatch* which would daunt all but David Attenborough.

gorilla's pubes, thicker than a sim. Stupid. *'Bloody hell, nan. You're thicker than a gorilla's pubes. Have you ever thought about going on The Chase?'*

growl at the badger v. Scots. To noisily *nosh* a *beaver.* To loudly *nod at a stoat, gnosh.*

hissing Sid n. One's *one-eyed trouser snake.*

inquisitive sea lion n. A *brown owl* lodged in the U-bend, leaving its snub-nosed end gently poking out curiously above the water's surface as if taking a look around for Sir David Attenborough or sardines.

kangaroo pouch n. A large *granny fanny,* big enough to fit your head in. A *horse's collar, welly top.*

leopard's back n. Worse than a *tiger's back;* a *chod bin* that has been peppered with *arse shrapnel.*

lizard rag n. Aus. A scaly piece of bedside cloth used for wiping excess *spoff* and *moip* from one's *bloodstick* after *popping the turkey in the oven.*

lizard's lick n. A feeble ejaculation that barely clears the *hog's eye;* the unimpressive result of excessive *working from home.* A bankrupt *money shot.* A *gwibble.*

llama's top lip n. A *camel's toe.*

manaconda 1. n. A ludicrously oversized *dildo* of home manufacture, eg. Four tins of beans in a rubber sock. 2. n. *Pant python, trouser snake, hissing Sid.* A *lirthy* male member.

milk the snake v. To practise *self abuse.*

miser's zoo n. Retail park mainstay Pets at Home; a chain of stores which inexplicably seem to remain profitable despite being visited principally by fathers bringing their young children to look at the animals while their wives pop into the shop next door to take back or exchange something. The pet shop was also referred to as the *cheap zoo* in *Flight of the Conchords.*

moose knuckles n. Can. *Camel's foot, Ninja's toe.*

one-eyed trouser snake n. A *spitting cobra* that is easily charmed by a *pink oboe* soloist.

panaconda n. A South American *dirt snake* of enormous length, that suffocates its victims if they get too close.

panda's eye n. A *ringpiece.*

park the tiger v. To puke, *yodel,* let out a *technicolour yawn.*

park viper n. A venomous *brown dirt snake* lying concealed in the grass, coiled and ready to strike at an unwary passer-by. *'Your grandad will have to join us later, I'm*

Roger's ANIMAL MAGIC ZOOLOGICAL WORDSEARCH

HIDDEN IN THE GRID below are all of the definitions in this *Roger's Profanisaurus* Zoological Selection. They may read up, down or diagonally, backwards or forwards. Some of them are probably spelt incorrectly like last year. And if you want a Viz Cheap Pen, simply send a **LARGE LETTER STAMP** to: *Roger's Zoological Profanisaurus Wordsearch, Viz Comic, PO Box 841, Whitley Bay, NE26 9EQ*. Please note, the awarding of a cheap pen is not contingent on completing the wordsearch correctly, only on sending us a large letter stamp.

```
V S E C B U Y K L P Z D E W O M B A T H O L E V B Y G S E W M K D C
D I N G O S B R E A K F A S T C T G I Y S K M L X Z E Y R I T F T A
E D C E A U H N B E D N H E T R M P A N A C O N D A M U T M L F G K
L E L E O P A R D S B A C K X C T I K N M L G D Q R E G I T E H T K
W W Z F B H K O V B N U H S L I A N S T E L I O T L M T G W A B U S
T A P W C D R H E D S C D B Y H O N A E M B J P Y F E A E M L H T F
E Y S E A Q U O K Y A E H K R E W K U J R P L G L G R E R M L I H F
G S W F M X H N L H I E C A P O M L F T Y S N R E L E A S E T H E S
H M V Y E L T I M D T I R W R L K M V N P I Z L M C F P F G L K P N
V O W Z L E E H F I L V B B X M M N R W N L I O L U O E A P U T F Z
M N A E S Q L R E S T X A K R L T C P O W Z V H O L P L C R T E L K
V K J D F L G B D D F N R K L E W H O L I F E A F P L R E A E Z F Y
D E A X O L R R O P O F L P T U G B E C B K U P L M U D W D M N L B
B Y M L O P A E F G J L Y A N L A I E S K V I M L G R D T M Z S R M
E M A D T Z W G N V O E P S M B H T T J N L E X J L I H L H R O L C
F O K R I L S I D W Y S D H J I L B L P F A I N S E D N I W E D I S
V U E L A H T T F I H T T L I E N A A S M H K K C B V R U N E G L H
G T S C H T E L A C A B I R F N L A O S T G P E E H S O E L I M I A
O H V E I H S A S U L J P V I L R G D W P P O A E A N A M L G D N R
R K T S T I L G D R W A E O E C N H O E L A V R C A G L J F E T W T
I N T R S C E N R L H U P F L I H A S P T E R I I L L I L D H S E T
L H D S A K N E F O M K S P M A M L F W R R L K E L V T R E L O P U
L E S A V E L B A Q W B X A I L R E G S A H A H V P L S R A M L H D
A G W P F R S L A C H L L N E N O B R O W N A D M I R A L D F X T S
S I L E N T R O A R B F A K S Q G D E M L S E E W I P L S B T F S L
A A Z S C H B K J M A N A T N L A S F A L P K W M N R E F A L E E T
L A E H E A B J T N A N E F T R L U E A R A L D W Q Q S R F L N O S
A W L I R N A E A N S S M Y D H L E N A N S L T S U M Z S H P A L R
D Z D T E G E H E A W T R S H E D I S L P A E L I F R T M L P D E A
D C V G U O T E H A O D A O P C E B R R S I F R L S E O M L F R S W
A X C K E R N T S T I Z O L P D L E A F R A O T M I O M L G R S C R
Y A V Y E I K A T S I M J Y F L S P H D S R I N K T L M F D S O F T
S W Y T S L A F G L L G O G R U I E M H G H P E L I C A N S Y A W N
B H T S I L S N A C T S E H O H Y P E D S E O L T V L H T D V H L P
V E Q M S A I M D X B I T R N E M K L I T R N N E M L F E R D W P B
W A W A S S Q U A T C H T H S L D E F X S P U T A S N A K E I N A B
S R D H S P P H N F E D G A P B L F S M J X T H I E L M T D C B N T
L P F I W U A C B Y E W D L D W A L B Y X A W K D A L M B V R T D W
E S H E T B B H T Y L N W D K R E C L H H S I F Y L L E J N A B R U
M H B C E E C W E T A B J U I L S W K M L F R S I I L H Y D E W C F
M K D G T S S E T P K A N G A R O O P O U C H B G O R I L L A S A R
M F D M L W N M L H T R S L X S R T L L K R D H U N M L G T D W K M
E S R A S O G N I D D A E D A F O T U O K C I T S Y S A E R G A L L
```

Definitions

afraid. He's been bitten by a park viper.'

pelican's yawn *sim*. A fanny big enough to hold 50lb of fish. A *hippo's mouth*.

playful dolphins *n*. A situation arising when no amount of flushing and weighing down with two-ply will rid the *chod bin* of floaters. 'Sorry gran, I flushed three times but there's still a couple of playful dolphins bobbing around in there.'

polar bear's arm *n*. A *fuck-off* bumper-size line of *Bacon powder*, of the sort typically enjoyed in the *bogs* of fashionable London clubs by sweating children's television presenters. 'And here's a polar bear's arm I snorted earlier. Get down spiders!'

pond walrus *n*. A lengthsome, wrist-thick, fully coherent *Sir Douglas*, possibly with whiskers and tusks, which languishes half in and half out of the water in the *bum sink*. A *foot stool*.

put a snake in a basket *v*. To go for a long, bendy *shit*. To *make a coil pot*.

release the scorpions *v*. To produce a *wind of change* powerful enough to have brought down the Berlin Wall.

rhino horn *n*. A well-matted tarantula among *arse spiders*. Definitely not an aphrodisiac.

rip in a bear's back *n*. A *ragman's coat, butcher's dustbin*, full Turkish, badly packed *kebab, beaver's guts*, untidy sock drawer; a pork pie that's been trodden on or an octopus climbing out of a wetsuit.

sideways monkey mouth *n*. The female *flapdoodle*. 'Phwooarr! If you freeze the frame at the exact right moment, you can see her pubes and her sideways monkey mouth and everything.' (Barry Norman reviewing *Basic Instinct* on *Film '92*, BBC1).

sidewinder 1. *n*. Some sort of snake that is often seen in nature documentaries, scuttling across the desert sand like a scaly brace and bit. 2. *n*. The elevation of one's left or right buttock in order to facilitate the surreptitious release of a *Judi Dench*. A *one cheek sneak* or *cushion creeper*.

silent roar 1. *n*. Trade name of the small pellets containing lion excrement, the smell of which scares cats from flower beds for up to six months. 2. *n*. A *feeshus* dropped in the toilet, the smell of which keeps everyone out of the bathroom for up to six months.

sitting on a brown snake n. Having to stay seated so you don't let the *bowl constrictor* escape.

snake charmer *n*. A girl who has an uplifting effect on your *pant python*, such that it rises up and sways about in her face.

tiger's back *n*. The decorative striped effect left in the *pan* after a particularly sticky *Meat Loaf's daughter* has gone to the beach.

tiger's face *n*. The *wind sketch* left in your *Bill Grundies* after a soggy *air biscuit* that

would certainly make Siegfried and Roy jump.

tiger bread 1. *n*. Visually alluring but strangely flavourless loaf that is sold in supermarkets. 2. *n*. Appearance of the sponge after giving one's inadequately wiped *ringpiece* a quick buff-up in the shower.

toilet snails *n*. Cryptozoological molluscs that slither around the *bog pan* in student houses, leaving brown skidmarks for which no-one claims responsibility.

toothless gibbon *n*. A *clapping fish*.

toucan's bill *n*. The firm, leathery and yellowed hood adorning a well-thumbed *starter button*.

urban jellyfish *n*. A rubbery, semi-translucent, parazoological beast typically found drifting in the stagnant canals and waterways of our towns and cities. *Jubber ray, dunky, Coney Island whitefish*.

wax the dolphin *v*. To *polish the lighthouse*.

wombat hole *n*. An elegant way to describe a woman's *cunt*.

wolf bait *n*. An unusually

meaty, pungent *fart*, similar to the smell encountered when opening a tin of Butcher's Tripe Mix.

wolf bite *n*. A really painful *arsehole*, eg. After a curry. 'Would you care to ride with us to Wenlock Edge, Captain Tremaine?' she asked. The Captain winced. 'I regret I must decline your kind offer, Mrs Dugdale,' he replied. 'I lately partook of a monstrous vindaloo with the Lord of Harpole, and I still have a wolf bite upon my postillion.' (from *Middlemarch*, by George Eliot).

110

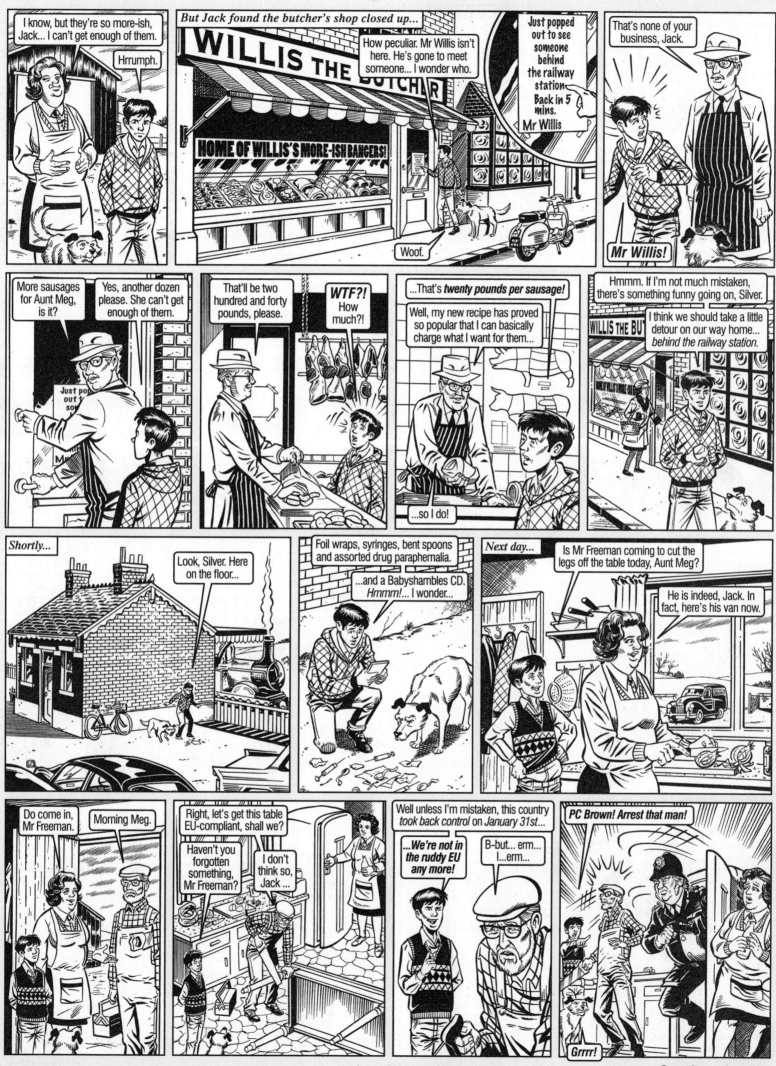

Continued over...

The End

Key to Living Longer is "Dying Later" ~ Scientists

A GROUNDBREAKING new study published in the *European Medical Journal* today claims that not dying early could well be the key to a longer life.

The study, which was researched and produced by Swedish scientists from the University of Gottenberg, found that time and time again, people who lived to a ripe old age were dying "significantly later" than people who passed away before them.

perished

Lead researcher Professor Gunilla Borgsdottir said: "Our findings suggest that dying is clinically proven to drastically reduce your lifespan. Studies showed that people who put off dying until they were 80 or 90 were living nearly TWICE as long as people who perished in their mid-forties."

"There have been many studies that have claimed the key to living longer is regular exercise or a healthy diet. These things are certainly important, but our research proves that not dying is far more important."

"The message is clear", the Professor added. "Die later and you'll live longer."

fresh

At time of press, the University has entlisted A-List celebs such as Joe Swash and Dappy out of N-Dubz to promote dying later on social media, using the hashtag *#DieLaterLiveLonger.*

CHEAP TRICK

ZZ **TOP** front man *Dusty Hill* was last night branded a *HYPOCRITE* by fans as news broke that he had spent $3,500 on a pair of *SUNGLASSES.*

For years, the Tex-Mex rocker has been advising fans to purchase inexpensive models in the band's 1980 hit *Cheap Sunglasses*. But yesterday, Hill was spotted coming out of a Bel Air opticians wearing a brand new pair of Louis Vuitton shades that retail for an eye watering three-and-a-half grand.

Not cheap: Louis Vuitton

cheap

"I feel let down" said ZZ Top fan Clunk Wangford. "'Go get yourselves some cheap sunglasses' we were told, and he spends a goddam fortune on a pair."

"It's a slap in the face for all Topsters," said Glint Triops, who had joined 2000 other fans protesting outside the offices of the band's record company Warner Brothers. "Seems like it's one rule for him, another for his fans, the hypocrite muthafucker."

hat

Hill was unavailable for comment yesterday after dying in 2021, but guitarist Billy Gibbons took to Twitter to put the story straight. "The three of us in ZZ Top buy our shades from Walmart or gas stations, and we never pay more that a dollar fifty a pair," he assured fans.

"Dusty was perhaps trying them on for a joke," he suggested. "Or perhaps he's gone to have his eyes tested and picked up the wrong pair when he left."

WITH LOVE FROM

A VISIT from the gas man is a familiar, twice-yearly experience for all British householders. But when we let him in to view the meter hidden away behind a clutter of dusty golf clubs, walking boots, vacuum cleaners and half-used tins of paint, it's not just the numbers on the dials he's taking note of.

According to a former professional meter reader, our innermost secrets are revealed by what we keep in our understairs cupboards. 28-stone FRAMPTON MUCOR, spent 18 months reading gas meters in his home town of Chorley, Lancashire, and during that time he got a privileged peek into the hidden lives of his customers.

He told us: "To be an effective gas man, you have to be a psychologist – a student of the human condition, if you will."

"Before you can read a customer's meter, you have to know what they are doing with their gas, and that means finding out what makes them tick and what turns them on. And during my year-and-a-half on the knocker, I used my hard-won professional skills to solve crimes, mend broken marriages … and even save countless lives."

"The gas man really is the fourth emergency service," he said.

Now Frampton has penned an extraordinary memoir about his days going from door to door in the Chorley area. And in these exclusive extracts from his book *Life in the Gas Lane* (Rocum Publishing, 49p), he reveals the sensational secrets of his meter-reading career.

EXCLUSIVE!

> *At the top of the stairs, I pushed the bathroom door open half an inch and peeped through the crack*

Drown and Out

❝ Early one morning, I was out doing my rounds and I called on a house in South Ribble. The young woman who answered the door was in her dressing gown, and she explained that she was just on her way up for a bath. I showed her my official ID and told her that I would let myself out as soon as I'd read the meter, and she went off up the stairs as I let myself into the cupboard.

As it turned out, it was quite a difficult meter to read, and I was in the cupboard for a good ten minutes trying to read it. Suddenly, I heard the water up in the bathroom stop, and my mind began to race. What had happened?

Maybe she had finished running her bath, turned the taps off, and got in it, I thought.

But then again, what if the woman had fallen, and knocked the tap off with her head as she fell to the floor? Admittedly, I hadn't heard a bump, but then again, she might of had a rug in the bathroom with a thick pile, and she was lying on it now, bleeding to death.

One thing was certain, I would never of forgiven myself if I'd left her there in a spreading pool of her own blood, so I crept out the cupboard and silently made my up the stairs. After all, she probably thought I'd left ten minutes earlier, so I didn't want to make her jump if all was well.

top

At the top of the stairs, I pushed the bathroom door open half an inch and peeped through the crack. You can't imagine my relief when I saw that all

Dial M for Meter: *The under stairs world of the professional gas meter reader put pressure on Frampton's own personal life.*

Headline does not truly reflect content of article about gas man

my worst fears had been unfounded; the woman was sat in the bath, completely uninjured, and was happily soaping her arms, long legs and ample breasts.

However, the bathmat was a bit rumpled at one side. It looked like a bit of a hazard to me, and I was suddenly gripped by the fear that as she got out the bath to dry herself she could trip on it and bang her teeth on the sink. I would never of forgiven myself if any harm had come to one of my customers, so I resolved to wait until she had towelled herself off and got her dressing gown back on.

Twenty-five minutes later, once I had watched her get out the bath, dried and safely back in her dressing gown, I crept back down the stairs and let myself out, closing the door behind me as quietly possible.

A meter read and a life saved; it's all in a day's work for a gas man.

Porn to be Wild

❝ You'd be surprised at some of the stuff people keep in their gas meter cupboards. In fact, some of the things we see would make your hair curl. But a gas man is like a priest taking confession – we never reveal the secrets of the meter cupboard. But even I was shocked at what I

Life's a gas, man: Mucor (right) was self professed '4th Emergency Service.' But he found his job often landed him in hot water.

METER YOU

found when a young housewife in Duxbury showed me under her stairs.

I flicked my torch about, looking for the gas meter, but something else caught my eye; a flash of lurid colour behind some old cans of paint. I investigated further, and what I found shocked me to my core; it was a pornographic DVD.

The vid clearly belonged to the woman's husband, and as I turned the box over in my hand and read the lurid description of the filth it promised, and looked at the disgusting screenshots of the depraved contents on the back of the box, I felt sick to my stomach. Worse, as a student of the human condition, I knew that anyone who owned one of these disgusting DVDs probably had a big collection of them hidden away elsewhere in the house to feed his depraved and perverted sexual appetites.

finger

Then a thought struck me. If his poor wife were to find these DVDs, the couple's marriage would be finished. No relationship could survive the discovery of such a pile of filth as the one I was imagining. I was going to have to intervene. It was risky, but I would of never forgiven myself if their marriage broke up due to my inaction. Tucking the DVD into the pocket of my gas man's mac, I came out of the understairs cupboard and asked the lady of the house if I could use her upstairs toilet.

But when I got to the landing, instead of going in the bathroom, I ducked sideways into the master bedroom where I had a hunch I would find the rest of the householder's sordid stash. And there, up on top of the wardrobe, I found the rest of his hardcore vids – each one more depraved than the last.

> **Nauseated by what I had found, I started filling my pockets with the filth, resolving to destroy it as soon as I was able**

Nauseated by what I had found, I started filling my pockets with the filth, resolving to destroy it as soon as I was able. But as I left the bedroom, I came face to face with the woman coming up the stairs, and she asked me what the eff I was doing. Only she didn't say eff, she said the eff-word. (Fuck).

Thinking quickly, I said I had taken a wrong turn at the top of the stairs, but she didn't believe me and started shouting and screaming at me, calling me all the names under the sun, including a filthy c-word. (Cunt).

She was still shouting at me as I left the house; she clearly didn't realise that I had just given her husband a second chance to save their troubled marriage. But I didn't get into the meter-reading game for thanks. Let's hope her husband saw the error of his ways and didn't mess it up again by giving in to his base desires.

Fire Down Below

> Police had been on the local news, warning residents about a bogus meter reader who had been working the area and preying on local housewives, so I was on the lookout for any suspicious activity when I headed out to do my rounds in Grimeford. On my first call of the day, the woman of the house invited me in and showed me to the meter cupboard under the stairs.

It was a big cupboard, and I found the gas meter in the back corner, obscured behind an ironing board and a basket of ladies' smalls waiting to be ironed. However, as I tried to move them out of the way in order to ply my professional trade, the basket toppled over, spilling skimpy

OVER 3 HOURS OF EXPLICIT MATERIAL

CAN YOU KEEP A SECRET?
XXX SECRETS
FAPWORTH DVDS

What have we grot here? One of the many pornographic DVDs that Frampton says he will eventually dispose of.

knickers and frilly bras all over the floor. As I knelt down to pick them up and replace them in the basket in a professional manner, I froze in horror.

tank

Examining the labels carefully in the torchlight, I noticed that many of the lingerie items did not bear any labels showing them to be flame retardant in accordance with nationally applicable safety standards. Every time she put them on, the lady of the house was putting herself at risk of serious burns to the arse, tits and fanny if she went near a naked flame.

I knew that I would never of forgiven myself if that had of happened when I could of prevented it, so I quickly stuffed the lethal grundies into my pockets to smuggle them out of the house. I planned to then immediately take them to the fire brigade for safe disposal, but I never got the chance to carry out my good deed. For the lady of the house had heard the commotion in the cupboard and came to see what was going on, catching me stuffing her scanties down the front of my shirt as my pockets were all full.

She began furiously screaming at me. I tried to explain about the grave fire risks she was running – even offering to carry out a free fire safety

> **Examining the labels carefully in the torchlight, I noticed that many of the lingerie items did not bear any labels showing them to be flame retardant in accordance with nationally applicable safety standards**

assessment on the scads she was wearing now – but she was having none of it. Looking back on it, she had probably heard the news report about the bogus gas man operating in the area, so her hysterical reaction was understandable.

As she chased me down the path, hitting me with a brush and calling me all the names under the sun, I reflected that it would all be worth it as long as she replaced the deadly lingerie stuffed into my overalls with safe alternatives carrying the BS Kitemark.

spud

Sadly, Frampton's meter-reading career came to an end not long afterwards. He told us: "I was out on a routine housecall, reading a woman's meter, and I ended up in her bedroom. I was fixing a faulty underwear drawer that could easily have trapped her fingers, when her husband came in and mistook me for the bogus sex pervert gas man who'd been all over the local news."

"I was convicted on faulty DNA evidence on counts of gaining unlawful entry to premises by impersonating a gasman, theft, and various sexual offences, and sentenced to eighteen months."

"I decided not to appeal the conviction, as I was already on probation for something else I didn't do."

"To make matters worse, the real fake gas man who had been preying on innocent housewives in the area decided to lay low while I was inside, so it made it look like I was even more guilty than I was. Which I wasn't."

"All in all, it was a sad end to a glittering career, even though I didn't technically work for the gas board; I was more of a freelance operative. But I do still have the figures off all the meters written down if the official authorities ever want them," Frampton added.

WINDS OF CHANGE

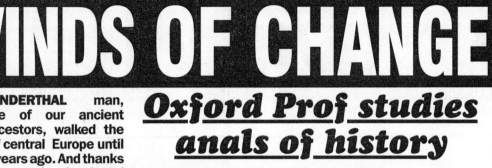

Oxford Prof studies anals of history

Jurassic fart: Dr Crispin Martinville (inset) says he now knows what olden days farts sounded like.

NEANDERTHAL man, one of our ancient ancestors, walked the plains of central Europe until 40,000 years ago. And thanks to the recently developed scientific technique of facial mapping, we now know what our primitive predecessor looked like, with his large nose, receding chin and heavy-set brow. But one Oxford scientist wants to add to our catalogue of knowledge of these early hominids... *by working out what their farts sounded like.*

Archaeologist Dr Crispin Martinville has been researching the sound of breaking wind for 20 years, and now he thinks he knows exactly what it sounded like when a prehistoric Neanderthal stepped on a duck.

Dr Martinville told *New Scientist* magazine: "From radio and CDs to iPods, we take the ability to listen to sound at our leisure for granted. But recorded audio is a relatively new phenomenon. All sounds before the invention of recording are lost forever."

"The clang of a Norman blacksmith hammering his anvil, the incantations of an Aztec priest – all these sounds are extinct, never to be heard by modern ears."

But there is one sound that Crispin believes is our most tragic loss.

"Despite understanding what is at the centre of the atom and at the farthest reaches of the universe, the farts of our ancestors remain a complete mystery," he said.

"Whether it's a medieval farmer squeaking one out as he bends to pick his beans, or a high-ranking Roman Centurion cutting the cheese before heading into battle, we simply have no idea what they sounded like."

guts

But now, using the latest scientific techniques in physiology, anthropology and archaeology, that is all set to change. And Martinville says that he can now reproduce the exact sound of a Neolithic man dropping his guts – the first time it will have been heard in nearly half a million years.

"The average Neanderthal was only five foot six tall," he explained. "With a shorter distance for their fart to travel from their colon to their anus, this would make for a short sharp fart when the sphincter expelled their gas."

"Imagine you stepped into the road and then suddenly jumped back as the short toot of a horn blared. It would probably sound something like that," he said.

But it's not just the Neanderthals' physiology that determines what their trouser coughs were like. According to Dr Martinville, diet played as much of a part in determining the sound as the physical structure of the colon.

"Neanderthals were essentially hunter-gatherers, with raw mammoth steaks constituting a large portion of their diet," he said. "All that rich meat, supplemented with a few berries here and there, would have given their gut contents a slightly gelatinous texture."

"Consequently, their farts would have probably stretched out and then popped – like a bubble rising to the surface of a boggy lake."

shopping

Martinville points out that the nature of human farts has altered over the course of our history, as people's shapes have changed.

"If you could go back in time, even as recently as Shakespearean times, you wouldn't even recognise the flatulence you heard as farts by modern day standards," he said.

"Not only have people's bottoms expanded through improved diets, such as sweet and sour chicken and pork fried rice, but vitamins from things like Fanta and cans of Lilt have meant that we have grown taller. The distance from stomach to bum-hole has increased, and with it the entire timbre of the human fart."

Dr Martinville was keen to explain why he is so interested in the archaeology of the noises our arses make. "A lot of academics accuse me of only having got into this field because of the women it attracts," he said. "But I genuinely care about this work and its importance."

"Growing up, I didn't know what ancient Mesopotamian farts sounded like, or the farts of those who invented the first cotton looms."

"It is my dream that in years to come, future generations will be able to hear the recreated farts of people from 1066 or Agincourt, and feel like they're actually there on the battlefield with them," he added.

CLASSICAL GAS

DESPITE specialising in Neanderthal flatulence, Martinville has also applied his expertise to look at other periods of our history.

He told us: *"When people discover I'm a Palaeohistorian of early human flatulence, the first thing they ask me is: what did the farts of Henry VIII's wives sound like? So let me answer..."*

DIVORCED

HENRY'S first wife was the Spanish Catherine of Aragon. A diet of paella and chorizo sausage would have made a heavy bowel gas that she expelled with a deep rumble. Whilst it's true that Henry divorced Catherine because she wasn't able to give him a son, a contributory factor could well have been the fact that she farted like an ox - much louder than Henry was physically capable of doing. In those days it wasn't the done thing for a woman to fart louder than her husband, especially if he was King.

BEHEADED

ALTHOUGH Henry's second wife Anne Boleyn was the daughter of an English nobleman, she was brought up in France, with its diet rich in cheese and red meat. A stableboy in the time of Henry VIII, hearing Anne crack one out as she mounted her horse, would have heard a typically French fart - rude, uncouth and slightly wet around the edges. Even the staunchest feminist would have to admit they understood why Henry beheaded her.

DIED

HAD recording devices been available at the Tudor Court, a young knight who wanted to prove his worth to his peers would have placed his medieval cassette machine in a bush in the rose garden where Jayne Seymour, Henry's third wife, probably went to walk after a lunch of roasted pheasant. What he would hear when listening back to the tape would have been an unhealthy fart that stuttered and came out with a gentle, ladylike gasps.

DIVORCED

A SIXTEENTH century dictaphone placed behind the cistern of the Queen's earth closet would have captured a few pre-dump farts before Henry's fourth wife, Anne of Cleves, unloaded her breakfast. A rather heavy-set woman, her German-born buttocks would have unleashed little bursts of air, like musket shots being fired. As King of England, Henry lived in constant fear of assassination, and it is very likely that he jumped every time he heard a volley of his consort's farts. She had to go.

BEHEADED

AN EXTREMELY early version of an iPhone, placed on the windowsill to a turret room where Catherine Howard played cards with other women of the court, would secretly capture her rectal noises. In that relaxed setting, Catherine would happily drop her guts, but there would be little to hear when the device was retrieved and the play button pressed. Because Henry's fifth wife was notoriously slight of build and a delicate eater, and it is certain - with a degree of 95% probability - that her farts were almost totally silent.

SURVIVED

WHEN Catherine Parr, Henry's final wife, farted, it would have made a noise like a minstrel blowing on a crumhorn. And although that was the Tudor monarch's favourite musical instrument, he didn't think the noises made by his twice-widowed wife's bottom were ladylike. In days when women were to be seen and not heard, we can deduce that having a loud fart would be a death sentence for Henry's Queen. It was only the fact that the ailing King died first that saved Catherine from the block.

LetterbOcks

Viz Comic, P.O. Box 841 Whitley Bay, NE26 9EQ : letters@viz.co.uk

I THINK you will find that *Far From The Madding Crowd* was written by Thomas Hardy, not William Shakespeare. If you want to know about other works of literature not written by Shakespeare, just ask. I know loads.

Barry Prunes, email

WHAT is it with Michael Gove pointing at us with his knuckle when he speaks? Has nobody told the fish-faced fucker that it's the end bit of your finger you're supposed to point with, not the bendy bit in the middle?

Douglas Fur, Newcastle

WITH reference to Mr Fur's letter (*above*). I was always taught it was rude to point, and in making this gesture with the middle bit of his finger, Mr Gove is emphasising his words, but doing so in a polite fashion. Perhaps Al Qaida and Isis should take a leaf out of his book and use this more civilised pointing technique when threatening atrocities on the west.

Hector Maestro, Tooting

* *Thank you for your letter, Mr Prunes, but we are well aware that Far From the Madding Crowd was written by Thomas Hardy. As far as we understand, we have never, in person, in print or anywhere else, suggested that it was written by William Shakespeare. To suggest otherwise is a serious accusation to make and one which we intend to pursue, whatever the cost. Could you send us the documentary evidence of us saying that Far From the Madding Crowd was written by William Shakespeare and we will pass it on to our legal department.*

I'VE only been to Newcastle twice in my life. Once when I was nine months old, and again last year on a stag do. I shat myself on both occasions.

Dominic Twose, L'ton Spa

BACK in May 2018, you reported that the Bayeux Tapestry included the first known battle in which combatants fought by pulling jumpers over heads. It's taken me a while to find it, but it also contains a horse's cock. I'm not sure if it's a French or an English horse.

Gwilym Hughes, email

ST★R LETTER

WHY do they boast these days that foods are 'triple cooked'? Back in my day, it was cooked once and then we ate the fucker.

Roger Vaughan, Leeds

IF there is one thing I've learnt from grumble movies, it's that they give us wholly unrealistic and unhealthy expectations about just how quickly a plumber will come to your house.

Iain Devenney, Abingdon

WHEN people say "It's about as much good as a chocolate teapot," they're forgetting that you can at least eat a chocolate teapot. So it's not like it's completely useless, and probably quite nice as well. Maybe they should put that in their pipe and smoke it. Although, again, if it's chocolate, they should probably eat it instead.

D Cooper, Malta

THE most overused phrase in the English language at the moment is "unprecedented times." But aren't all times unprecedented? I'm no Doctor Who, but surely that's just how time works?

Sylvest Crumbhorn, Hull

WHY ARE those two American astronauts wearing belts in space? It's not as if their trousers will fall down. Over to you, Brian Cox.

Martyn Pointer, email

WHEN my wife asked me what a pair of lady's knickers were doing in the back of the car, I pointed out that they weren't doing anything, since knickers are inanimate objects. In retrospect, it was perhaps not the best time for witty repartée.

Toby Treacle, Tincleton

YOU used to publish my letters regularly and used to send me *Viz* coffee mugs. The trouble is that the colour ran the first tme they went in the dishwasher. I will in future send my stories to *Scientific American*, as I believe their mugs are much more robust.

David Haslam, Datchworth

WHY is it that Labour leader Keir Starmer spells his first name like he does, and not 'Kier.' I was always taught it's *'i before e, except after c.'* If he brazenly flouts this rule, what others does he think he can get away with?

Billy Wiffles, Bath

I JUST watched *Bargain Hunt* on BBC1, and in this particular episode, one team made a loss of 100 quid, which is roughly 66% of the cost of my TV licence. Little wonder there's not enough left in the pot to pay female presenters properly.

Dave Shorter, St Neots

I WONDER if any of your readers have noticed how so many great things begin with the letter 'M', and how so many crap things start with 'T'. For instance, marmalade, milk and mashed potatoes are all super. And tuberculosis, tummy ache and tax are all pretty nasty. Having said that, monsters aren't very nice and I do like a bit of toast, so it's not quite 100%.

Jeff Doormat, Brighton

ACCORDING to my Apple Watch, I just burnt seven "active calories" whilst taking a shit. Can any of your readers beat that?

Bill Marney, Brentwood

HERE'S some sheet music I saw for sale on eBay. Honestly, the things they wrote musicals about in the olden days.

Dr Julie Thorn, Hexham

MINISTER, YOU'VE BEEN ACCUSED OF MISLEADING THE PUBLIC IN YOUR ELECTION MANIFESTO... HOW WOULD YOU RESPOND TO THAT?

WELL, IF I CAN JUST BE FRANK FOR A MOMENT...

NOW, IN ANSWER TO YOUR QUESTION...

THEY say money can't buy you happiness, but I was always upset about never having clean teaspoons in the cutlery drawer. Then one day I visited a car boot sale and bought a job lot of two dozen hardly-rusted ones for £2. Now I'm as happy as Larry. So you *can* buy happiness, and it turns out it's pretty cheap!

Geraint LT, London

YOUR fly-tipping feature *(page 22)* implied that Carmel magistrates fined Clint Eastwood $1500 for dumping rubbish in the Hollywood Hills. However, Hollywood falls under the jurisdiction of LA County, whilst Carmel is in Monterey County, some 300 miles away. The $1500 would also be for a second offence, with fines between $250 & $1000 for a first time offender.

Tony Baker, Wallsend

HERE is a photograph of my remote-controlled cocktail sausage. I wonder if any other *Viz* readers have pictures of remote-controlled meat-based products?

Pete Flannery, Dalston

APPARENTLY, there's a species of bacteria called Micrococcus. But what were they expecting from a microbe? Anything larger would be frankly unwieldy.

Desmond Bullen, Sale

THE Prime Minister always seems to be telling us to "use common sense". Well that's all well and good, but what about those who haven't got any? I know I certainly don't.

Jane Hoole Garner, St. Ives

I SAW these beauties on the side of the Leeds-Liverpool Canal and thought they were about the right intellectual standard for your publication. *Anita Bush, email*

I TOOK a photo of my cock with my plant identifier app, and it came back with *Zingiber officinale*. Can any botanists please tell me if I should take this as a compliment, or a slight on my manhood?

Nigel Quicksand, Bristol

I HAVE just watched the BBC's Jenny Hill reporting on COVID precautions being taken by football teams in Germany, and she said that Eintracht Frankfurt will be disinfecting their balls at half-time. No wonder the infection rate in the UK is so high; we are only told to wash our hands.

Adrian Martin, Glasgow

AS I sat in the bath just now, it occurred to me that in all the years I've been using Head & Shoulders, not once have I ever used it to actually wash my shoulders. This realisation has left me in something of a quandary and I'm now concerned I've been wasting my money on this product for some time.

Ben M, Rochester

WHOEVER says "talk is cheap" has obviously never called Babestation.

Lenny Sherman, London

I FOUND this disgusting map in the *Penguin Atlas of Medieval History*, of all places. It shows the Venetian Republic at the time when it was penetrating the Mediterranean. It's even got hairy balls.

Don, Newbury

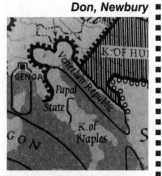

WHY are there so many different types of cheese on sale in the supermarket? This is exactly the letter you asked for in response to Harold Abrahams' letter about nothing *(page 99)*, so if you don't print it, it will leave us honest readers thinking that you actually just make most of this shit up.

Chris Tomlinson, Norwich

THE recent delay in SpaceX Falcon 9's launch due to rain makes you realise the difference between the Baby Boomers that went to the moon and the current snowflakes aiming to get to a Meccano Travelodge in close orbit. Had it been a bit drizzly in 1969, the astronauts would have simply put the wipers on double speed and lit the blue touch paper with a rag soaked in petrol.

Stuie, Bunny

"MOTHER" Teresa didn't even have any children! Yet another example of the fake news media twisting facts to suit their agenda.

Mark Airey, Manchester

Kids fail to say the funniest things...

ABOUT WIGS!

I TOOK my grandson to see a thatched cottage yesterday in the hope that he might point at it and say, 'Look Nana, that house is wearing a wig!' thus giving me a delightful anecdote for your letters page. But the selfish little arse just sat there in total silence. To be fair, he is only eight weeks old, but still.

Mavis Obelisk, Catford

* Are YOU an old woman whose grandchild has failed to say the funniest thing to you about wigs? Write to the usual address and tell us about it. Each letter we print wins a more amusing grandchild for you and six friends.

TÖP

SUBURBANITES. Cheer up prudish neighbours by covertly writing humorous sweary words with liquid lawn feed in a watering can on their lawns. Or, on a large lawn, a massive luscious green comedy cock and balls with a drop of spunk is particularly amusing.

Mike Tatham, St. Andrews

MAKE people think you're a politician by thanking them for their question when they ask you something, and adding that their question is very good. Then don't answer it.

Rick, Manchester

PORN directors. To help boost the revenues of your ailing industry, ink 'Advertise Here' along with your phone number on the buttocks of all your actors.

Gerry Paton, London

AVOID a world class pasting by not attempting Jedi mind control and Mr Spock's Vulcan death grip on lap-dancing bar doormen.

Les Lloyd, email

A SHALLOW tray of honey, sprinkled with breadcrumbs and placed on an outdoor table is a good way to attract small birds, who will then be unable to get away for whatever reason you might want to do that.

Sam Dabidozi, Sandwich

CONVINCE visitors you own an Alexa by making your wife hide in a cupboard with a set of encylopedias.

Fat Al White, Wrenthorpe

WHEN queuing for the McDonald's drive thru, make sure you take a snack and a drink to keep you going during the 4-hour wait.

Geoff Greensmith, email

BBC iPlayer users without a TV licence. When asked to select whether you have a licence or not, outwit Auntie by clicking on the "I have a TV Licence" box.

Tim Buktu, Timbuktu

toptips@viz.co.uk

123

TIME is running out. According to boffins, we have just 10 years to save the planet. If we don't act now, the climate will literally explode, and the warning signs are there for all to see. Australia has already burnt to a crisp, and unless something is done, a *real* disaster could be just around the corner.

Whilst the environmentalists' message is an admirable one, it is falling on deaf ears, because the people who deliver it are such miserable, sour-faced, boring fuckers. We believe it's time to draw a line in the scorched sand and make Saving the Planet FUN, with this free *Viz* Climate Emergency Boardgame.

INSTRUCTIONS

Cut out the eco-warrior playing pieces and glue them onto a piece of recycled cardboard using palm oil-free glue. Then, draw some dots on a sustainably produced sugar cube to make a dice. Take turns rolling the dice and moving your eco-warrior along the board.

COUNTERS

Thurnberg

Attenborough

Monbiot

Sting

Cut out the four counters, folding the base back on the dotted line under each to stand them up

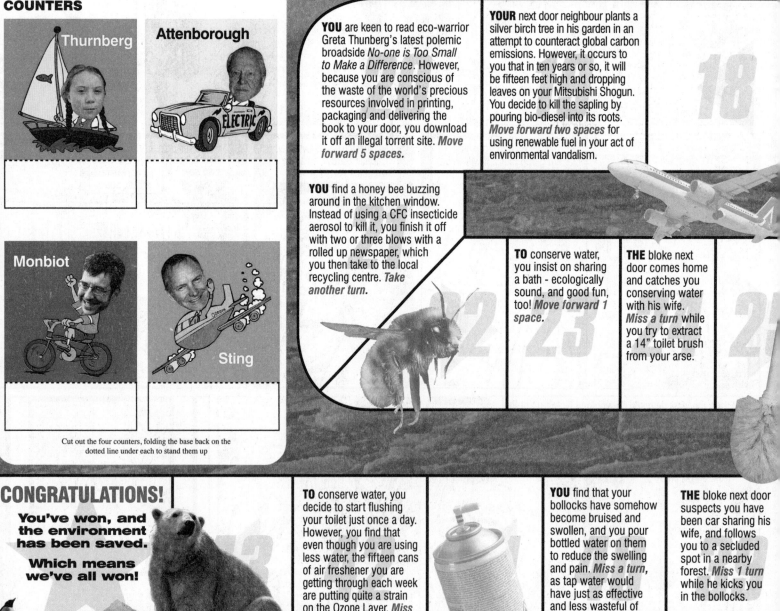

START

1

AFTER a particularly fierce Vindaloo, you let out a massive fart that adds to the earth's greenhouse gases. *Miss a turn* while you light a match to offset your arse's carbon footprint.

3

YOU buy a V8 diesel 4x4 that does 6mpg. However, when you get back from the dealership, you go on the internet and make a generous donation of £1 to a tree-planting charity in order to make amends. *Have another turn.*

YOU are keen to read eco-warrior Greta Thunberg's latest polemic broadside *No-one is Too Small to Make a Difference*. However, because you are conscious of the waste of the world's precious resources involved in printing, packaging and delivering the book to your door, you download it off an illegal torrent site. *Move forward 5 spaces.*

YOUR next door neighbour plants a silver birch tree in his garden in an attempt to counteract global carbon emissions. However, it occurs to you that in ten years or so, it will be fifteen feet high and dropping leaves on your Mitsubishi Shogun. You decide to kill the sapling by pouring bio-diesel into its roots. *Move forward two spaces* for using renewable fuel in your act of environmental vandalism.

18

YOU find a honey bee buzzing around in the kitchen window. Instead of using a CFC insecticide aerosol to kill it, you finish it off with two or three blows with a rolled up newspaper, which you then take to the local recycling centre. *Take another turn.*

22

TO conserve water, you insist on sharing a bath - ecologically sound, and good fun, too! *Move forward 1 space.*

23

THE bloke next door comes home and catches you conserving water with his wife. *Miss a turn* while you try to extract a 14" toilet brush from your arse.

2[5]

CONGRATULATIONS!

You've won, and the environment has been saved.

Which means we've all won!

TO conserve water, you decide to start flushing your toilet just once a day. However, you find that even though you are using less water, the fifteen cans of air freshener you are getting through each week are putting quite a strain on the Ozone Layer. *Miss a turn.*

YOU find that your bollocks have somehow become bruised and swollen, and you pour bottled water on them to reduce the swelling and pain. *Miss a turn*, as tap water would have just as effective and less wasteful of Mother Earth's precious resources.

THE bloke next door suspects you have been car sharing his wife, and follows you to a secluded spot in a nearby forest. *Miss 1 turn* while he kicks you in the bollocks.

YOU realise with horror that many of the objects in your home are made of Polyethylene Terephthalate -a plastic that will take millions of years to break down in landfill. To prevent this happening, you set fire to it all in the garden. *Have another turn.*

YOUR old-fashioned 2-stroke lawnmower uses fossil fuels and belches out toxic smoke and carbon particulates. However, using a pushalong would be too much of an arseache. To save the planet, you cover your entire garden in six inches of concrete. *Move forward 3 spaces.*

WITH dismay, you notice that the climate is getting uncomfortably warm. To counteract this worrying trend, you invest in the planet's future by buying a powerful air-conditioning unit, which you leave running around the clock. *Move forward 2 spaces.*

YOU change the landing light for a modern, low-wattage, eco-efficient flourescent bulb. *Miss two turns* while you get up for a piss in the night and fall down the stairs in the gloom.

TWO people can live more eco-efficiently than one, so when your wife goes to the supermarket, you move in with the woman next door to save on heating and lighting. *Move forward 1 space.*

THE woman next door's husband comes home early, and catches you saving on heating and lighting with his wife. *Miss a turn* while he kicks your head in.

YOU have always fancied taking your family for a dream holiday in Disneyworld, but after reading a Guardian article by George Monbiot, you are horrified to learn that each passenger on a longhaul flight to Florida is responsible for releasing 2 tonnes of carbon into the atmosphere. So you save 8 tonnes of emissions by leaving your wife and kids at home, and going on your own. *Have another turn.*

YOU decide to get fit and save the planet at the same time by buying a mountain bike. *Move forward 2 spaces* while you strap it to the back of your car and drive 60 miles to the Lake District, where you pedal a couple of miles along the side of Derwentwater before driving home and putting it up on Gumtree.

YOU are horrified when you find out the number of food miles involved in the production of supermarket tomatoes, so you decide to grow your own in a polyethylene greenhouse heated using 12 gallons of paraffin a week. *Move forward 2 spaces.*

YOU are going to burn an old sofa in the back lane, and douse it in unleaded petrol. However, you realise that when struck, matches give off sulphur dioxide, one of the gases held responsible for the Greenhouse Effect. *Have another turn* while you you set it ahad using the renewable energy of the sun's rays through a magnifying glass.

INSTEAD of using single-use non-degradable disposable nappies, you insist upon old-fashioned, re-usable terry towelling ones for your kids. *Move forward 4 spaces* while your wife scrapes the shit into the toilet and puts them into a bucket of bleach while you watch *Match of the Day*.

RUNNING your tumble dryer half-empty wastes energy, so to be a good neighbour, you jump over the fence and take the woman next door's bras and knickers off her line to fill up your load. *Move forward 2 spaces.*

AT the supermarket, instead of buying a disposable 5p carrier to throw away after use, you invest in the planet by stumping up 30p for a 'bag for life'. *Move forward 2 spaces* as you get home and stuff it in the cupboard under the sink with all the other ones you've bought.

YOU decide to shame your neighbours into living a greener, more eco-conscious life by daubing accusatory graffitti on their front door using lead-free organic paint. *Move forward 2 spaces.*

YOU realise that your old car is a gas-guzzling, pollution-belching dinosaur, so you decide to sell it to someone else who keeps driving it round. *Have another turn.*

YOU decide to go for a drive to a nearby, secluded spot in a nearby forest for a quiet nap. Coincidentally, the woman next door fancies a nap in the same place, so you decide to "car share", halving both your fuel use and emissions. *Move forward 1 space.*

PASSIONATE, energetic sex with your wife leaves you panting out carbon dioxide - one of the worst greenhouse gases. To save the planet, you decide to tell her you've got a headache and have a leisurely, low-carbon wank instead. *Move forward 2 spaces.*

TO prevent foxes and swans strangling themselves, you cut the plastic rings from your beercan sixpacks before discarding them in country laybys. *Move forward 2 spaces.*

"I'm No Tit-Man"
~Starmer

SIR Keir Starmer yesterday denied being a tit man after claims in an unauthorised biography accused the Labour leader of 'living a lie' by publicly pretending to prefer women's arses and thighs while secretly admiring the shape and size of their breasts.

There have long been rumours that the Labour Party leader went through a rebellious phase of being a tit man during his university years.

And an unnamed source in the book, *Your Starmer for Ten* by former ITV weather man Hutton Cranswick, claims that whilst studying at St Edmund's Hall, Oxford, Starmer would openly talk about his preference for women's breasts over their buttocks and the tops of their legs.

leg

Despite the accusations, the self-proclaimed leg and arse man and former Attorney General braved the media as he arrived at Parliament for Prime Minister's Questions, but refused to comment on

Labour leader moves to quash rumours

the accusations when challenged by reporters.

"Let's be clear about this, I'm not a tit man," he said. "Tits don't really do anything for me."

hand

But Leader of the House, Jacob Rees-Mogg, stood up in the chamber and asked the Labour leader directly to come clean about which bits he preferred.

guard

"It is a simple question, and I confess to being rather perplexed as to why The Right Honourable Gentleman can not give a straight answer and quell the rumours concerning his being a tit man," the lanky streak of piss told MPs.

watch

And, to raucous shouts of "Tit man! Tit man!" from the Tory back benches, Rees-Mogg added: "Unless the Labour leader denies the accusations, he is guilty of misleading this house."

fanny

But Sir Keir would not be drawn into the argument and responded calmly and forensically when he rose. "Mr Speaker, the Leader of the House knows well my preferences. They have been logged in the Register of Members' Interests and are a matter of public record," he said.

"Furthermore, if he wants to lay an accusation of my being a tit man at my door, I would invite him to do it outside of this chamber where he will not enjoy the protection of Parliamentary privilege."

Division: *Labour leader Starmer (left) denies preferring womens breasts (above left) over and above their buttocks and thighs (above)*

The shadow chief whip, Valerie Vaz, later told reporters that Starmer had said all he had to say on what has been termed "Tit-man gate" and that the Labour Party considered the matter closed.

tits

But chairman of the influential 1922 Committee, Sir Graham Brady, said that he intended to introduce a private members bill calling on Starmer to appear before a cross-party Select Committee to answer questions about whether he prefers tits to arses and thighs.

~Reuters

STARMER'S LLAMAS

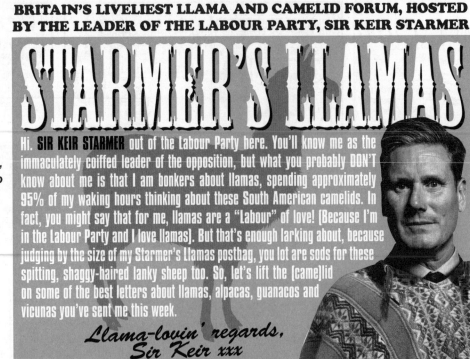

Hi. **SIR KEIR STARMER** out of the Labour Party here. You'll know me as the immaculately coiffed leader of the opposition, but what you probably DON'T know about me is that I am bonkers about llamas, spending approximately 95% of my waking hours thinking about these South American camelids. In fact, you might say that for me, llamas are a "Labour" of love! [Because I'm in the Labour Party and I love llamas]. But that's enough larking about, because judging by the size of my Starmer's Llamas postbag, you lot are sods for these spitting, shaggy-haired lanky sheep too. So, let's lift the [came]lid on some of the best letters about llamas, alpacas, guanacos and vicunas you've sent me this week.

Llama-lovin' regards,
Sir Keir xxx

SEEING as how llamas have two 'L's at the beginning of their name and they spit when they talk, it seems fairly obvious to me that they're trying to pass themselves off as Welsh. But they're not Welsh: they're South American, and they should ruddy well accept it. When oh when will llamas embrace their own Andean culture instead of clumsily appropriating ours?

Mrs Gwyneth Llewellyn, Llandudno

HOW arrogant of Mrs Llewellyn (*above*) to assume that llamas are trying to copy the Welsh. Their appropriation of two 'L's at the beginning of their name could simply be a tip of the cap to my husband, the popular 1980s hip-hopper LL Cool J. And when you consider that 'spitting' is also a slang word for rapping, it becomes even more likely that these humble beasts are, in fact, trying to emulate the New York-based '*Rock The Bells*' hit-maker. Perhaps next time, Mrs Llewellyn will consider all the facts before she puts pen to paper.

Mrs Ada Cool J, New York

WHEN I was a boy, you never even heard llamas mentioned, but here in 21st Century Britain it's just "llama this" and "llama that" everywhere you turn. Now that we've finally been freed from the shackles of the European Union, can we *please* stop going on about foreign animals like llamas and get back to focusing on decent, green and pleasant British beasts, such as cows, chickens and field mice.

Colonel Montgomery Farage-Littlegaunt, Chipping Norton

I READ last week that llamas are highly sociable animals, and since I was planning a barbecue for my birthday, I decided to invite a few over. Well, I've never been so disappointed. The smug-looking creatures didn't say a single word to either me or my guests – they just kept themselves to themselves at the other end of the garden. And when I tried to offer them some potato salad, they spat in my face. Sociable my foot.

Mrs Edith Witch-Trials, Dundee

WITH their long eyelashes, spindly legs and permanently smug expressions, it strikes me that llamas are essentially the supermodels of the animal world. I don't know about anyone else, but I can certainly imagine a llama striding purposefully up and down a catwalk in some outlandish frock and then tumbling out of the Groucho Club at 3am, high on cocaine.

D Attenborough, London

MR ATTENBOROUGH (*above*) is talking out of his arse. Llamas are notoriously protective over other animals, and will often 'guard' sheep and goats by chasing off coyotes and other predators. This clearly makes them the *bouncers* of the animal world. I don't know about anyone else, but I can certainly imagine a llama standing in front of a velvet rope, chewing gum in a bomber jacket and telling a fox to fuck off because it's not wearing a tie.

M Strachan, London

MR ATTENBOROUGH and Mrs Strachan (*above and above*) are both talking shite. Llamas stick their tongues out when they're annoyed and have unusually high blood sugar, which means they are both cheeky and diabetic. As such, they are quite clearly the *Bernard Mannings* of the animal kingdom. I don't know about anyone else, but I can certainly imagine a llama up on stage, sweating profusely in a dickie bow whilst telling racist jokes and making unpleasant comments about its mother-in-law.

C Packham, London

I USED to work at Chester Zoo where I was responsible for maintaining the daily nourishment of various South American tylopods. But with patience, graft and dedication, I worked my way up from that lowly position to the job I currently hold today – General Secretary of the British Agricultural Workers' Union. So, I supposed you could say – if you really wanted to – that I used feed llamas and now I lead farmers. This is true, but since both Chester Zoo and the BAWU have lost all the paperwork relating to my employment, anyone looking into the matter might come to the conclusion that I have made it up.

Mervyn Ballsack, Farnham

I WATCHED a documentary the other day in which I learned that llamas have been used to transport meat by Andean cultures for centuries. As a butcher whose delivery van had recently broken down, I thought it might be a quirky idea to start doing my rounds on a llama instead. I had one imported from Peru, and I've since become the talk of the town, clip-clopping up and down the high street on my shaggy-haired ungulate beast, distributing chops and sausages to my customers as I go. Not only is the llama much cheaper and easier to maintain than my old van driver, but he doesn't go running to the police every time he catches me interfering sexually with the meat.

Gerald Giblets, Scholes

Kids don't get the simplest jokes... ABOUT LLAMAS!

"**I TOOK** my two-year-old grandson to the zoo last week so that he could see the llamas. However, when we arrived at the enclosure the animals were nowhere to be found. We had to wait almost twenty minutes before one of them peeked its head out through the leaves and walked towards us. Quick as a flash, I turned to my grandson with a chuckle and quipped: "Better ungu-late than never!" But rather than roaring with laughter at my amusing pun on the scientific classification for even-toed hoofed mammals, the humourless arsehole just sat there stony-faced. I don't know why I bother sometimes, I really don't.

Agnes Prole-Arthreat, Prestwich

Has YOUR fun-sucking killjoy of a grandchild failed to grasp the most basic joke about llamas? Write in and tell us about it. Each letter we print wins a three-week intensive course in llama-based comedy to get the sanctimonious little prick up to speed.

IT'S COMPETITION TIME!

TO WIN A DECADE'S SUPPLY OF LLAMAS IN OUR FANTASTIC PHOTO CONTEST

FROM LAND'S END to John O'Groats, we can all tell the difference between the various breeds of even-toed camelid. But what about if you only can only see their arses? Would you still be able to spot the difference then? Take a look at these four pictures of Artiodactyla mudflaps and see if you can distinguish which chuff belongs to which. We've given you a couple of cheeky clues to help you on your way...

1 *A-llama* bells will be ringing if you can't guess which popular two-toed ungulate this backside belongs to!

2 You're sure to be *guanaco-ver the moon* if you can classify the booty of this shaggy-haired South American mammal!

3 *Vic(una)tory* will be yours if you can match this pair of bestial buttocks to the Cetartiodactylic creature they're attached to!

4 There'll be Wild Bactrian *Cam-ell* to pay if you fail to identify this rump belonging to a beast from the suborder Tylopoda!

Tweet your answers @Vizcomic and make sure to include the address to which you would like your decade's supply of llamas to be sent. The property in question must be at least 600 acres in size and rich in wild bromgrass, alfalfa and lichen

10 THINGS YOU NEVER KNEW ABOUT *LLAMAS!*

1 **LLAMAS** are the only mammals on Earth who communicate by humming, apart from hummingbirds, giraffes and the Dave Clark Five.

2 **BELIEVE IT** or not, llamas have THREE stomachs! "Mental, isn't it?" says TV naturalist **DAVID ATTENBOROUGH**. "It's like something out of fucking *Blade Runner*. And this'll really blow your wig off. Cows've got FOUR stomachs. I mean: for fuck's sake! Four! Isn't nature fucking bonkers?" the national treasure added.

3 **AN ANAGRAM** of 'llamas' is 'small', with an 'a' left over – which is ironic because llamas *aren't particularly small*. They regularly grow to around 6ft in height – which is nearly THREE TIMES the height of adult human U2 vocalist, **BONO**.

4 **THE SMALLEST** ever llama was not an animal... but the *Dalai Lama*! In 2006, the world's smallest man, Calvin Phillips, was elected the 12th Dalai Lama, making him the most diminutive Tibetan Buddhist leader in history. During his six-year tenure as head of the Buddhist faith, Phillips wore a red handkerchief as a monastic robe and shaved his head with a razor blade the size of a SIM card from an iPhone 11.

5 **BERGERAC** star **JOHN NETTLES** is the only living British actor to have been bummed off a llama. The steely-frowned Cornish thespian was trekking through the Andes as a student in the 1960s, when his trousers and pants got snagged on a jagged rock. Seeing an opportunity, a nearby llama anally mounted the *Midsomer Murders* icon and proceeded to frot itself to orgasm. "It's not an experience I'd be eager to repeat," Nettles told *Bride* magazine. "But it's certainly provided me with a memorable after-dinner anecdote."

6 **THE OWNER** of the largest number of llamas on Earth is none other than superstar rap fave **P DIDDY!** The Harlem born hip-hopper possesses a whopping 9,708 domesticated South American tylopods, which he keeps in various rented paddocks across the globe. "If I'm honest, I've got too many," Diddy told *Woman & Home* magazine. "I got pissed one night and bought ten thousand of the motherfuckers on eBay. I've given away a few hundred to mates, but I've still got more llamas than I know what to do with."

7 **INNUMERABLE** pop songs have been written about llamas, such as 'Llama' by Phish, and innumerable others, which we unfortunately don't have the space to list here, due to their aforementioned innumerability.

8 **BELIEVE IT** or not, American cumshot icon **PETER NORTH** is afraid of llamas! The freelance stick-vid man has a clause in all his contracts which states that he will not venture within six feet of any two-toed lamoids. "It's not a medical thing", North told *The Independent On Sunday*. "I just don't like them."

9 **MANY** of our favourite telly celebrities keep llamas as domestic pets – such as snooker ace **PETER EBDON**, Jam frontman **PAUL WELLER** and *Game of Thrones* favourite **LENA HEADEY**.

10 **MANY** of our favourite telly celebs don't keep llamas as domestic pets – such as BBC anchorman **CLIVE MYRIE**, soccer analyst **JAMIE CARRAGHER** and *Spectator* bellend **TOBY YOUNG**.

LLAMA LLAFFS 'N' LLOLS!

We're crackers about YOUR cheeky even-toed ungulate chuckles

Ho! Ho! Ho!

Q: What's a domesticated South American camelid's favourite 1970s supergroup?

A: Emerson, Lake & Llama (Emerson, Lake & Palmer)

D Letterman, New York

Q: What's a domesticated South American camelid's favourite 1980s pop trio?

A: Banana-llama (Bananarama)

J Seinfeld, New York

Q: What's a domesticated South American camelid's favourite 44th US president?

A: Barack O-Llama (Barack Obama)

V Putin, Moscow

Q: What does a domesticated South American camelid say if it has organised a picnic and it discovers at the last minute that an extra person will be attending?

A: "Alpaca-nother sandwich" (I'll pack another sandwich)

K Jong-un, Pyongyang

We literally can't get enough of your bonkers cetartiodactylic japes. Keep them coming in – every single one we print wins a lifetime's supply of ten, twenty and fifty pound notes for you and 3,000 friends.

LLAMA Q&As
with
The AB of C off of the C of E
DR JUSTIN WELBY

YOUR ecumenical queries about even-toed lamoids, answered by the Archbishop of Canterbury

Dear AB of C, **I'VE ALWAYS** loved llamas but I've never been able to own one as my husband is severely allergic to their phlegm. So you can imagine my envy and covetousness when my next-door neighbour bought herself a lovely shaggy llama. I watch the beast jealously all day through our living room window as it struts about my neighbour's front garden, chewing the lawn and spitting at her. I know the Bible says thou shalt not covet thy neighbour's ox or thy neighbour's ass, but since it doesn't explicitly mention anything about not coveting thy neighbour's llama, do you think I'll still be all right for a spot up in Heaven when I shuffle off this mortal coil?

Edna Blue-Haze, Ardwick Bridge

The AB of C says: *"I'm afraid the simple answer is no, Edna. If you read the recently released 'special edition' of the Bible which features bonus 'deleted commandments', you'll see that in the original version of Exodus 20:17, God clearly states: "Thou shalt not covet thy neighbour's ox, nor his ass, nor his ossifrage, nor his llama, nor his anything that does flyeth through the air nor cheweth upon the cud nor that that liveth in the firmament but doethn't hath fins nor scales." As such, I'm afraid you should probably use what remaining time you have left on this Earth to steel yourself for an eternity of unthinkable torture at the hands of the foulest legions of Beelzebub's despicable horde."*

Dear AB of C, **IN DANTE** Alighieri's iconic 14th Century religious poem, *The Divine Comedy*, he depicts Purgatory as a vast, towering mountain, which the sinful must climb in order to atone for their wickedness before they ascend to Heaven. Since llamas are especially good at trekking up mountains, it strikes me that these beasts have an unfair advantage over the rest of us when it comes to performing their allegorical afterlife penance. A llama that has lied and cheated and gambled and whored will still reach Paradise weeks before I do, and the worst thing I've ever done is expose myself to a women-only yoga class.

Bert Fruit-Machine, Prestwich

The AB of C says: *"Being omniscient, God is well aware that llamas are better at climbing mountains than you and all His other glorious creations. So I would imagine He'll have some kind of plan, perhaps putting them on the outside track of the Purgatory mountainside, meaning they have more ground to cover than everyone else. In future, if you think you've found a fault with any aspect of God's great plan, just remember that if it's occurred to you, then it's probably also occurred to Him."*

Dear AB of C, **WHY SHOULD** we consider YOU to be the foremost authority on llama-related theological matters when Tibetan Buddhist leader 'The Dalai Lama' quite literally has llamas in his name? Surely if I want to know something about llamas with reference to religion, I'd be best off writing to him, wouldn't I?

Jeremy Realthing-Yeah, Oxon

The AB of C says: *"Having a thing in your name does not automatically make you an expert on that thing. For instance, if you had a question about nettles, you'd write to Monty Don, not John Nettles. The only exception to this rule is Crocodile Dundee, who, to be fair, did know a lot about crocodiles, even though, to be fair, he was a fictional character. Of course, feel free to write to the Dalai Lama about anything you like, but don't come crying to me when you're burning in a sulphurous lake of fire for all eternity for worshipping a false idol."*

Have YOU got a question about llamas, alpacas, vicunas, guanacos or camels in the afterlife? Why not write in to: The AB of C off of the C of E, c/o Viz Comic, PO Box 841, Whitley Bay, NE26 9EQ

NO TIME LIKE THE FUTURE FOR BARRY

BARNSLEY accountant Barry Ropewalk hit a milestone last Saturday when he celebrated his fortieth birthday with friends and family. But when he awoke the following morning, the fun came to an abrupt halt as he discovered that fate had a cruel surprise in store.

"It was a wonderful occasion. We hired the function room above our local and pretty much everyone I know came," remembers Barry. "One of my mates DJed and there was karaoke later on. It was the perfect evening."

"I'd been looking forward to the party for months, so when I woke up the morning after, I was excited to look forward to it some more," he said. "But something had happened. Suddenly, looking forward to my fortieth birthday party just wasn't the same."

wife

Barry's wife Linda explained that up until yesterday, his fortieth birthday party had been in the future, and this had been why he had been able to look forward to it. When the confused accountant asked her when it would be in the future again, she broke some devastating news.

"Linda told me that the party was no longer in the future, and that I would never be able to look forward to it again," he said. "She told me that it was now in what she called 'the past'."

lands

Linda explained to her distraught husband that although he couldn't look forward to his 40th birthday party any more, he could now look back on it with fond memories, something he couldn't have done previously.

"I know she was only trying to cheer me up, but this just didn't sit right. How can something be in the future one day, then not be in the future any more?" said Barry. "It simply makes no sense."

Time, gentlemen, please: Barry enjoyed his birthday in local pub, but later discovered that he no longer looked forward to it.

According to physicist Professor Brian Cox, Barry had made a fundamental error in his reasoning. He told us: "We live in a realm of four dimensions of space and time. We can go anywhere we like on the ground, backwards, forwards and sideways."

"We can even go up and down in an aeroplane or hot air balloon. But when it comes to time, we can only go in one direction."

wich cuckoos

Barry says he is coming to terms with the realisation that he can not look forward to his last birthday ever again. "I now understand that there's a vast fathomless chasm of time, the past, stretching from the birth of the universe to just one femtosecond ago, and that things in the future are constantly, remorselessly, being consigned to the past" he told us. "It's all come as a bit of a shock."

Despite his dismay, Barry is determined to learn from his experience. "Knowing that looking forward to something will eventually come to an end has made me more determined to make the most of the anticipation," he said.

"This has all been a bit of a rollercoaster ride, but I've been consoling myself by looking forward to Christmas 1985 when I got a BMX," he added.

UNEASY LISTENING
Bruce sprains his avuncular

RADIO 2 daytime favourite *KEN BRUCE* has spoken of his recent agony after spraining his avuncular live on air.

The 69-year-old DJ explained that the incident occurred two weeks ago during the 'Popmaster' slot of his popular mid-morning show.

"Jeremy from Glossop had just failed to name three hits by Wet Wet Wet, and I was enjoying a hearty chuckle when I felt something pull at the top of my chest," said Bruce. "I didn't really notice the pain initially, but then I read out a charming note from Sylvia in Essex about how her grandson made a hat out of some cheese."

"I began a light chortle and felt a sharp twang in my shoulder."

pop

Fearing something was wrong, the quick-thinking DJ immediately put on *Building a Bridge to your Heart* by Wax to buy himself some time.

He said: "I needed to get to the bottom of what was wrong, so whilst the song was playing, I called Dr Marion Alan-Davis, the Radio 2 medic, who arrived just as the track was finishing."

Despite being in considerable discomfort, Bruce managed some quick banter with the traffic presenter and put on *Hip to be Square* by Huey Lewis and the News, buying enough time for Dr Alan-Davis to perform a standard DJ examination.

She then gave Ken the bad news that he had a bad sprain to his avuncular. He was told to spend a fortnight taking it easy with absolutely no on-air chuckling, and under no circumstances was he to be obliging or warm-hearted.

gravy

"It's nigh-on impossible to be a mid-morning DJ with a dicky avuncular," Bruce told his fans on Twitter. "I had no choice but to rest up and, thankfully, I'm now fine."

Fully rested, Bruce has been given a clean bill of health and is now back on air. "The old avuncular is back to factory settings and I'm looking forward to once again enjoying delightful stories of how his listeners lost their slippers or nearly fell in a pond," he said.

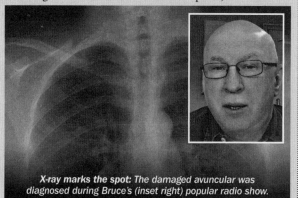
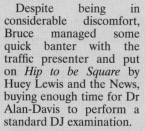

X-ray marks the spot: The damaged avuncular was diagnosed during Bruce's (inset right) popular radio show.

THE MOTORWAYS are the arteries of our country, criss-crossing all parts of the United Kingdom, except most of Wales and the top half of Scotland. And when we're on a long journey, the Motorway Service Station is an alluring oasis that provides a welcome respite from the rigours of the open road. Indeed, there's nothing more alluring and exciting than the opportunity to enjoy a twenty-minute slash'n'dash visit to one of these wonderful, quintessentially British institutions.

Whether you're looking to fill up with ludicrously overpriced petrol, enjoy a gourmet meal, or sit down for a relaxing dump only to find there's no paper, service stations are a sight for sore eyes when they hove into view. But what exactly can we expect to find when we waddle through the doors at one of these oh-so-convenient roadside oases, desperately nipping one in? Let's frantically pull over across three lanes of busy traffic at the last second and take a look.

1 The Toilets

95% OF motorway services stops are to answer an urgent call of nature, so after we park our cars, the first thing most of us do is to park our breakfasts. And with anything up to 1,000 weary motorists an hour making use of the facilities, keeping the conveniences clean and hygienic is a job for an army of lavatory cleaners. So the best that the single, minimum-wage mop-pusher on duty can do during his shift is to try to keep at least one of the bogs un-blocked at any one time, in the style of a Big Top plate-spinner.

If you're just after a "number one", however, you'll be in in luck, as chances are most of the pineapple-cubed urinals are more-or-less functional, and users can relieve themselves whilst reading carefully targeted ads for car insurance, digital tyre inflaters and erectile dysfunction helplines. And on their way out, male toilet users can take their choice of a dazzling array of vending machines selling everything from Viagra and condoms to ring-shaped battery-operated gizmos that buzz when you put them on your cock.

The ladies' toilets are largely the same as the men's, except that the vending machine dispenses sanitary towels and eau de cologne, and there is invariably a large queue of women waiting patiently for their turn in the trap. The general ambience of the place is slightly sweeter than the gents' counterpart, due in part to the presence of small vases of flowers by the sinks, but mainly because women never use their facilities to crimp off a length of cable.

2 The Food Court

AFTER the toilet visit, most travellers' thoughts turn to food, and the modern motorway service station's Food Court is a veritable gourmet's paradise, offering hungry travellers a mouth-watering array of fare. Whether you fancy a quick Big Mac and fries from McDonalds, a quick chicken burger and fries from KFC, or a tasty burger and fries from Burger King, you'll be spoilt for choice. And of course, for those who don't fancy a burger, there are some mouth-watering pre-wrapped sandwiches sweating in the fridge at WH Smiths. And crisps by the till.

And, just occasionally, a service station decides to 'think outside the box' by offering a unique cuisine option that challenges convention and takes on the generic fast food giants. Be it sushi, gourmet falafels or artisan salads, you'll be able to spot these brave innovators a mile off as they'll be the only place in the entire foodcourt with no customers.

3 The Shopping Mall

WHEN we've satisfied our hunger, it's time for a little retail therapy. Today's motorway service station is a mini shopping mall, complete with an array of big-name retail outlets offering a bewildering variety of high-end shopping experiences. Here motorway travellers can purchase everything necessary for their journey, as well as plenty of things that nobody in their right mind could ever need, including three-quarters-sized scarecrows, children's and adults' wetsuits, and carved wooden ducks.

Another popular concession is a store selling Mobile Phone Accessories. This retailer serves a valuable didactic function, as anyone who has forgotten their charger when embarking on a long road trip and has had to cough up ten times the usual rrp for an emergency replacement will be unlikely to make the same mistake again.

4 The Games Arcade

Those who fancy a break from life in the fast lane may prefer to slip into the services' exclusive gaming section. Here they can experience a taste of the glamorous, James Bond-style Monte Carlo high-life as they listlessly feed £2 coins into an Ant & Dec's Saturday Night Takeaway fruit machine that is set to pay out 85% of the money fed into it as winnings (that is to say, it will simply keep 15% of all the money fed into it).

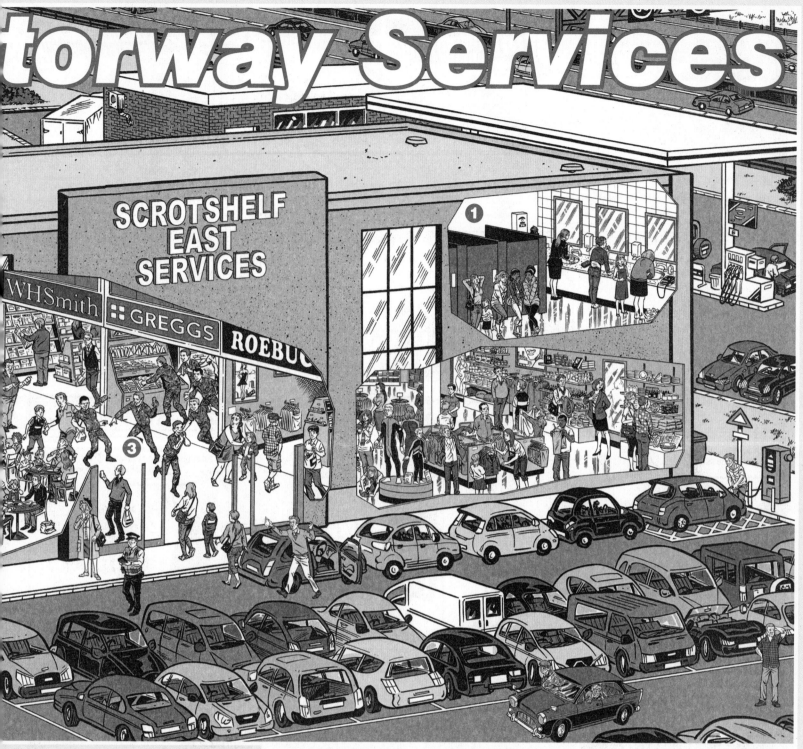

And if you're looking for relaxation after spending 5 gruelling hours behind the wheel on the M1, what better way is there to wind down than by clambering into a small, plastic bucket seat for ten high-octane minutes of frantic Gran Turismo 7 Japanese street racing? It's a great way to recharge your batteries and set yourself up for the next 7 hours on the road in your diesel VW Sharan.

5 The Accomodation

Some motorway journeys are so long that they cannot be completed in a day. Fortunately, most motorway services include a budget hotel, providing a welcome respite from the rigours of the road for weary travellers. The on-site branding may suggest that these provide a cosy stop-over for families wishing to break their journeys to their holiday destinations; but in reality they are full of sales reps putting a room service microwave burger and the porn channel on their expenses, before wanking themselves to sleep.

CAN YOU SPOT...?

• An old couple in their car who can't find the exit back to the motorway and are embarking on their tenth circuit of the services complex

• A doughnut vending machine that, for all anyone knows, has had the same doughnuts mouldering in it for the last six months

• A thirsty man who has just paid for a bottle of water with a £20, wondering why there are no notes in his change

• A man buying a chewable toothbrush, somehow unaware that it may not be a good idea to put anything bought from a vending machine in a gents' toilet into your mouth

• A powdered egg salesman who has just lost £4 in a cock buzzer vending machine, wondering whether to get someone to open the machine or simply write off his loss

• An old woman whose day-trip bus driver has got fed up of waiting for her and left

• A queue of 5 electric cars with flat batteries that have taken an 80-mile white knuckle detour for a shot on the single working 2-hour "rapid charger" that may or may not have the correct connector

• A driver who has now been sat in the queue for the electric charger for 2 hours and 3 minutes, being fined a statutory £85 charge for exceeding her 2 hours free parking limit

• A man who has lost the will to live, failing to sell AA memberships from under a big umbrella

• A platoon of squaddies on their way to Catterick, laying waste to Greggs in a tactical strike on the pasties and sausage rolls

• A bewildered middle-aged man who has forgotten where he parked his car, trying to decide how much longer to look for it before he reports it stolen

• An old couple who have been coming to the services for tea once a week for more than 40 years, because "it was a treat" in the 1970s

• A football manager accepting a 'bung' from a Far Eastern betting syndicate

• A pair of sickly saplings in the car park that have been planted to offset the carbon emissions of the 10,000 cars who call at the services each day

NEXT WEEK: *What to See and Do in the MOT Viewing Area at KwikFit*

DON'T TAKE THAT!

FORMER *TAKE THAT!* frontman Gary Barlow opened his heart to reporters yesterday, telling them how the pressures of fame at the height of his pop success had made him pile on the pounds into an offshire account.

Barlow, known as the one who could play the piano a bit, revealed that things first started to go awry in the late nineties. He said: "One day we were a struggling band, the next we were on a world tour with a four album deal."

"If I'm honest, I didn't handle it very well, and I started to invest in an index-linked, enterprise, investment venture capital scheme."

cheques

"Even after I quit music in 1999, the royalty cheques just kept coming in. I was just sat in my big house in Cheshire, and my bank balance just got bigger and bigger. I simply didn't know what to do with all the money," he said.

"I was so embarrassed by it all, but the thought of paying tax and contributing to the welfare of others just seemed silly. So I just kept piling the pounds into an offshore haven."

Barlow continued living the high life and packing on the cash throughout the noughties. But one day, after getting out

Pressures of fame made me put my money in offshore tax havens ~ Barlow

of the shower, he caught a glimpse of his bank statement on the bedside table.

"I couldn't believe how bloated my account had become," he said.

bombs

It was the sight of his distended balance – along with a BBC Panorama report into high profile tax avoidance schemes – that finally led the stout-walleted singer to act.

I decided I had to shed a few million pounds, so I did," he said.

"A lot of people think that the song *Back for Good* was about some bird who'd kicked me into touch, but in reality it was about all the cash I'd been forced to hand over to the Inland Revenue to keep my OBE," he added.

CUTBACKS TO THE FUTURE!

CONTROVERSIAL plans to balance the books announced by Nottinghamshire County Council yesterday have raised eyebrows amongst ratepayers. For the cash-strapped borough intends to save money in the latest financial year by cutting services... *in the 1920s!*

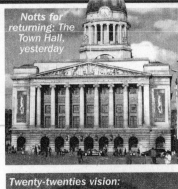

Notts for returning: The Town Hall, yesterday

The scheme, thought to be the first of its kind in the country, will see the cash-strapped local authority employing *Back to the Future*-style 'time engineering' to make cuts in the third decade of the twentieth century in order to protect council services in the present day.

"It's really quite simple if you think about it," Alderman Tom Finch told reporters. "We're simply going to go back in time to the twenties and cut services across the board. We don't need them now, because those days are gone."

"That frees up much-needed money for the present day residents of Nottinghamshire to spend on things like improved bin collections and mending holes in the road."

library

One area thought to be ripe for cuts a century ago is Nottinghamshire's former library services.

"We've been looking through the borough records, and back in the twenties there were twelve libraries in Nottingham City Centre alone," Finch told reporters. "Nobody needs that many libraries, and bending the laws of physics in order to sell off eleven of them will allow us to keep our one remaining library open at least three days a week in the present day."

billiard room

But the plans to save money on past salaries have upset many people, not least of all Nottinghamshire County Council employees.

"They intend to go back and halve the wages of everyone who was working for the council a hundred years ago," said a planning officer who wished to remain anonymous. "Not only that, but they intend to remove paid holidays and put all the staff on zero hours contracts."

conservatory

"I mean, in a sense it doesn't matter so much, because they're all dead. But it will set a precedent, and what's to stop the council in a hundred years' time from coming back to today and cutting my salary now?" she added.

Twenty-twenties vision: Alderman Tom Finch.

Council launches adventurous budget scheme

Chief accountant at Nottingham County Council, William Whiffles, confirmed that around £1.5m of ratepayers' money has been funnelled into research and development on the time machine that will be used to bring about the cuts. In testing, the machine has yet to go back in time, but Whiffles said he was confident that a working model would be ready soon.

ballroom

"We hope to have cracked the problem of time travel in time for the next Spending and Budgets Committee meeting at the start of the third quarter," he told the *Nottingham Clarion and Ocarina*. "This scheme will have cost a lot of money, but when we get it to work it will pay for itself many times over," he added.

study

The technology involved in the ambitious programme is a closely-guarded secret, and no-one from the council was willing to give any information about how the time machine will eventually work. But reporters covering a recent planning meeting spotted Nottingham Mayor Ron Futter entering the Town Hall debating chamber wearing a rudimentary space suit with wires sticking out of it and all smoke coming off his hair.

LetterBocks

Viz Comic, P.O. Box 841 Whitley Bay, NE26 9EQ : letters@viz.co.uk

WHY doesn't anybody shit themselves out of fear in the movies? If I was wandering through a haunted house in a *Woman in Black* situation and a deranged supernatural harpy jumped out at me, my knickers would be fuller than Santa's sack on Christmas Eve. Come on film-makers, show some realism and cut out the heroic Hollywood bullshit.

Harriet Jumpjet, Scarborough

OUR recent pizza order was delivered by a bloke in an Audi TT. Who knew there was that much profit to be made selling bread discs with tomato sauce and cheese on top for £20 a pop?

Mike Tatham, St. Andrews

I THINK video games have given us unrealistic expectations about street-fighting. I've seen a few dust-ups as an adult, but none has involved fireballs, hurricane kicks or a green bloke with electric skin. Come on, computer boffins, how about a game where two hairless men in smart shirts and crap shoes shove each other before one does a headlock and they both fall over the kerb?

Gavin Forknife, Wednesbury

MY office has this running joke where they set the fire alarm off once a week and we all have to get up and go outside. Whilst this was funny the first few times, it is starting to wear thin now.

Christina Martin, Bexhill-on-Sea

I'VE only shit myself twice, but both times I was wearing the same pair of knickers. Coincidence?

Debi Fish, Doncaster

∗ *Hmm. We're afraid that something doesn't quite ring true about that story, Ms Fish. Surely, when the first incident occurred, the knickers would have been swiftly discarded, not emptied and washed to wear again. So we're going to open this to the readers for discussion. Do YOU think Debi Fish of Doncaster shat herself twice in the same knickers, or is she making the story up as a means of getting her name on the letters page? Write and tell us what you think, marking your letter or email "Debi Fish of Doncaster shitting herself twice in the same knickers."*

I HAVE noticed that jazz musicians often comment that the music they are playing is 'too funky!' In which case, perhaps they could try toning the funk down a little bit instead of just complaining about it.

John Godbolt, Bristol

I'M A huge fan of both Clint Eastwood and sticky toffee pudding. One was mayor of Carmel, California, whilst the other is made in Cartmel, Cumbria, but I always get the two places mixed up. Imagine my embarrassment when I flew all the way to Carmel in California and asked the mayor if I could buy a sticky toffee pudding from him. Honestly, the look on his face!

Neil Johnson, Durham

STAR LETTER

WHY is it that almost every sentient creature on the planet manages to turn on a tap or crawl over to a pond when they're thirsty, but plants just sit there expecting you to pour drinks into them like they're Emperor fucking Caligula? What's worse is we let them get away with it. You should see the way Monty Don fawns over them on *Gardeners' World*. Pathetic.

Josh Cluderay, Wensleydale

ON your Big Vern strips, could you please write the word 'BLAM!' a little smaller? Only my eye tends to catch it when I'm halfway through the story and it spoils the surprise ending.

Micky Bullock, London

I'VE just seen the Duchess of Cambridge, Kate Middleton interviewed on TV, and I noticed she says "Oh gosh" where I'd say "Fuck me," and she says "My goodness!" where I'd say "Fuck off!" Exactly the same message communicated in both circumstances, and I can only conclude that in her own way she's got a mouth like a fucking docker.

Lee Kern, email

I ENTERED a roundabout and didn't see a Nissan Micra, the colour of which I can only describe as 'tarmac grey'. I fully accept that it would have been my fault had I collided with it, but come on, Nissan, give us a fucking chance.

Claude Golightly, Wells

WHY do nurses wear their watches upside down on their tits? I mean, why don't they just wear a watch and stop pissing about?

Terry Farricker, Blackpool

THESE 'clothes' are an absolute con. It seems that after taking them off to go to bed, we're supposed to put them back on again the following morning. You couldn't make it up.

Col P. Fawcett, Durham

AFTER years of being unable to retract my foreskin down as far as the maker's nameplate, I tried snipping through my banjo string. Sadly this didn't have the desired effect and I now have a deep seated penile infection. Perhaps I should have left it to the professionals.

Dave Headwards, Dorset

∗ *You should have, Dave. Every man to his trade.*

INSPIRED by a sign on a bench in our local park saying "He spent many happy hours sitting here," I asked the Beate Uhse sex shop in Hamburg if they'd put up a similar sign in my memory in wank booth number four when I died. But they told me to fuck off. In German.

Leonard Wankbender, Edinburgh

I'D like the so-called scientists to explain what the point of toads is when we already have frogs. But I won't hold my breath.

Dave Mclean, Newport

∗ *It's a very good question, Dave, and perhaps a Viz reader with herpetological knowledge could enlighten us. Or perhaps this is a question for Viz-reading philosophers or religious leaders. If you fall into any of these categories and fancy having a bash at answering this question, write in tell us what the point of toads is when there are frogs. There's a free Viz pen for each correct answer.*

IN 2003, US Marines used a 50 ton M-88 military tow truck to topple the statue of Saddam Hussein in Baghdad. The other week in Bristol, the statue of Edward Colston came down with a few tugs on a rope by protesters. This statue was clearly a hazard to heath and safety whenever a half decent wind was blowing. The Colston statue has now been made safe by lobbing it in the Avon, and the protesters should be thanked by the local council.

Michael Bach, Blackpool

GANDHI CAPP

WHAT DO YOU WANT, MAHATMA?

AN INDEPENDENT INDIA BASED ON A PRINCIPLE OF RELIGIOUS PLURALISM

AND A PINT OF MILD.

BY dressing up like ghosts in their scary white suits, beekeepers are asking to be attacked by their poisonous little insect pets. The bees must be terrified. Surely it would calm them down, and probably win their respect, if their keeper was to dress up like a giant but friendly bee in a suit of yellow and black furry stripes, with a pair of deely boppers, and some makeshift wings improvised from two old pillow cases. It's not rocket science.

Phil Kitching, Isle of Jura

DOGGING these days isn't what it used to be. Last weekend I was standing, cock in hand, peering in at a couple parked up in their car who were just sat eating sandwiches. What's the world coming to?

Gaz Thomas, Redhill

I WAS as saddened as anyone to learn that Dame Vera Lynn had passed away. However the description of a 103-year-old woman as a 'forces' sweetheart' sickened me to the core. Surely modern soldiers can fantasise about women their own age.

James Brown, Edinburgh

DOES anyone know what BBQ stands for? I know the first letter stands for barbecue, and the second B probably stands for burgers or something. But what the Q stands for is anyone's guess. I for one am totally perplexed.

Glenn, Halifax

I DREAMED that I went to a record signing event with Debbie Harry of Blondie. When I got there, I was told that she was in a cupboard and you had to push your records under the door for her to sign. I pointed out that as I hadn't seen her go into the cupboard, it could be anyone in there. I took a picture of the cupboard on my phone but as it was a dream, it hasn't come out. What an abominable way to treat your fans.

Hugh Grainger, Bromley

❋ *That really is an appalling way to behave on Ms Harry's part. Have any other readers been treated as badly by a pop star at a signing event in a dream? Perhaps you dreamt you met the Rolling Stones in HMV, but they made you put a bag over your head so you couldn't see them. Or perhaps Fatboy Slim was eating fish and chips out of newspaper at a signing and got greasy fingerprints all over your 12-inch record cover. Or maybe Led Zep guitar ace Jimmy Page refused to sign his autobiography and stamped it instead with an inked rubber stamp. No, hold on, that last one actually happened.*

COBRA CORNER

ANIMAL experts tell us that snakes are more scared of humans than we are of them. What nonsense. When I encountered a king cobra while on holiday in India, I shat myself but the snake didn't.

Martin Harwood, Bradford

ON A trek through the mountains of Brazil, I encountered both the highly venomous Coral Cobra *(Micrurus decoratus)* and its perfectly harmless look-a-like, the False Coral Cobra *(Erythrolamprus aesculapii)*. You can tell them apart as one has an extra band of white in its markings, although I can't recall if that's the killer or the imposter. Luckily, there's a rhyme to help people remember which is which. It goes…

> *Duas cobras, uma venenosa, uma não,*
> *Mas qual é qual e qual não é,*
> *O mortal tem duas faixas brancas,*
> *O impostor três, tão seguro de manusear*

Unfortunately it's in Portuguese and I don't understand a word. Sorry, I can't be of more help.

Ross, Paw

POSTIES are lazy fuckers aren't they? Temporarily stopping deliveries on Saturdays based on some cock-and-bull story about a pandemic. What do posties actually do for their money? I only receive one or two items of post a day, so come on, it's not exactly a tough job is it?

Phil, Bedford

READING a Wikipedia article on English kings, it struck me that until about 100 years ago it was all the rage for male members of the Royal Family to wear wigs. From Charles I to George III to William of Orange, they were all at it. I bet the current crop of male Royals are absolutely fuming that this trend has died out, since those poor bastards have barely got a dozen hairs between them! I don't see why Edward or William or Philip doesn't ask Her Maj to reinstate the regal wig rule and spare them all their slap-headed blushes.

N Witchell, Sandringham

I WAS mightily impressed to learn that Bruce Dickinson of Iron Maiden has a pilot's licence and personally flies the band all over the world. With this in mind, the Happy Mondays could have utilised Bez a bit better in the early days. Instead of wasting money teaching him to play the maracas, a few flying lessons would have saved them a small fortune over the years.

Tecwin Porthole, Derby

I GOT a bollocking off my GP's surgery for missing appointments. Apparently it costs them sixty quid every time. Surely, if I tip them off that I am going to be ducking it, they save the money and we could split it thirty quid each.

Tom Crumbs, Hull

WHY do they always build skyscrapers and tower blocks upwards? If they built them sideways they'd save a fortune on cranes and scaffolding. Architects? I've shat 'em.

Mark Procter, Burnley

TOP TIPS

GENTS. Avoid having to spend £5,000 on a Marriage Vow Renewal Ceremony in Florence by not getting caught shagging a woman from work over the photocopier.

Torbjorn Wallpaper, Hull

DETECTIVES in crime dramas. When studying CCTV footage, look for the bloke coolly walking away from the scene and not jumping out of his fucking skin when the whole place explodes behind him. He's the one that did it.

John Sharp, London

INCREASE the romance of your wife finding you have blocked the toilet by leaving a trail of rose petals scattered across the bathroom floor, leading to the pot.

Ian Baker, Weston-s-Mare

BALLET companies. Avoid needing ballerinas to dance on tiptoes by hiring taller ones.

Mike Holland, Canberra

CHEFS. If you are chopping mild onions that aren't making you cry, simply chop them while watching the last few minutes of *Titanic* or the first few minutes of *Up*.

John Moynes, Dublin

ELIMINATE the need to spend up to £500 on costly anal bleaching treatment by never dropping your kecks, bending over and looking at your arse in the bathroom mirror.

H Baumgarten, Crewe

ECO warriors. A biro refill inserted into a courgette makes a lovely, environmentally friendly pen.

Harriet Jumpjet, Scarborough

BADLY programmed web forms. I know 'c' isn't a valid email address. Hold your horses and let me finish typing. *Christina Martin, Bexhill-on-Sea*

GLUEING a potato waffle to the front of your face mask will convince people you have a top-of-the-range face mask with its own cooling radiator.

Herbert Sausage, Wakefield

YOUTUBE. Change the text on your 'Skip Ads' button to 'Fuck Off,' as that is what people are invariably shouting every time they press it.

Eldon Furse, email

toptips@viz.co.uk

Sergio Padt (Goalkeeper)

"When I was doing my swimming badges at school, we were taught to make an improvised float if we fell into any water. We all had to jump into the pool in our pyjamas, then take off the trousers under the water and "swoosh" them over our heads to fill them with air. It was simple but very effective. I can't help thinking that if all 3,500 people on board had tied their pyjama trousers together, fixed them to the front of the ship and flapped them full of air, this enormous float would have kept the ship on the surface long enough for rescue vessels to arrive. Of course, in those days, pyjama bottoms had fly buttons, so it would have been important to make sure they were fastened first."

Bart van Hintum (Left Back)

"The RMS Titanic famously went down with 10,000 bottles of wine for the enjoyment of the first class passengers on board. The corks from all those bottles could have been quickly removed by skilled White Star Line cocktail waiters. None of the 2,400 passengers on board wore slip-on shoes, which were many years in the future, and so boasted 4,800 shoelaces between them which could have been used to lash the corks together to build a hugely buoyant life raft. I firmly believe that this impromptu vessel could have made the difference between life and icy death for thousands of passengers."

Mike te Wierik (Centre Back and Captain)

"By the time the 150m long iceberg was sighted, it was already too late for Captain Smith to attempt to steer his giant ship away, and he knew that a collision was just minutes off. But I believe that if an alert had gone out to all the passengers instructing them to quickly fill and boil the kettle in their cabin and bring it to the ship's bow, the disaster could have been averted. Pouring thousands of kettles worth of boiling water onto the mountain of ice would have been enough to melt it and avert disaster. Admittedly, at over a million tons in weight, it may not have melted completely, but it would certainly have produced a less serious rip in the ship's hull."

The Disa

THE White Star Line's **RMS TITANIC** was the largest ship afloat when, on 10th of April 1912, she set sail for New York on her maiden voyage… a voyage that she was never to complete. We can all vividly remember where we were and what we were doing when we heard the news that the 46,000 ton passenger liner had struck an iceberg off the coast of Newfoundland and sunk to the bottom of the Atlantic.

The catastrophe cost over 1,500 lives as the ship slipped under the icy water in little over 2-and-a-half

Ramon Pascal Lundqvist (Midfield)

"The crew had about three minutes warning that the ship was about to strike an iceberg. It must have been a terrifying time, but if the captain had had a clearer head, he could have ordered at the passengers to stand at the bows of the ship. This would have caused the Titanic to dip down at the front, meaning the collision would have holed it safely above the waterline. Immediately following the collision, the passengers could have all legged it to the very back of the ship, ensuring that the holed portion of the hull was lifted up way above the sea's surface for the rest of the voyage to New York, like a BMX cyclist doing a 'wheelie'."

hours. It was indeed a tragic accident of epic proportions. *But was it an accident that could have been avoided?* Or if the sinking was inevitable, could actions have been taken to save more lives?

We asked the first team players of Dutch Eredivise side **FC Groningen** how they thought the crisis could have been handled better. And the 2015 Johan Cruijff Shield runners-up had some novel suggestions which, had they been employed 108 years ago, could have changed the course of history.

Sinking TITANIC

Joel Asoro (Forward on loan from Swansea City)

"We all know that hindsight is a marvellous thing, but it seems that Captain Edward Smith missed an opportunity to save his vessel. Just before sinking, the stern dropped and The Titanic rose vertically out of the water. At this point, the captain should have given the order to put the ship's powerful the engines on full throttle. In this upright position with the propellors going full thrust, the Titanic could have "trod water" until help arrived. Admittedly, it would have been uncomfortable for the passengers who would have to sit on the walls of their cabins, but it would have been a small price to pay for saving 1,500 lives."

Gabriel Gudmundsson (Forward)

"The ship was holed below the water line, so it makes sense that if it was turned over, the breach would then be safely above the water. In my opinion, all the passengers should have climbed up on top of the ship's 4 iconic funnels and started to sway from side to side, like we used to do on the top deck of the bus going coming home from school. Getting a bit of momentum going, the ship would have rocked too and fro and eventually have toppled over. The passengers could then have swum back to the surface and climbed onto the now buoyant hull to await the arrival of the rescue ship, the RMS Carpathia."

Ko Itakura (Defender on loan from Manchester City)

"The Titanic was 'Party Central' for the first few days of her voyage, with extravagant balls and dances arranged every evening. To create a party atmosphere, the quartermaster must have had tens of thousands of balloons in his stores. These could have been handed out to passengers to blow up and pack into the ship's hull. If all 2,400 passengers had inflated just 10 balloons each, the 24,000 colourful toys would have provided enough buoyancy to keep the ship afloat for a couple of days, enough to get her and all her passengers and crew safely to New York."

Danny Buijs (Manager)

"I was once on a boating lake in Heerenveen and a load of rowing boats got wedged together near a bridge. The park keeper came and pushed us apart with a boat hook - a ten foot pole with a curved metal end. Perhaps there was one of these boat hooks on the RMS Titanic that Captain Smith could have employed to push the iceberg away. However, it might have taken more than one of these implements to ward off a block of ice weighing over a million tons, but if all the passengers armed with a mop or brush leaned over the front like Kate Winslett in that film and gave it a shove, perhaps disaster may have been averted. I suppose we'll never know."

Next week in the Disaster Files: *How the Hi-de-Hi stars would have prevented the 1883 eruption of Krakatoa.*

CANDID CANVAS

New survey reveals red-hot habits of British campers

CAMPING is a pastime that is often associated with dull, unimaginative couples, people with no sense of adventure who holiday in the same place year after year after year; those so wary of the unknown that they shun hotels, staying only under canvas, surrounding themselves with things that are familiar. These people, you might think, also have tedious and humdrum sex lives, making love just a few times a year, always in bed, always in the dark, and always in the missionary position.

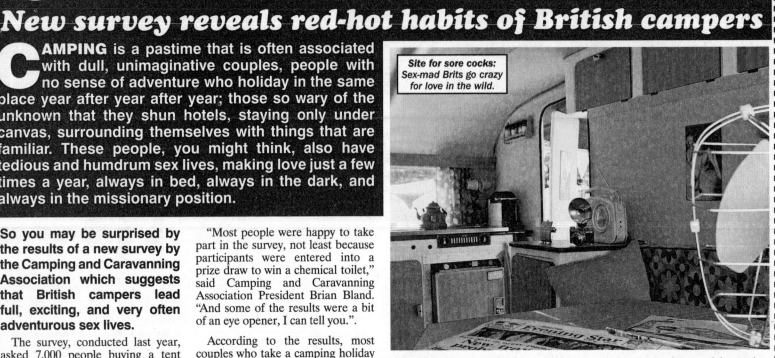

Site for sore cocks: Sex-mad Brits go crazy for love in the wild.

So you may be surprised by the results of a new survey by the Camping and Caravanning Association which suggests that British campers lead full, exciting, and very often adventurous sex lives.

The survey, conducted last year, asked 7,000 people buying a tent to fill out a questionnaire asking if the tent was a first purchase or an upgrade, and how often they planned to use it.

erotic

The questionnaire then went on to ask for intimate details about the purchasers' sex lives, including the number of partners they have had, their preferred sexual positions, their favourite erotic fantasies and fetishes, and whether or not they have ever been treated for venereal disease.

"Most people were happy to take part in the survey, not least because participants were entered into a prize draw to win a chemical toilet," said Camping and Caravanning Association President Brian Bland. "And some of the results were a bit of an eye opener, I can tell you.".

According to the results, most couples who take a camping holiday every year enjoy sex on average five time a week, with those owning a four-man ridge tent becoming intimate every day and twice at the weekend.

And contrary to stereotype, the Missionary Position did not feature amongst campers' favourite sexual postures, with 59% of frame tent owners preferring Reverse Cowgirl, whilst 78% of dome tent owners plumped for the Seated Wheelbarrow. The Snow Angel proved to be the favourite position of congress for couples with a three-berth trailer tent.

cherries

"Most campers lost their virginity at seventeen, with those who pitch a geodesic dome tent popping their cherries a year later," said Bland. "So much for campers being prudes."

And it seems that when it comes to sexual fantasies, camping enthusiasts are anything but dull.

"We asked the tent buyers to describe in detail their favourite erotic fantasy, and some of the stories we got were red hot," said Bland.

"Fantasies about group sex were very common amongst men owning knuckle joint tents of any size, whilst ladies who owned this type of tent preferred fantasies about sex in forbidden places like a library or church."

Bland hopes that the results of the survey will change people's preconceptions about campers and lead to an increase in the popularity of camping holidays.

HAPPY CAMPER FUN

Here are a few games and puzzles to keep you amused in your tent whilst it's pissing down outside.

1 *My first is in Tractor, but never in Horse*
My second's in Heather and also in Gorse
In Never and Nothing my third you will see
My last you will find at the start of Torquay
I am cloth house, held up with a pole
With guy ropes and tent pegs to maketh my whole

What am I?

2 A ridge tent is 3m long, 2m wide and held up with 1m pole. If the tent is filled with wood of density 0.69g/cm^3, which is then placed in a full bath of water and the overspill collected and placed in a pan, and then heated up using a butane gas cooker, what is the minimum size gas canister in litres that would be needed to raise the water through 50 Kelvin. Assume the latent heat capacity of water is 334KJ/Kg, the standard enthalpy of combustion of butane is -2.8781-2.8769MJ mol^{-1} and the tent is 15m above sea level.

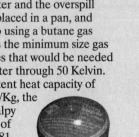

3 *Oh, dear!* The three members of the indie band Scouting for Girls have gone camping, but they've got their guy ropes in a tangle. Can you help lead vocalist Roy Stride, bass guitarist Greg Churchouse and drummer Dr Pete Ellard find out whom's tent belongs to which?

Answer: A tent

Answer: A 10 litre canister

Answer: Tent A belongs to Greg, Tent B belongs to Roy and Tent C belongs to Dr. Pete.

Paris's Camping Tips

HI, PARIS HILTON here. Now I've stayed in the penthouse suites of my daddy's hotels all around the world, so I'm used to luxury. But I also once spent a night in a tent, so I'm an expert on how to rough it under canvas. And I'm going to share that expertise with you in a series of helpful camping tips.

WHEN you go camping, remember to take plenty of bottles of Dom Perignon champagne with you, as it is unlikely that the smaller campsite shops will stock it. If they stock any champagne at all, it will probably be something inferior, like Krug or Pol Roger Brut Reserve.

CAMPING fees can be costly, especially on the larger, more well-equipped sites. Negotiate with the owner to see if they will let you stay on the best pitch for nothing in return for mentioning the name of their campsite on your blog, or in a tweet to your BFF.

CHOOSE a pitch well away from the shower block.

This will ensure that you have to walk past all the other tents in your bathrobe in the morning, thereby gaining maximum exposure and increasing the chances of someone papping you for the papers.

MOST campsites allow guests to bring dogs providing that they are on a lead or in a handbag. If you have a large dog, such as an alsatian or rottweiller, Louis Vuitton will make you a custom handbag to fit it for as little as £100,000.

DON'T forget your video camera so you can make a grainy sex tape inside your tent to release onto the internet. In fact, why not take a camera crew to follow you around all the time so you can make a tawdry reality show for a low-end American TV channel?

SCIENCE CAMP

Dr Adam Rutherford answers YOUR questions about the science of camping

Dear Adam, **WHAT** is the fastest wind that a tent could stay up in?

Ed Bumfluff, Crewe

Adam says: That's a very good question, Ed, and the answer depends on a number of different variables. Camping scientists developed what they term the Fundamental Tent Equation which addresses this question, namely:

$$v_{max} = 1 + \int_0^\infty \sqrt{\frac{(4t\rho \sin\emptyset)}{(a^2 - c) + n}}$$

Where v=windspeed, n= number of poles in the tent, t=tension in the guy-ropes, ρ=tensile coefficient of the tent pegs, a=the surface area of the tent, $\emptyset$=angle of incidence of the wind and c= the percentage competency with which it was erected.

Dear Adam, **WHAT** were the earliest humans to make tents?

Jack Percival, Stockholm

Adam says: Anthropologists have made discoveries that indicate that Homo neanderthalis were making shelters by draping animal skins over a frame of mammoth tusks as far back as 40,000 years ago. However, these Neanderthal shelters were for living in rather than going on holiday in, so they can't really be classed as tents.

Dear Adam, **I'VE GOT** a Baylis wind-up torch with a port to plug in another appliance. How fast would my wife have to turn it to run a 55-inch telly in our tent?

Bramwell Tollpuddle, Hull

Adam says: That's an interesting question. If we assume that your torch pulls about 3 watts to work, which requires it to be wound at about 2 revolutions per second, then this means that for a standard 57W LED TV, your wife is going to have to crank the torch around 38 times per second. If you have the more power hungry 98W OLED version, she's going to have to step it up a bit to just over 65 revolutions per second, or 3,920 rpm.

Dear Adam, **WHAT** is the best angle to knock a tent peg in so it won't come out?

Hector Twelves, Goole

Adam says: The more shallow the angle of the peg to the ground, the more it will resist the pull on it exerted by the tension of the guy rope. However, a shallow angle will mean that the soil above the peg will not exert much of a downward force to keep it in place. The best compromise is to erect the tent so that the guy-ropes subtend an angle of 90° to the peg, so always remember to take a large protractor on any camping trip.

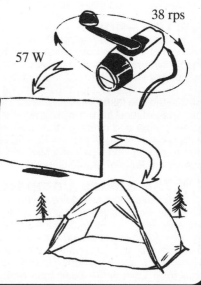

38 rps

57 W

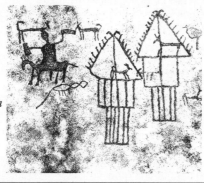

149

FOUR MONTHS into the pandemic, the government acted swiftly to quarantine anyone coming into the UK for 2 weeks to make sure they did not bring Coronavirus into our heavily infected country. However, the French spitefully took the same decision, thereby spoiling it for any Brits planning continental breaks. So this year's buzz word is going to be **STAYCATION**. And as millions of us gear up to holiday at home, the chances are that a good many of us will end up CAMPING.

There is nothing like sleeping in the great outdoors with only a thin piece of nylon between you and the stars and the bloke farting six feet away. But for many of us, this will be our first time under canvas, and the campsite will be an alien world. So let's have a look at some of the people and some of the things you might see on a *Great British Campsite.*

1 The Campsite Shop

This little building by the gate is a cornucopia of wonders, selling everything the camper could need, as long as it's tins of beans, tins of spaghetti hoops, or a loaf of flavourless long-life bread. Of course, with campsite overheads so high, the owners are forced to add a small mark-up on their prices, but with the nearest shop over two miles away, the convenience of the on-site store means that customers are happy to pay a little extra. Plus, it gives everyone a little glimpse into the future as they get to see what food prices will look like in the year 2525.

2 The Shower Block

There is nothing like a nice, hot shower in the morning, and for those who wake up under canvas, the shower block is their first port of call. Although very welcome, the washing facilities on site are a little more rough and ready than you may be used to at home, but the smell of Jeyes fluid and the black mould on the cinder block walls are all part of the camping experience. You will need to be quick, however, as a £2 coin in the shower slot will get you just long enough under the feeble stream of luke-warm water to get your shampoo worked up into a lather.

3 The Cafe

Many hardened campers will only eat what they can cook themselves on their portable butane stoves, and consequently spend their holiday eating Stagg tinned mince and boil-in-the-bag rice. But for those without cooking facilities, the site takeaway is on hand. With a wide range of food from beef burger and chips to chicken burger and chips, all their culinary needs will be taken care of, all at a fraction (ie 99/100) of the price you would pay at a Michelin-starred restaurant in Paris or Monte Carlo.

4 The Novice Campers

There's a first time for everything, so the saying goes, and spotting a novice camper is easy. The most obvious sign is that they are attempting to put up their brand new tent inside out, and - unaware that a mallet would be necessary - are hammering in their tent pegs with a shoe. Later in the week, after darkness falls, they will be seen going from tent to tent asking if they can borrow a torch before going back to their pitch and trying to smash open a tin of beans with the wheelbrace from their car.

5 The Seasoned Campers

Year after year, these seasoned campers return to the site for seven nights under canvas in their luxurious, state-of-the-art multi-room tent. With its moveable room partitions, extra-large double-glazed windows with built-in curtains, and zipped access point for effortless connection to mains electricity for lighting and cooking, it's an impressive piece of kit - a real home from home where they can sit and watch the telly all evening, just like they do the other 51 weeks of the year.

Can You Spot.......?

● A couple of first-timers who have decided to take some photos of their tent to put up on eBay, before packing up and going home on day two.

● A group of kids whose parents are perfectly happy for them to play football using the side of another family's car as a goal.

● A couple who have hit the depths of despair after realising that their 7-nights under canvas will work out £150 more expensive than last year's 14-night break the Maldives.

IF YOU HAVE TO ASK THE PRICE, YOU CAN'T AFFORD IT.

● A group of pissed-up youths trying to light a barbecue with some petrol - a scenario that can only end up like a scene from *Saving Private Ryan*.

● A man who has passed out after blowing up a king-size inflatable airbed without a pump.

● A couple of dogs having a fight, the sound of which has attracted a small crowd and a few bets.

● A man watching a woman in a bikini, desperately hoping that she'll start to do some exercises that result in her bra flying off.

● A campsite official going round telling people that site rules forbid them from doing whatever it is they happen to be doing.

● A young couple who have been at it inside their two-man tent since five minutes after they pitched it the previous morning.

● A man who's been awake all night listening to the young couple at it in the next tent.

● A Dutch family with a motorhome three times larger than your house that makes everyone else's lights dim when they plug in the electrical hook-up.

● A man dressed like Ray Mears who refers to himself as a 'woodsman', bleeding profusely after taking half his thumb off while trying to whittle some willow tent pegs with a machete.

● Two serious campers whose discussion about the best way to knot a guy-rope has descended quickly to disagreement, through name-calling, and into fisticuffs.

● Some poor sods who have been given the pitch next to the chemical toilet, whose only crime was to book and pay in advance.

● A family who wanted to 'get close to nature', on their fifth can of Raid, killing everything that comes within ten feet of their tent.

● A man trying to flirt with a young woman whist emptying a 25-gallon drum of his family's shit into the camp waste collection tank.

10 THINGS YOU NEVER KNEW ABOUT CAMPING

SOME people think that camping in the UK is all about sitting shivering in a damp tent, trying to pick ants off your sandwiches and listening to the rain hammer down on the canvas. And they are exactly right. But we had better get used to it, because a combination of deadly viruses, unemployment and economic collapse means we can forget about sunning ourselves on the golden beaches of Spain, or relaxing by palm tree-shaded hotel pools in the south of France. It's a fact that we'll be holidaying under canvas in the UK for the foreseeable future. But exactly how much do we know about camping? If the answer is 'not much', then we had better start learning. Let's get the ball rolling with…

1 FOR HIS role as Sid Boggle in the 1969 film *Carry on Camping*, Sid James adopted a "method acting" approach in order to get in character. The actor spent most of 1968 sleeping in a tent in the garden of his Highgate house, so that by the time filming started in October of that year, he was completely in character. His performance as a sexually frustrated 56-year-old bachelor earned him praise from many in the business and he was tipped to take the Best Actor award at the 1970 Academy Awards. Unfortunately for Sid, that accolade went to Bernard Bresslaw, who played Bernie Lugg in the same film, with Peter Butterworth, who played miserly campsite owner Joshua Fiddler, taking the award for Best Performance in a Supporting Role.

2 ALTHOUGH there is no patron saint of campers, Catholics heading for the campsite can still get heavenly help when they need it. If they mislay a tent peg, for instance, they could ask St Anthony, the patron saint of lost things, to find it. St George, the patron saint of boy scouts, could be asked to intervene if they are having trouble putting up their tent. And Saint Fiacra, the patron saint of haemorrhoid sufferers, could be beseeched to intervene if their piles swell up and they don't have any Anusol at the campsite shop.

3 AND THE patron saint of hernia sufferers, St Conrad of Piacenza, looks after anyone who has just tried to take a soaking wet, 6-berth canvas family tent off the roof rack of their car.

4 FOUR INTO a *Two-Man Will Go* was to be a 2019 gang bang porn flick set inside a two-man tent. Filming was fraught with technical difficulties from the start, with the male star, three female stars, the director, the cameraman, the lighting engineer, the sound man and a fluffer all crammed into a 6-foot by 4-foot Millets CampMaster tent. When the director called 'Action!' there was simply no room for the male lead to get a bone on, and the production was canned.

5 IF YOU take your tent across the Channel to France, you'll find that camping in that country is a very different experience from camping in Britain. Time is an hour in front, everyone speaks French, and they all drive on the wrong side of the road.

6 CAMPING comes with many problems, not least of which is that there is no door to knock on when you want to attract the attention of the occupants of a tent, perhaps to borrow a tin opener or complain about their radio. According to The Camping and Caravanning Club of Great Britain, the widely accepted method is to stand by the front of their tent and shout "Hello! Knock! Knock!" followed by a short, embarrassed laugh.

7 FOR MANY years, camping scientists worked on a solar-powered doorbell which could be fitted to the front flaps of any standard tent. However, in testing, it was found that the button would only work if the fabric was extremely taut, otherwise the entire mechanism and the door itself just sagged in a bit, and the project was abandoned.

8 THE SAME scientists spent many years trying to develop a letterbox that could fit into a tent, allowing campsite owners to pop in leaflets about camp shop opening times and cafe menus. However, under testing, all the spring mechanisms developed proved too heavy and caused sagging of the canvas. This, along with the inability to get a 100% waterproof seal led to the research being abandoned.

9 DUE TO its unpleasantness, for most people, camping is a holiday activity limited to just a couple of weeks each spring or summer. Scouts founder Robert Baden-Powell reversed this trend, spending fifty weeks each year under canvas, only coming in the house for a fortnight when he was on his holidays.

10 THE TINIEST ever tent was owned by the world's smallest man Calvin Phillips. The lightweight 2-man ridge tent measured just 8" at its highest point, and packed down to fit into a rucksack the size of a Weetabix. Whilst camping in it, Phillips and his wife – the world's smallest woman Ada Phillips – slept in sleeping bags the size of McDonald's Apple Pies.

THAT'S TENTERTAINMENT!

Your chance to WIN a glamorous camping holiday with the stars!

WE'VE all dreamt of going on a glamorous camping holiday with our three favourite showbiz celebrities. Whether it's a week in a four-man ridge tent with the Supremes, a fortnight in a lightweight dome tent with Shirley Bassey, Bill Roach and Fiona Bruce, or ten nights with Sean Bean, Lionel Richie and Lulu in a pyramid tent, a star-studded jaunt under canvas is right at the top of everyone's bucket list.

Well now's your chance to make that pipedream fantasy into a 24-carat star-studded reality, because we've teamed up with the Variety Club of Great Britain to offer one lucky reader the chance to enjoy a fantastic 2-week camping holiday with the THREE celebrities of their choice! And that's not all – we'll even throw in £35 spending money!

For your chance of winning, simply complete the entry form below, putting five features of the new Hillington portable camping toilet into order of preference, most important first. Then complete the tie-breaker and list the three showbiz stars you'd like to go on a camping holiday with.

Put the following great features of the new Hillington camping toilet in order of importance from 1 (most important) to 5 (least important):

  a. Stylish and functional design
  b. Comfortable, adult-sized seat and lid
  c. Large 5 litre removable waste bucket with carry handle
  d. Low risk of tipping in use
  e. Attachable toilet roll holder

1. ☐   **2.** ☐   **3.** ☐   **4.** ☐   **5.** ☐

Name: .... Address: ....

....

The stars I would like to share a tent with are: 1. ....

2. .... 3. ....

Tiebreaker: I would like to receive promotional mail about chemical toilets because (15 words or fewer) ....

Send to: *That's Tentertainment Competition, Viz, PO Box 841, Whitley Bay NE26 9EQ.*

Terms and Conditions. All holidays must be taken at the Pig Shovel Farm campsite, Newton Aycliffe, County Durham, between October 1st and October 15th this year. £35 spending money in the form of vouchers to be spent at the campsite shop. Winner provides their own tent and sleeping bag. As a condition of taking part in this promotion, the showbiz stars have made it clear that they won't be responsible for helping put the tent up, cooking meals, or emptying the chemical toilet, so those will be jobs for the competition winner.

Stars' Camping Fears

CAMPING is undoubtedly great fun – pitching the tent, snuggling inside your sleeping bag, and waking up at half past four to the sound of birdsong are all part of the experience. But sleeping in a tent also has its dark side – the strange noises in the night, the sense of vulnerability, the prices at the camp shop. We asked some A-list celebrity campers about their biggest fears when settling down under canvas, and what they do to overcome them.

Jeremy Paxman

WHENEVER I go camping, I'm always worried about a sink hole opening up and engulfing my tent. I watched a programme on National Geographic a few years ago and those things open up really fast and go down for miles. So before I go camping, I always do a thorough research of the campsite to see if there is any history of subsidence or geological suffosion in the area. Then, after I've pitched my tent, I drive back home and sleep there just to be on the safe side.

JK Rowling

I'M TERRIFIED of being struck by lightning when I go glamping. And because I've got so much money, I've always got the biggest tent on the campsite, which means that in an electrical storm, I'm the one most likely to be struck. So after I've pitched my enormous tent, I get a scaffolding company to erect a 'Faraday Cage' around it to protect it from lightning bolts. The scaffolding has to be made out of platinum, which makes it really expensive. But I'm extremely rich and what price safety?

Idris Elba

I LOVE camping, but I'm terrified that while I'm asleep, a car will suddenly roll into my tent and squash me flat. A lot of these campsites have sloping ground and it's not unheard of for the handbrake cable on a parked car to ping. So when we go camping, as well as the tent, the cooker and all the other paraphernalia, I also take along a hundred or so house bricks. Then, every night before turning in, I go round the entire campsite and wedge a brick under the front wheel of each car. It's a lot of hard work, but at least it means I get a good night's sleep.

Ian Dunt

I FUCKING love camping, but I'm shit fucking scared of animals coming into my fucking tent in the night. I know there aren't fucking wolves or bears or anything like that in the UK, but there's fucking beavers now, and them fucking coypu things, and them bastards have got fucking front teeth like little fucking daggers. So when I go camping, I take a 2000v electric fence and set the fucker up around my tent to keep the fuckers out. It's powered by a bastard big diesel generator which is noisy as fuck, but it's okay because I take fucking earplugs.

THEY'RE shiny, they're crinkly, and they stop enemy powers from interfering with your mind. They're TIN FOIL HATS, and unless you wear one, chances are some foreign governments or MI5 are tapping into your thoughts, gathering information and implanting false memories RIGHT NOW. With this sobering thought in mind, it would be madness not to wear one all the time. But how much do we know about these marvellous weapons in our fight against sinister interference? Here are…

10 THINGS YOU NEVER KNEW ABOUT TIN FOIL HATS

1 **THE FIRST** tin foil hat was made in 1965 by Gritley Mews from Yorkshire. The 25-year-old bicycle mechanic had been invited to a fancy dress party, and decided to go as a robot, covered head to foot in tin foil. It was only when he put on his robot head that he realised that the foil stopped aliens from outer space controlling his thoughts.

2 **IF YOU** have run out of tin foil, an aluminium saucepan will do the job in an emergency. But be aware that pans are not as snug fitting as tin foil hats, and some of the invasive rays may get in the gaps up the side and penetrate your brain.

3 **JAMIROQUAI** frontman Jay Kay famously owns over 5,000 hats. What is not so well known is that all of them are lined with tin foil in order to prevent MI5 from influencing his song-writing to make him produce propaganda. "Those spooks will stop at nothing," the funkadelic space cowboy told told *NME*.

4 **THE KGB,** the intelligence branch of the Russian government, is known to be working on a machine that produces a special sort of wave that is able to penetrate a layer of tin foil. In order to counter this, tin foil hats from now on should be made out of turkey Bacofoil, which is much thicker and Soviet special wave-proof.

5 **IN AN** attempt to keep the population docile and obedient, North Korean prime minister Kim Jong-un has banned tinfoil. Being caught in possession of any kind of kitchen foil is punishable by 25 years in prison. As a result, not only can the Pyongyang government now tap into everyone's thoughts, but all chickens roasted in the hermit kingdom come out of the oven a bit on the dry side.

6 **THE BILDERBERG** Group, a secretive cabal of bankers and politicians, were once planting revolutionary thoughts directly into the brain of the world's smallest man, Calvin Phillips. However, Phillips was able to deflect the group's sinister electromagnetic oscillations by making himself a tin foil hat out of a Wrigley's spearmint chewing gum wrapper.

7 **AMERICAN** inventor Charles Martin Hall took out a patent on the industrial production of tin foil in 1888. The same year saw French inventor Paul Hérault simultaneously come up with the same idea. But the inventors of what would be called the Hall-Hérault process, churning out the material which would later be turned into hats in order to thwart hostile agencies, both died in 1914, both at the age of 51. Coincidence?

8 **YOU MIGHT** be surprised to learn that tin foil isn't actually made out of tin at all, but aluminium. It's called tin foil because it was originally used to line roasting tins, which aren't made out of tin either… but steel! You couldn't make it up.

9 **MANY** tin foil hats have an optional spike on the top made from scrunched up aluminium or a small piece of coat hanger. These hats work as normal, blocking invasive, government-generated mind-reading microwaves, whilst the extra aerial picks up short-wave radio signals from fellow members of the resistance.

10 **YOU DON'T** need to wear a tin foil hat when driving your car, since the car itself acts like a large tin foil hat on wheels, deflecting space rays from the other side of the universe. Obviously if it's a convertible car, your brain is vulnerable to these extra-terrestrial rays, so it's Clunk! Click! and on with the tin foil hat.

BILDERBERG GROUP MADE MY DOG SHIT ON THE CARPET ~CLAIM

Leeds man has PROOF that elite group are controlling his pet.

A LEEDS man has been reported to the RSPCA by his neighbours after sellotaping tin foil to his dog's head. But Les Corduroy, 46, claims that far from being cruel, his action was in the animal's interests.

The part-time car park attendant says that a sinister group of international bankers, financiers and politicians bent on world domination has been controlling the mind of his lurcher, Ragnar, and that they made the 6-year-old animal soil the living room carpet whilst he was out.

swift

"I left Ragnar in the house while I nipped to the pub for a swift lunchtime pint or two," he told the *Leeds Bugle and Ocarina*. "When I got back just before midnight, he'd shat in the front room."

Corduroy was immediately suspicious, as his dog was fully housetrained and hadn't done its business indoors for several months.

"He hadn't shat on the carpet for ages, probably getting on for six months, so I knew something was

up. And I hadn't fed him that day because he'd eaten a dead pigeon in the morning, so he shouldn't have needed a shit neither," he said. "And then it struck me."

"A bloke in the boozer was telling me about this group of bankers and heads of business called the Bilderberg Group, who were using mind control techniques to start a new world order with them in charge."

"He said they infiltrate the brains of city traders and dealers and force them to buy and sell stocks and shares against their will in order to control the markets. It was obvious that they were using Ragnar as a guinea pig to test their techniques, seeing if they could make him shit on the floor," said Les.

elddis

Corduroy decided he would clear the mess up in the morning, in case the group used their mind control techniques to make his dog defecate a second time. But whilst having a nightcap, he hit upon the idea of covering his pet's head in aluminium foil in order to keep the shadowy group from accessing its brainwaves.

"I'd got some Bacofoil in the cupboard under the sink, so I wrapped it round his head," he

Foiled again: Lurcher Ragnar (main pic) had foil wrapped around head by owner Corduroy (inset above).

said. "It was a bit tricky doing round his ears, but I got the all important bits covered, and I held it in place with sellotape."

And Corduroy's suspicions were proved correct. "The following morning, there was just the one original shite in the front room," he said. "The tin foil hat had clearly worked."

In fact, with his dog's protective headwear left in place, Mr Corduroy's carpets remained clean for the following week.

But as one problem was solved, another cropped up, as two officers from the RSPCA

yesterday called round to tell him that he must take the foil off Ragnar's head.

"The woman from across the road must have grassed me up," he said. "They told me it was cruel and that I had to take it off immediately or face prosecution."

"She's always had it in for me, the nosey cow. Just because of a thing that happened when I first moved in and didn't understand the bins."

"Anyway, I told the bloke I'd take the dog's foil hat off if they came round and cleared his shit up afterwards," he added.

TIN FOIL TITFERS

J UST for fun, we've made some unusual tinfoil hats. Can *YOU* work out who would wear them as they go about their daily business?

Tin Foil Titfer 1

'Ello! 'Ello! 'Ello!

'Copper' load of this tin foil hat. Whoever wears this will be an arresting sight. And the beat on the street says you'll work this out quite constable-y.

Tin Foil Titfer 2

Pay attention at the back.

Ten out of ten if you can guess the wearer of this headgear. And if you don't, then see us after class for six of the best.

Tin Foil Titfer 3

Salve, citizens.

All roads will lead to where you'd find the wearer of this tin foil protective headwear. *Si enodatio molestiam vobis affert, ansam accipite: galea centurionis est!*

FROM JOHN'S END to Land O'Groats, we all love our celebrity A-listers. They captivate us with their acting, singing and television presenting, and they seduce us with their dazzling good looks. But more than all that - they inspire us with their heroic good deeds.

Matt Damon, Angelina Jolie, Jamie Oliver… the list of stars who somehow manage to find time in their hectic schedules to promote, support and donate to a myriad of charitable causes seems literally endless.

But is it really? Are these performers who we place on a pedestal as generous as we think they are, or is their philanthropy simply an illusion concocted by their PR staffers?

We sent *Viz* investigative reporter **MAHATMA MACAROON** undercover to discover whether our favourite stars truly are the big-hearted Samaritans they would have us believe. And what he found out will **DISGUST** and **HORRIFY** every right-thinking, rational reader.

For, as this article lays bare, rather than being the philanthropic do-gooders they claim to be, these billionaire, Ivory-Tower-dwelling stars are in fact a bunch of hatchet-faced, penny-pinching Scrooges who literally wouldn't piss on the common man if he was **ON FIRE** in front of them.

Prepare to be shocked, saddened and sickened to the core, as we expose… *The Tight-Uns of Stage 'n' Screen!*

BY **VIZ** UNDERCOVER REPORTER **MAHATMA MACAROON**

CELEBRITY TIGHT-UN NO.1: BRIAN MAY

CORKSCREW-**H A I R E D** guitarist Brian is well known for his love of woodland creatures, and he has long been a vocal supporter and benefactor to many top wildlife charities.

But just how much of this ostensible good-deedery is merely 'woke' virtue signalling? When push comes to shove, will the glam-rocking badgerphile **ACTUALLY** put his hand in his pocket to help out Mother Nature?

I intend to find out.

Sporting a big grin, a clipboard and a hi-viz tabard that I bought from a pound shop, I pose as a 'charity mugger' outside May's lavish Surrey mansion. These irritatingly chirpy 'chuggers' throng our modern high streets, cheerily cajoling us into giving generously to good causes, and I'm intrigued to see if a supposedly 'big-hearted' A-lister like the Queen plank-spanker will be as benevolent as the common man.

Having scrawled the words 'HEDGEHOG AID' across my tabard with a sharpie, I stride out in front of the rock icon as he leaves his 10-bedroom house.

'All right, mate', I trill, breezily. 'Have you got a few seconds to talk about a new wildlife charity?'

The judge's-wig-haired pop fave is clearly LIVID at the thought of being hit up for a few coppers from his immense fortune, but he manages to hide his miserly fury expertly. 'Sure, I'd love to hear about it,' he lies through his teeth. 'What's it about?'

I promptly launch into a long, improvised spiel about the fictional woodland foundation I've just invented, and before you know it, May is jotting down his bank details on my clipboard, cordially agreeing to make a monthly £20 donation to my non-existent good cause.

So far, so charitable. *But when I return home later to process the payment, things take a darker turn.*

As I set up the direct debit from May's account into mine, my finger accidentally slips five times, and I mistakenly put him down for £2,000,000 per month. It's a steep sum for your average Joe Bloggs, but a drop in the ocean for a mega-wealthy philanthropist who 'claims' to love all creatures great and small. Assuming Brian will be happy to dig a little deeper into his vast fortune, I go ahead and process the transfer.

Within an hour, my assumption is proved pitifully naive. I log on to my online banking app to see that not only has May **CANCELLED** the payment, he has also **BLOCKED** all further transactions to my bank account.

I feel sick to my stomach. This pre-Raphaelite-haired hypocrite loves to harp on about all the 'good work' he does for environmental charities, but he won't cough up one *single solitary penny* to help an - albeit fictional - hedgehog foundation.

Tightwad Brian found fame back in the 80s with the hit song 'We Will, We Will Rock You'. But if you had him pegged for a kind-hearted, decent human being, then I'm afraid… He Will, He Will Shock You.

CELEBRITY TIGHT-UN NO.2: GEORGE CLOONEY

OSCAR-WINNING heartthrob George is the undisputed king of Hollywood do-gooding. For decades, the *From Dusk Till Dawn* hunk has generously donated his time and money to countless humanitarian charities across the globe, raising millions of dollars for worthy causes.

Or is he just 'method-acting' the part of a charitable do-gooder?

To find out, I head over to Pinewood Studios in Slough, where I'm told Clooney is currently filming his next big-budget blockbuster. Dressed up as an octogenarian Oxfam shop volunteer in a cardigan, floral dress and blue-tinted Dame Edna wig, I approach the security guards at the studio entrance.

Adopting a sort of Dot Cotton voice, I explain that I'm here to collect a donation of clothing from Mr Clooney. I have to chuckle as the bomber-jacketed guards fall for my ruse hook, line and sinker, allowing me straight past once I've immobilised them with a taser I had stashed in my handbag.

Creeping onto the sound stage, the flashing red light tells me that Clooney is currently busy filming a scene. Not wanting to disturb the *Ocean's 11* icon, I head straight to his plush trailer to begin gathering up some of the donations that his track record suggests he would be only too happy to make.

The door is padlocked, but I am able to open it with a technique involving two spanners that I saw on YouTube. Once inside, I quickly stuff six bin bags with expensive suits, shirts and shoes - as well as several Nespresso coffee machines. As I stride back out across the studio lot, I have the satisfying feeling that at least one top A-Lister has lived up to his benevolent reputation.

However, just as I am about to leave the compound through the fire exit, I am apprehended by the two shaven-headed goons I mugged off earlier. They yank my wig from my head, grab my bin bags and then hurl me violently out onto the street, showering me with four-letter abuse.

As I dust myself down and walk home, I feel the now-familiar sting of crushing disappointment. Clooney is probably receiving the thick end of $10 million for his part in this tawdry new flick - and yet he can't even spare a few measly items of clobber for a little old lady from Oxfam.

The doe-eyed Tinseltown fave famously made his directorial debut with 'Confessions of a Dangerous Mind'. Perhaps it should been called 'Confessions of a Tight-Fisted Bastard'.

EEN! So-called 'charitable' celebs exposed as sickening skinflints

CELEBRITY TIGHT-UN NO.3: GARY LINEKER

SILVER-HAIRED footy fave Gary is renowned for his charitable nature, not only presenting the BBC's *Sport Relief* programme, but also regularly donating large sums of his licence-payer-funded fortune to all manner of benevolent foundations.

But when it comes to the crunch, is the crisp-peddling *Match of the Day* man **REALLY** prepared to shell out for a good cause, or is he trying to sell us a dummy?

Dressed as a 'wacky' student, complete with red nose, spinning propeller cap and bra-and-pants-embossed apron, I knock at the ex-Spurs icon's luxurious Leicester mansion. When he answers, I inform the ample-lugged silver fox that I am planning to sit in a bath of beans to raise money for the Red Cross, and ask if he would like to sponsor me.

Working hard to disguise his irritation at having to dip into his deep pockets, Lineker nails on a rictus grin. 'That's brilliant, good on you,' he seethes. 'Put me down for £100.'

It's a generous offer and no mistake. *But of course, I'll only find out whether Gary's good for it if I actually go through with the stunt.*

Lineker signs my sponsor sheet and I nip to Aldi to bulk-buy two industrial-sized pallets of baked beans before hiding in the bushes in the footy ace's garden until he leaves. After jemmying open the window of his downstairs bathroom, I spend the next hour filling the ex-Barca fave's jacuzzi with 400 cans of tomato-sauce-slathered pulses. Once the job's done, I strip naked and lower myself in.

Soon enough, I hear a key in the door. I have to chuckle as I imagine the BT Sport legend's reaction when he finds me in here. He's sure to be howling with laughter and reaching gladly for his chequebook, *isn't he?*

But as the bathroom door is flung open, I am greeted by a very different Lineker to the one I'd pictured.

'What the f*** is going on?!' the supposedly magnanimous pundit bellows. Although he didn't say 'f, star, star, star'… he said *fuck*.

'What the f*** are you doing in my bathroom?!' again using the f-word (*fuck*).

Disappointment courses through my bean-smothered body. Just a few hours ago, this shameless hypocrite was pledging a hundred nicker for my light-hearted stunt. But now he realises he actually has to cough up the cash, he's flying off the handle.

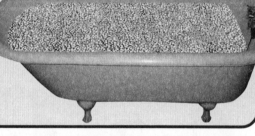

It's enough to make you sick.

As Lineker runs to call the police, I haul myself out of the bath, dripping all tomato sauce everywhere as I leap out of the window. As I hear sirens approaching, I high-tail it into the nearby woods, naked as the day I was born, and take a moment to process my shock and despair at what's just happened.

Lineker loves to present himself as a big-hearted do-gooder on Sport Relief. But it turns out the only 'relief' this sanctimonious fraud feels is when he doesn't have to put his hand in his pocket.

CELEBRITY TIGHT-UN NO.4: JAMES MARTIN

TELLY CHEF James is a small screen culinary icon, beloved by every person in Britain, with the exception of cyclists, people who aren't from Yorkshire, and people who don't like daytime cookery shows. But the big-hearted cook is also well known and admired for his generous contributions to various food-based foundations.

Or so the Google results for 'James Martin charity work' would have us believe.

In reality, will the God's-Own-County-obsessed gastronome *actually* cough up for a good cause when there are no cameras or journalists around to capture his generosity? I make it my mission to find out.

Since Hampshire-based James is a dyed-in-the-wool Yorkshireman, I'm assuming he'll be more likely to give generously if I pose as a 'reet proper Northern' charity worker. As such, I arrive at his swanky Winchester home wearing a flat cap, Gannex raincoat and *Last of the Summer Wine* t-shirt, whilst chomping on parkin and cradling a whippet.

Martin answers the door looking confused and and a little wary. 'Ayup, mi duck,' I say in a flawless

Yorkshire dialect. 'I'm from t' food bank up in t' Pontefract. 'As tha' got owt tha' could gi' us in't way o' scran, like?'

Martin eyes me cautiously, clearly **FUMING** at the thought of dipping into his bottomless bank account, or possibly just annoyed that I've showered him with parkin crumbs. But he masks his rage with a friendly grin, telling me that he'll fetch some bits from the kitchen.

He returns a minute later with a cardboard box full of bread, milk, vegetables and other foodstuffs. 'Eeh, I'll g' t' foot o' our stairs!' I cry in mock-Northern delight. 'That's a reet champion load o' tuck an' no mistek.'

'Any time,' Martin smiles.

As I walk back down the garden path holding James' donation, those two words ring in my ears: *'Any time'…* Taken literally, that means that the *Saturday Kitchen* icon would be happy to help out my fictitious food fund at any hour God sends. *I decide to put that pledge to the test.*

A few hours later, at 3.30am, I'm back in Martin's plush front garden. Aware that the bicycle-shunting cuisiner is probably asleep by now, and not wanting to wake him by knocking at the door, I quietly jemmy the back window with a crowbar.

Once inside, I creep into Martin's classy kitchen and open the fridge. My heart swells with gratitude

as I see the mountain of mouth-watering goodies on display. Unloading the lot into a large burlap sack, I imagine the looks of joy on the non-existent faces of my imaginary food bank customers when they see this charitable bounty.

After dropping a jar of pickle relish, however, I hear whispering voices upstairs, and moments later, the sound of police sirens fills the air.

Martin *explicitly* told me that he would be prepared to give generously at 'any time' and yet the tight-fisted telly fave has summoned the law rather than offer up a few more morsels to help some make-believe families in need.

As I flee into the surrounding forest with Martin's food and a few items of silverware, I reflect on my disappointment that yet another so-called 'altruistic' A-Lister has proved so sickeningly stingy.

Cordon Bleu? More like Cordon Bleurgh.

NEXT WEEK – Mahatma is once again left feeling shocked, saddened and disgusted after he burgles Bono's house dressed as a Salvation Army tuba player.

IT'S A FUNNY OLD WORLD

with Martin Itsa & Jeremy Funnyoldworld

RAISIN HEL
Los Angeles, USA

BRITISH STAGE and screen icon **DAME HELEN MIRREN** has shocked fans by launching a high profile bid to enter the *Guinness Book of World Records*... for eating the most raisins in the space of an hour. "I love raisins, me. In fact, cards on the table, I probably like them more than I like acting," she told Hollywood gossip columnist Fanny Batter. "I'll be training with some of Tinseltown's top dried grape specialists to make sure I blow the 'currant' record out of the water," the *Caligula* star quipped.

LIDL BUY LIDDLE
Munich, Germany

THE GERMAN supermarket giant **LIDL** has shelled out an undisclosed fee to purchase the journalist, broadcaster and twat **ROD LIDDLE**. Lidl bought Liddle at around 9pm Central European Time yesterday evening, with executives for the discount food chain said to be "delighted" with the deal. "We offered Rod a generous sum of money and now we own him," confirmed Lidl CEO Heinrich Bittbei-Bitt. "We're not sure yet what we'll get him doing – possibly stacking shelves or working on the tills. Or maybe we'll get him to pen a shit column for our in-store magazine."

APPLES AND PEAR-SHAPED
London, UK

FINANCIAL markets were in meltdown today after the Cockney Animal Pound plummeted to its lowest level since the 1970s, as a result of continued uncertainty over Covid-19. At close of trading this afternoon, a 'pony' – previously worth £25 – equalled just £21.39, whilst a 'monkey' (£100) was equivalent to just £86.54. In order to shore up liquidity, Cockney Chancellor **'BIG' NOBBY DAKIN** announced new emergency Bow Bells zoological currency measures in the form of a 'vole' (£2.50) and a 'chaffinch' (99p).

Marty 'n' Jez xx

More weird 'n' wonderful global current affairs titbits next time, folks!

UK AND TRANS-LUNAR TRAJECTORY BREAKS

LETTERBOCKS

Viz Comic, P.O. Box 841 Whitley Bay, NE26 9EQ : letters@viz.co.uk

THEY say that you should never judge a book by its cover. But you judge a tin of paint by the lid. It just goes to show, it's one rule for 'la-di-da' books and another for tins of paint.

Peter James, Bristol

I RECENTLY spent some time on Björkö, a small island in the Baltic sea near Stockholm. The island has just one pub, a restaurant and a Viking museum, and my visit coincided with that of a local Norsemen reenactment society. Have any other readers been stared at when they walked into a pub because they weren't dressed as a Viking?

Jack Dury, Stockholm

I BET those fellas with hairy backs and big hands who used to rip telephone directories in half on the telly are feeling a bit redundant now. Perhaps they should move with the times and try folding SIM cards 12 times or something.

Kevin Bevin, Consett

I'M sick of how negative the mainstream media has become. Almost every day we hear about people who have died, but there are never any stories about those who have come back to life like Jesus did. Come on, let's have a bit more balanced reporting, please.

Ben Nunn, Caterham

MY wife just asked me if I thought that aliens from another planet had banjo strings on their cocks. I couldn't help thinking that she seems to have jumped into the alien life debate midstream, and there are a lot of questions need answering before we get to that one.

Tobamory Dupree, Crewe

THE saying 'If at first you don't succeed try, try again' doesn't seem to apply when attempting to nick a pair of my sexy neighbour's knickers off the line. I was caught by her husband who gave me a right good hiding, and my subsequent attempts just seemed to make him increasingly angry and the beatings more vicious. When my legs have mended I might give it one more go, but that'll be it.

Stanley Metaxya, Croydon

STAR LETTER

AFTER visiting the famous south coast Listening Dishes that were used during the war to hear the approach of enemy planes, I wondered if the *Viz* science correspondent or some of your readers could answer something that's been puzzling me. If, under the reciprocity principle, someone, my wife for instance for no particular reason, stood at the focal point of one of these dishes and dropped a good one, would it be possible to blow off a Frenchman's beret?

Phil Buckley, email

HOW come we don't see much cheating going on on TV game shows and quizzes these days? You would have thought that those so-called brainboxes would be smart enough to pull the wool over the quizmaster's eyes and get away with it.

Paul Kelly, Dublin

EVERYONE likes Han Solo's pal Chewbacca off of *Star Wars*, but if I ran around stark bollock naked shooting at people with a crossbow I'd quite rightly be sectioned under the Mental Health Act. It just goes to show it's one rule for celebrities and another for the rest of us.

Dan Kelly, Bridgwater

I RECENTLY visited the ABBA Museum in Stockholm and was fascinated to see a reconstruction of a kitchen that might have looked a bit like one in which one of the members of ABBA may have written one of their hits in the 1970s, perhaps *Mama Mia*, or *Waterloo*. If not, it was certainly how a lot of kitchens in Sweden would have looked at the time those songs were penned. Well worth the £40 entrance fee, I can tell you.

Crawford Golightly, Hull

I OFTEN see signs on rural roads saying "Oncoming vehicles in middle of road." Well I don't know what I'm supposed to do about that. Wouldn't it be better to put a sign on the other side saying "Get on your own side, you bastards"?

Micky Bullock, London

IN 1938, the Olympic swimmer turned Tarzan actor Johnny Weissmuller opened a swimming pool in my home town. Sadly it was 46 years before I was born, so I missed my chance to meet him.

Dave Shorter, Saint Neots

ALL my friends have had children recently and they inevitably insist on bringing them everywhere, and talking about how 'special' and 'unique' they are. The thing is, I find their kids really boring and I'm tired of pretending they're interesting, but I don't know how to tell them. Do *Viz* readers have any advice on how to broach this delicate subject?

Tom James, Berkhamsted

* *Well, readers, what do you think? Perhaps 'honesty is the best policy', for Tom, or maybe your advice to him would be 'if you can't say anything nice, then don't say anything'. Write in and tell us how you would broach the subject of your indifference to your friends' children.*

WHEN the lockdown ended in New Zealand, we were told to go back to work, which is very annoying, as I retired in 2013.

David Blakey, Auckland

MY wife has her heart set on a large glass dining table for our house, but I'm worried that some of the acts that I've seen performed on these items of furniture on various specialist DVDs will result in horrific flashbacks that will spoil every meal, particularly spaghetti bolognese. I can't really use this as a reason for not getting one, though. Can any of your readers think of a plausible excuse that won't result in divorce?

Hector Alsophila, Nottingham

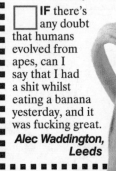

IF there's any doubt that humans evolved from apes, can I say that I had a shit whilst eating a banana yesterday, and it was fucking great.

Alec Waddington, Leeds

KATHY BURKE & HARE

BACK in 1941, my grandfather's house in Birmingham was destroyed by a bomb that had been dropped from an aeroplane. He reported it to the police but they didn't even bother to investigate. No arrests were ever made and to this day the perpetrators are still at large, still laughing about it with all their mates, no doubt.

D Williams, Donegal

I CAN'T remember the last time my cats stroked me, or tickled me under the chin. Or indeed the last time they provided me with a free pre-prepared fast food meal. It seems like a one way street with this particular pet. Come on cats, give a little back.

David Haslam, Datchworth

CAN Covid-19 get in via your bottom? I'm going to the zoo today and I am bound to need a shit at some stage and I'm a little concerned that someone may have coughed on the seat.

Stuie, Bunny

∗ *That's a very good question, Stuie. Perhaps the government's chief medical officer Prof. Chris Whitty could write in and tell our readers if they can catch Covid-19 off of toilet seats at the zoo.*

FOLLOWING yon from my previous letter *(this page)*, I think you should be able to hire paintball guns at zoos. The animals look bored stiff and the occasional thwack off a paintball (no head shots allowed) would spice up their routine a bit and keep them on their toes. The zoo could charge extra for the privilege, earning much needed money to fund their conservation efforts.

Stuie, Bunny

THE other day, my wife said she was rinsing some vegetables for tea. But when I looked in the colander, it was full of tomatoes, which are actually a fruit. Women, eh?

Herbert Pocket, Deal

AS a wig-wearing football fan, I find it disappointing that our top-flight players have embraced every anti-baldness measure except hairpieces. Bobby Charlton plumped for a combover, Alan Shearer pioneered the head shave, and Wayne Rooney shelled out for a hair transplant. Yet still, in 2020, not one single professional footballer has stepped out onto the pitch in a wig. Come on, you slap-headed soccer stars – get out the toupée tape and stick a wig on the old bonce.

Oliver Reaction, Chipping Norton

I DON'T know why so many high court judges feel the need to wear wigs. They are supposed to be figures of authority who command our respect with their clear-sighted moral acumen. But it's pretty hard to view them as such when they can't even come to terms with their own baldness. I've never had any brushes with the law, but if I do ever find myself in the dock, I'll be sure to only accept the judge's ruling if he has fully embraced his male pattern hair loss.

Archie Recidivist, HM Prison Brixton

MONSTERS aren't as scary as many people assume. Mummies, zombies and Frankensteins shuffle around slowly and are easily out-run. Draculas are afraid of garlic, crosses and sunshine and so are simple to vanquish. Ghosts are a much more tricky opponent, but they don't worry me because they aren't real.

Tom Tit, Orkney

WERE deeley boppers named after Cat Deeley, or the other way around?

Matthew Breeze, email

∗ *What an interesting question, Mr Breeze, and we have to admit we have no idea. Are you the inventor of deeley boppers, and if so, did you name the product after the model and TV presenter? Or are you Cat Deeley, and if you are, can you tell us if your mum and dad named you after the novelty headwear? Although, thinking about it, Deeley would be your surname, not your given name, so that doesn't work. Forget it. What a fucking stupid question, Mr Breeze.*

In response to Mr McLean's letter about the point of toads *(page 142)*...

...THE theological answer is simple. The Lord foresaw the post-lapsarian state of man would be such that we would treat frogs horribly - licking them for their hallucinogenic juices or using them as johnnies like what the Romans did. Consequently he made toads, which give you warts as everyone knows, so as to confuse us and cause us to accidentally pick them up instead, thereby punishing us with horrid fleshy growths on our hands/genitals for our foreordained maltreatment of amphibians.

Rev. F Butler-Gallie, Liverpool

∗ *An interesting take, Rev. Butler-Gallie. In the interests of balance, perhaps Richard Dawkins or the late Christopher Hitchens would like to write in and counter this argument.*

...MR McLean's letter betrayed a shocking ignorance of basic cladistics. 'Toads' and 'frogs' are merely vernacular terms without clear taxonomic significance, so in the words of the physicist Wolfgang Pauli, Mr McLean is 'not even wrong' when he ask this question. I expect higher standards from *Viz* readers.

Prof Mark Huxham, Dunbar

...THERE are many differences between toads and frogs. Toads have dry, warty skin and much shorter legs, as they prefer to crawl around rather than hop. Frogs, on the other hand, have long, splayed legs made for hopping, and slimy skin, very much like your mother whose legs are also often wide apart and pretty much permanently covered in various, slimy fluids. Although the vaginal warts also make her a bit toad-like to be fair.

Trim McKenna, Surbiton

∗ *And here we go again. Another puerile attack on our mothers' integrity in the guise of an informative letter by Mr Trim McKenna. Well, we are not joining in. As Michelle Obama famously said, "When they go low, we go high." We're going to show Mr McKenna how to behave, something his mother should have done if she wasn't too busy giving reach-arounds to all the tramps of Surbiton in return for a swig of their meths.*

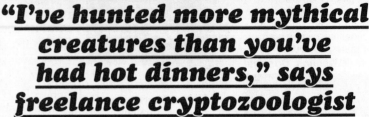

"I've hunted more mythical creatures than you've had hot dinners," says freelance cryptozoologist

Beast behaviour: *Cryptozoologist Pustules spends his spare time attempting to assemble proof of mythological monsters.*

ASK any man what his dream job would be and you would expect him to say footballer, train driver or astronaut. But you'd be surprised at the answer you are most likely to hear… *Cryptozoologist.*

That's according to RON PUSTULES – a freelance cryptozoologist and registered sex offender, from Trawden, just outside Burnley.

"People are constantly asking me how I got into the cryptozoology game," chuckles 30-stone Ron. "The truth is, I've been fascinated by mythical beasts ever since my childhood, and it's always been my ambition to track down, unearth and – ultimately – to understand these fantastical critters that live undiscovered in our forests, lakes, jungles and skies."

Speaking to his local paper, *The Trawden & Winewall Intruder,* Pustules, 66, outlined the ins and outs of his unorthodox trade: "I'm sort of like the David Attenborough of animals that don't exist," the thrice-divorced father of ten explained. "These fabled creatures you might have read about in books – the Yeti, the Bigfoot and the Loch Ness Monster – are my bread and butter."

"My aim is to build a cache of conclusive evidence for their existence via notes, photographs and video footage, in order to study their behaviour and anatomy, and then, hopefully, make a few bob by shooting them with a tranquiliser dart and flogging them to a zoo."

Incredibly, many of these legends of folklore have materialised at Pustules's former place of work – the Lovecraft Leisure Centre & Gymnasium in Barrowford. He told the paper: "I was employed there technically as a drain cleaner, but rumoured

EXCLUSIVE!

sightings of all manner of mythological beasts soon began swirling among the leisure centre's customers."

"Before long, I was forced to put down my U-bend plunger and don my cryptozoological hat and binoculars in order to investigate."

And a tearful Ron added: "What I uncovered was a conspiracy that went all the way to the top and, ultimately, cost me my job, my livelihood and my freedom."

SAS-QUATCH OUT... HE'S BEHIND YOU!

Ron's first brush with a cryptozoological being occurred just a few days into his brand new career as a janitor's assistant at the leisure centre.

Due to a few dozen misunderstandings, I'd been sacked from my previous twenty jobs and placed on the sex offenders' register. But the manager at the Lovecraft Leisure Centre was kind enough to take a chance on me, possibly because I had accidentally forgotten to mention all the sex offender stuff on my CV.

I started the job, and to my surprise

I found that I enjoyed it. I would make my rounds every morning, my trusty plunger and an industrial-sized tub of caustic soda in my hand, giving a cheery wink to the lycra-clad female clientele who I'd see squatting, jumping and stretching through the window blinds of the gym.

But before too long, things took a sinister turn. I began to overhear whispers among some of the lady customers about a 'disgusting hairy beast' who roamed the building's corridors, and was occasionally caught leering in at the all-women yoga classes.

I felt my heart race. I'd read enough Wikipedia articles on cryptids to know exactly who… or rather *what* they were referring to: **BIGFOOT**.

Also known as the 'Sasquatch', Bigfoot is a hirsute, ape-like beast hailing originally from the American Pacific Northwest. How on earth the hairy fucker had found his way into an East Lancs leisure centre, I wasn't sure.

But there was one thing I was sure of …*I was going to catch him.*

beast

I arrived at work early next morning with my camera poised and ready around my neck. For a cryptozoologist, there is no bigger fear than your equipment malfunctioning at the very moment you sight a folkloric beast. So to check my camera was working, I snapped a few practice shots through the gym window of the ladies limbering up before their spin class.

I'd taken a few hundred or so of these test photos, when one of the women suddenly screamed and pointed a trembling finger in my direction.

My heart nearly burst out of my chest. *The mighty Sasquatch was surely right behind me!* I spun round, expecting to see the ferocious, missing-link-like figure towering over me. But there was no one there! The hominid brute must of scarpered.

The ladies were now sprinting towards

me, clearly eager to get another sight of the nightmarish entity that has haunted American folklore for centuries. But I was one step ahead of them. I tore off down the corridor, ready to snap the photo that might make me a millionaire. Unfortunately, though, as I turned the corner, I slammed straight into my supervisor, Mr Dodder.

To cut a long story short, the ladies had got the wrong end of the stick and assumed I was trying to take pictures of *them*, rather than of a marauding Sasquatch. I laughed out loud at the preposterousness of the idea – but incredibly Mr Dodder took their side and hit me with a verbal warning.

It was the ladies' word against mine, as well as some substantial CCTV evidence, so I took the slap on the wrist with good grace, and resolved to forget all about the Bigfoot rumours.

ANOTHER FINE NESS

Pustule knuckled back down and focused on his janitorial duties. But it wasn't long before rumours began to circulate of another fabled beastie sighted at his place of work.

About two weeks after the Bigfoot sighting, I was unclogging some matted hair from the swimming pool drain, when I happened to catch my trousers and pants on the diving board and tumble half-naked into the water.

to check my camera was working, I snapped a few practice shots of the ladies limbering up before their spin class through the gym window.

It was an accident that could have happened to anyone. But as I swam to the side of the pool to get out, I noticed something strange. There were a couple of wooden slats missing from the ladies' changing room window, which meant that – at the right angle from in the pool, you could see directly inside.

My stomach turned as I watched several unsuspecting female clients striding about absolutely Billy Bollocks in the communal showers. It was clear to me that this 'loophole' could very easily be exploited by any twisted pervert that

got their sick kicks off watching nude ladies soap themselves, and I made a mental note to come back every day and check that it wasn't being misused.

governess

Not long afterwards, a fresh crop of strange rumours had begun circulating. During a four-hour stint cleaning a blocked cubicle in the women's lavatory, I overheard whispers about a 'grotesque, bloated creature' that had been spotted gliding ominously through the swimming pool, its cold unblinking eyes staring right into the ladies' locker rooms.

I gasped silently as I realised the truth: *these ladies had caught a glimpse of THE LOCH NESS MONSTER!*

An icon of cryptozoological folklore, 'Nessie' is an aquatic dinosaur – a living fossil that has somehow survived since the Jurassic era. She usually keeps to the Scottish Highland Loch named after her, so I can only think she got into the leisure centre swimming pool through the pipes.

I was wary that my last brush with a mythical monster had led to trouble, but a peek at Nessie herself is every red-blooded cryptozoologist's dream. I simply couldn't pass up this opportunity to capture concrete evidence of the beast's existence.

vixen

The very next day, I snuck into the empty pool just after the 'Yummy Mummies

Loch on, Ronnie: Could Pustules catch a glimpse of Nessie?

Water Aerobics Class' had finished. My trousers and pants had once again become ensnared on the diving board, but I was so excited about seeing Nessie that I barely noticed. I'd bought a waterproof case for my trusty camera, and I waited for the long-necked plesiosaur to appear. Whilst waiting, I took a few photographs of the missing changing room blinds to

> **"My trousers and pants had once again become ensnared on the diving board, but I was so excited about seeing Nessie that I barely noticed."**

show to Mr Dodder. Once he saw the problem, he would surely give me the nod to repair them.

I quickly snapped a few hundred pictures of the absent slats and, unavoidably, the nude milfs behind them. And then suddenly I heard a blood-curdling shriek that turned my stomach to ice.

One of the slim, birthday-suited young mums was pointing at something behind me. 'Oh my God!' she screeched. *'That disgusting beast!'*

comet

My heart was thundering. I knew I was about to come face to face with the most iconic creature in pseudoscientific history. But as I plunged down into the chlorinated depths and scanned around, Nessie was nowhere to be seen!

She must have heard the shapely milf's scream and slithered down one of the pipes to the filter. I swam frantically and began clawing at the duct beneath the water, desperate to squeeze myself through and take chase. But before I could, I felt a hand grip my shoulder and pull me up to the surface.

It was my supervisor, Mr Dodder. I began telling him how I'd just had a brush with the planet's most fabled aquatic reptile, but he'd already put two and two together to make five. He gabbled some ludicrous story about how I'd been caught 'ogling customers in a state of undress'. I tried to prove my innocence by showing him my photos of the missing window blinds, but that only seemed to enrage him further.

He docked my wages and hit me with a final warning – *if I became embroiled in another cryptozoological caper I could well lose my job altogether…*

CREATURE (DIS)COMFORTS

Unfortunately, the very next day, Pustule became embroiled in another **"***cryptozoological caper and lost his job altogether.*

I won't go into the details, but I'd heard rumours that a Thylacine had been spotted in the ladies' sauna and I decided to investigate. These dog-like marsupials were believed to have become extinct a century ago, and I was keen to get a photograph of the first living specimen in 100 years. However,

Triple trouble: Ron found the leisure centre infested with (top to bottom right) a centaur, a chupacubra and a Beast of Bodmin Moor.

I was discovered taking photographs underneath the slatted benches, and I was sacked on the spot.

I left with my P45 in my hand, and as I drowned my sorrows with a few bottles of white cider in the precinct, I pondered why Mr Dodder had been so stubborn in his refusal to listen to the truth.

Many people are sceptical about the existence of these non-existent creatures, and rightly so, but why Mr Dodder should have been so closed-minded was baffling. And then suddenly, it hit me.

Dodder was a Bilderberg Group agent, working for the 'Illuminati', who had charged him with keeping the planet's secret fauna of fantastical monsters hidden from human awareness. It was the only explanation.

This was a conspiracy that went all the way to the top of the East Lancashire leisure industry. And I was going to prove it.

cupid

Later that night, after another litre or two of White Lightning to steady my nerves, I snuck back to the leisure centre. I'd forgotten to hand in a spare set of keys that I'd had cut, so I was able to gain access to the building and Mr Dodder's office. I was on the lookout for documents that proved my former boss's involvement with history's biggest cryptozoological cover-up.

But what I found was something FAR more unsettling.

Stood behind Mr Dodder's desk were three ungodly figures – a half-man-half-horse, a scaly dog with the head of a lizard and a vast panther-like creature, with glistening red eyes and sharp yellow fangs. I'd watched enough David Icke YouTube videos to know exactly what these monstrosities were… **A CENTAUR, A CHUPACABRA and THE BEAST OF BODMIN MOOR!**

Startled by my arrival, the beasts began rampaging wildly around the

office. The centaur galloped about, scattering Mr Dodder's neatly ordered papers, toppling his filing cabinets and smashing some framed photographs of his wife. The Beast of Bodmin Moor urinated and defecated freely across the carpet, presumably to mark its territory. And for some reason, the Chupacabra wrote 'DODDER IS A BALD TWAT' in marker pen on the wall.

sid

I pulled out my phone to film this brain-boggling display, only later to discover that I had the camera switched to 'selfie' mode. Consequently, all I'd captured was my own face as I lurched around Mr Dodder's office in what appeared to be a state of drunkenness, but was actually terror.

At some point I must of been kicked in the face by the centaur, because I can't remember much of what happened. But I woke up a few hours later with a sore head to find the mythological beasts had disappeared and Mr Dodder was stood over me with a face like thunder.

He knew full well that I'd exposed him as the clandestine cryptozookeeper he really was. And I knew full well that he would pull every Illuminati trick in the book to keep me quiet. Sure enough, Dodder used his connections to have the coppers called, and I was soon in the back of a police car.

Furthermore, his contacts in the police forensics department were able to 'prove' that the urine and faeces in his office matched my DNA.

I'm on bail at the minute, but I'm looking at a couple of years inside with another ten years on the sex offenders' register when I get out. And all because I was brave enough to peek through the **"**

NEXT WEEK: *Ron is badly beaten by security staff after investigating rumours of a Kraken in the fitting room at Miss Selfridge.*

168

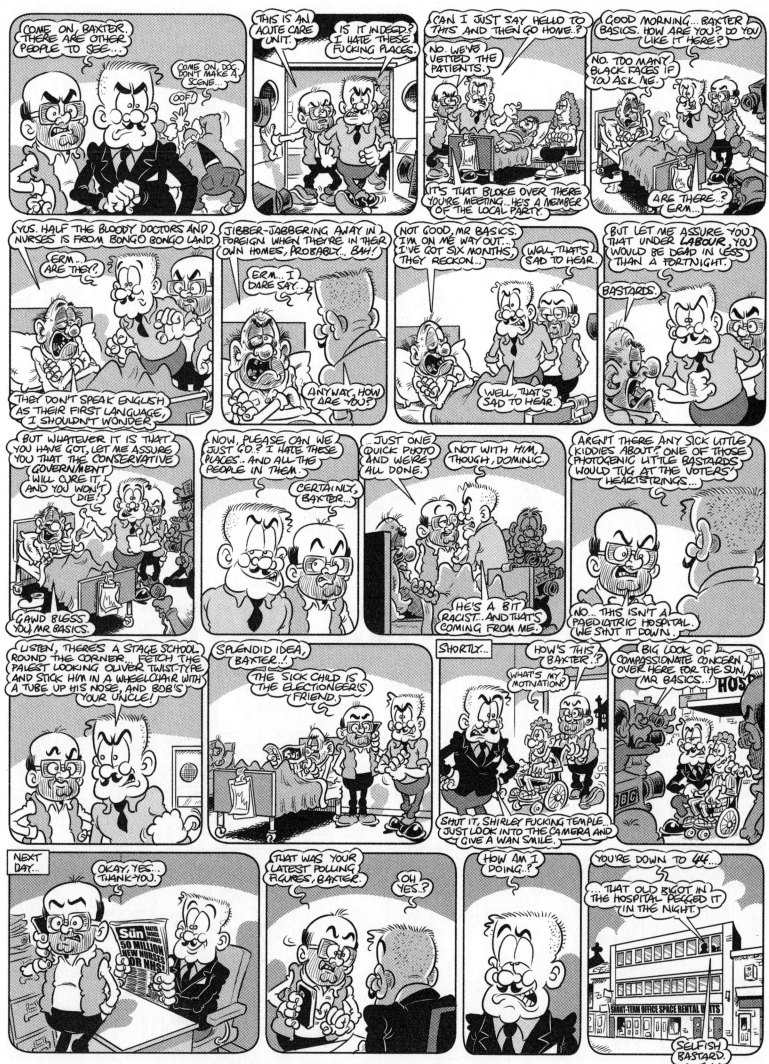

172

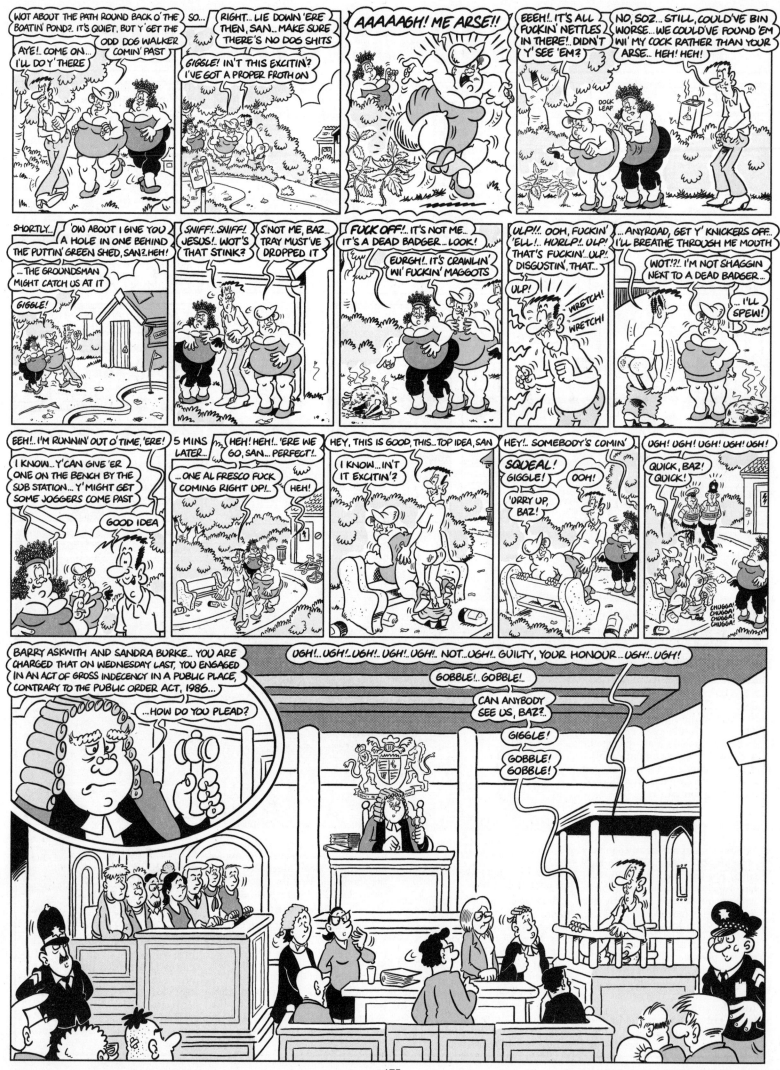

MAJOR MISUNDERSTANDING

RM/DJ '20

OH, LORDI!

A DIPLOMATIC row was brewing yesterday between the Finnish government and their Swedish counterparts over ownership of the famous Eurovision masks worn by the rock band Lordi.

The horrific monster masks, which date back to 2002 AD, were worn by the band during their Eurovision winning performance of *Hard Rock Hallelujah* in 2006, and are currently on display in Stockholm's ABBA museum, curated in a special wing dedicated to artifacts from the famous song contest.

Finnish

Finnish diplomats say that, historically, the natural home for the exhibits should be one of the many museums of art and culture in Helsinki. But the Swedish government has refused to hand them back, leading to tension between the Scandinavian neighbours.

Railway

Diplomatic negotiations regarding the possible repatriation of the seven masks, made from latex and PVC, have been ongoing since 2007 and have thus far remained on friendly terms. But the tension was raised last week when Finnish Minister for Antiquities and Culture Ari-Pekka Mäkinen accused the

EXCLUSIVE!

Scandi drama: Mäkinen and Ekblöm yesterday

Swedes of stealing the masks after the contest in Athens.

"Some members of the Swedish entrant's delegation broke into Lordi's dressing room whilst the band members were out celebrating their victory and looted the famous masks," he told a delegation of UNESCO members at the United Nations.

"These priceless cultural treasures should be returned immediately to their home country where they belong, and where they can be appreciated by the Finnish people."

But Swedish Foreign Minister Annika Ekblöm claims that the masks had simply been discarded after the show, and that the Swedes had saved them for future generations.

Telephone

"Our entrant for that year, Carola Häggkvist, who finished in fifth place with Invincible, found them in a bin outside the Finns' dressing room," she told the delegation.

"Had she not taken them, they would have been collected by the Athenean bin collectors, thrown into landfill and lost forever," she added.

Scrap metal: Discarded artifacts related to the Finnish Eurovision band are subject of bitter diplomatic row.

The delegation also heard from the chief curator of the British Museum who was demanding the return of the two skirts ripped off the Bucks Fizz girls. The dresses, which disappeared after the show in 1981, are now on display in the Song For Europe Museum in Bosnia Herzegovina.

TAKE YOUR PICNIC

THE GREAT British picnic is about to undergo a dramatic change. That's because, as the United Kingdom leaves the European Union in 2021, the humble SCOTCH EGG is set to be rebranded!

The popular dish, consisting of a boiled egg wrapped in sausage meat and breadcrumbs, has been a picnic staple for decades. But Downing Street believes the time has come for Scotch eggs to reflect not just Scotland, but the whole of the Union.

A Number 10 spokesman told us: "In January, the United Kingdom will be going it alone on the world stage. And we want the rest of the world to associate these delicious, meaty eggs with Great Britain, and not just a small part of it."

"Calling these savoury treats 'Scotch eggs' is selling the UK short. We need a world-beating name for these delicious yet not particularly nutritious titbits," he added.

eggs

The new name for Scotch eggs has yet to be decided, but Downing Street confirmed yesterday that the contract to come up with the rebrand, worth up to £750k, has been awarded to a marketing firm owned by Dominic Cummings and Michael Gove.

"Whatever the creatives come up with, the new name will reflect the

EXCLUSIVE!

identity of all four nations of the United Kingdom," said Gove.

"Not only that, but it will bespeak of Global Britain's position as a world leader in the egg- and meat-based snack industry," the fish-faced bellend continued.

"Britannia egg, Albion egg and Empire egg have all been suggested as possible alternatives, but no decision will be made until we have reached £750,000 in expenses," he said, pointing at the reporter with his knuckle.

dirk

However, opposition leader Keir Starmer was unhappy about the Prime Minister awarding such a lucrative contract to a No. 10 adviser and a fellow cabinet minister, and expressed his displeasure at Prime Minister's Questions. "I'm sure the Prime Minister awarded the contract to Mr Cummings and Mr Gove's company after their tender

beat off the competition in a fair and transparent process on a level playing field, but some cynical people might not think that," he told the house.

"Would it not be better to put it to the British public and let them decide what to call these iconic foodstuffs?" he continued forensically.

"Although obviously, not if they choose something stupid like Eggy

McPorkface," he added.

But Scottish Nationalist leader Nicola Sturgeon was less than happy about any changes in the name of what she called a traditional Scottish treat.

"It's a Scotch egg. The clue is in the name," she told reporters outside Hollyrood Palace. "Although, it should really be Scottish egg, rather than Scotch," she added.

Go to work on an egg: *Downing Street confirmed that traditional picnic favourite, the Scotch Egg, will receive a £750k rebrand.*

EGG FLIP

FROM next year, ask for a Scotch egg in a shop and you'll be met with a blank stare. Because by then they'll be called something else. But *what*, exactly? We called some well known celebrities, as well as a tosspot and a bellend, to ask what new name they would give to the Scotch egg.

NIGEL FARAGE
XENOPHOBIC PARTY LEADER

I'd call it an *English Pub Egg*. And I love nothing better than popping down my local in my Barbour jacket and my fucking tweed cap to enjoy posing for a photo with a delicious pint in my hand and one of these yummy non-foreign treats just by my mouth, breathing all stale Embassy Regal fumes onto it.

COLIN FIRTH
LADIES' FAVOURITE ACTOR

When I was filming *Pride and Prejudice*, they had Scotch eggs in the catering van, and I used to eat about two dozen a day. When I did that scene where I came out of the lake, my arse was quacking like a duck as I walked up the hill. Fortunately, the sound engineers managed to take the trumps out in post production. But for that reason, I'd call a Scotch egg a *Fartin' Egg*, or a *Fartmaker*.

BRIAN COX
D:REAM PHYSICIST

Scientists traditionally tend to call things by a name that describes their structure. Deoxyribonucleic Acid, for instance, is so-called because it is acidic, it is found

in the nuclei of cells, its structure is based on the sugar ribose, and that sugar has been deoxygenated. Similarly, I would call a Scotch egg a *Pork Encapsulated Egg*. That doesn't sound very appetising, but in the same way that deoxribonucleic acid is shortened to DNA, the pork encapsulated egg could be reduced to PEE. Although that sounds even less appetising.

JIM AL KHALILI
EGGHEAD BOFFIN

I agree to some extent with Professor Cox in that the Scotch egg should be renamed to reflect its structure and function, but I think he has 'reverse engineered' the name. It is not an egg surrounded by pork, rather a ball of pork with an egg at the centre, or more scientifically, an *Ovum-centred Pork Spheroid*.

DAVID STARKEY FORMER
ACADEMIC FORMER TV PRESENTER

I'm not sure what I would call it, but it would probably be something highly offensive – racist even – that would lose me whatever jobs I've got left, if any.

CHARLOTTE CHURCH
SINGER WITH THE VOICE OF AN ANGEL

We always had Scotch eggs when I was growing up in Wales, and my mum always used to refer to them as Welsh eggs or *Wy Cymraeg*, which is Welsh egg, only in Welsh.

JAMES MARTIN
CYCLIST AVERSE TV CHEF

In case anyone didn't know, I'm from Yorkshire, and having to call them Scotch eggs really boils my piss. I'd call them *Yorkshire Eggs*, or *God's Own County Eggs*.

ELIZABETH II
REIGNING MONARCH

I love a Scotch egg, me, but obviously the ones we have here at Buckingham Palace are made out of boiled swans' eggs. And my husband and I always refer to them as *Balmoral Eggs*, because that's the only bit of Scotland we like.

So you want to... GO ON A PICNIC?

ACCORDING TO a junk email from Marks and Spencer, this summer is the summer of the picnic, and what greater fun could there be than to pack our sandwiches, cakes and pop into a basket, find a nice spot in the country and enjoy an al fresco feast? It sounds idyllic, but the traditional picnic is not without its risks. Many people have a picnic in the country and return home relatively unharmed, but some are not quite so lucky after falling foul of picnic pitfalls. Recognising the dangers is essential if you are to weigh-up all the factors and decide whether or not to go on a picnic.

So, before you rustle up some sarnies, make a flask of tea and head for the countryside, here are just a few of the things you need to consider.

EVERYONE wants their picnic to be nice and peaceful, so find a nice, quiet spot in the country. But remember, it is not only picnic goers who want to stay away from the crowds. In seeking seclusion, you may come across people you would rather not meet; drug dealers in the midst of a transaction, the Real IRA hiding a cache of weapons, or a couple of 'Goodfellas' burying a 'whacked' rival mafia boss in the weeds. Disturb these scoundrels in the midst of their illicit activities, and no amount of sweet talking or offers to share your lemon drizzle cake is going to get you out of your pickle. In short, it's Goodnight, Vienna.

IN ADDITION to being arrested for a crime you did not commit, there is every chance your picnic will end in you being arrested for one that you did. Trespassing on someone's land is not a criminal offence, but it could land you with a fine of up to £1,000, which could easily end up ten times that after court costs. Similarly, taking your radio to a picnic and playing it to more than four people is a breach of the Performing Rights Society regulations, of which the courts take a dim view. And think carefully before you decide to spread jam on your scone. Being in possession of a knife, albeit a butter knife, in a public place is a far more serious offence, one which will land you with a criminal record and up to 10 years in prison.

MANY people think that the rain is the worst weather for ruining a picnic. But in actual fact, it is the sun we should be more scared of. Anyone heading out for a picnic in a place like California's Death Valley is asking for trouble. Here, temperatures regularly soar above a scorching 50°C, and picnickers frequently finish off their pop within minutes of laying out their spread. Worse, they then discover that the butter on their sandwiches has turned into liquid, the Penguin biscuits have melted onto their wrappers and the carrot cake, so moist when they set out, has baked to an inedible hardness in the relentless, scorching sun. As their skin blisters and cracks in the dry, furnace-like heat, they decide to pack up their basket and head home, only to get lost in the featureless terrain. What started as a fun day out ends with them wandering off into the parched wilderness, a mass of painful burns and delirious with dehydration, awaiting the blessed relief of death.

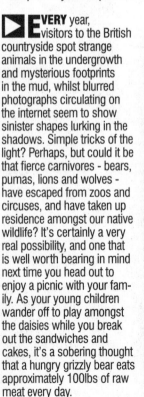

EVERY year, visitors to the British countryside spot strange animals in the undergrowth and mysterious footprints in the mud, whilst blurred photographs circulating on the internet seem to show sinister shapes lurking in the shadows. Simple tricks of the light? Perhaps, but could it be that fierce carnivores - bears, pumas, lions and wolves - have escaped from zoos and circuses, and have taken up residence amongst our native wildlife? It's certainly a very real possibility, and one that is well worth bearing in mind next time you head out to enjoy a picnic with your family. As your young children wander off to play amongst the daisies while you break out the sandwiches and cakes, it's a sobering thought that a hungry grizzly bear eats approximately 100lbs of raw meat every day.

THERE is nothing worse than settling down on the edge of a field for a picnic, only to discover a dead body behind the hedge, the victim of a grisly murder. You might think that calling the police to report your find would be an end to the matter, and you could go on with enjoying your picnic. But think again. As the discoverer of the body, you become the prime suspect…the focus of the police's investigations. Similarly, if you have your picnic and fail to notice the body, you are still in hot water. When it is eventually discovered, the crime scene will be littered with forensic and DNA evidence pointing to you - your saliva on a pork pie crust, your fingerprints on a Quavers packet. Either way, in the absence of any other suspects 'in the frame', you will arrested for a crime you didn't commit and almost certainly fitted up by the police.

SHOPPING for a picnic is great fun. We all enjoy loading up our trolley with Scotch eggs, bottles of pop, small buns and Mr Kipling cakes. But these items are a clear indication of what you are planning, and would-be burglars lurking in the aisles can spot them a mile off. Any felon watching you fill your trolley in the supermarket has simply to follow you home and stake out your house, confident that at the first hint of sunny weather, you and your family will be off to the countryside. You may enjoy a wonderful, carefree day picnicking, but it will all be spoilt when you return home to find your back door has been kicked in, your house has been ransacked, all your possessions have gone and there's a pile of human faeces on your living room carpet.

WASPS are a constant source of annoyance at a picnic, but for anyone allergic to their venom, a single sting could prove fatal. Even worse, if one of their paper nests falls from a tree onto your picnic, it will burst into a cloud of 20,000 angry wasps which you and your loved ones will be unable to outrun. Even if to those not allergic, a thousand stings from this angry swarm is more than the human body can tolerate, and a slow, painful death will inevitably ensue. Even if you survive the wasps, your picnic could still be spoilt by screwflies laying up to 500 eggs under your skin, which develop into maggots, devouring your flesh behind a writhing, itching boil, driving you to the edge of madness. These parasitic flies are only found in the semi-tropics of Central America, but as climate change brings warmer summers to the UK, it's not inconceivable that these foul insects are already here.

THE BRITISH countryside, with its grassy, open spaces, sun-dappled meadows and shady woodland glades, is a great place to get away from it all. But these secluded spots, well away from prying eyes, are also a draw for a far more sinister group of visitors - Devil worshippers - and woe betide any innocent picknickers who accidentally find themselves mixed up amongst their mysterious, diabolical rites. Nothing is guaranteed to ruin a family picnic more than mum or dad getting dragged away by naked satanists, to be spread across a stone altar and stabbed through the heart with a dagger decorated with runes and inverted crucifixes, whilst a cohort of masked, naked, priapismic diabolists ravish each other to a blood-soaked climax in honour of Beelzebub.

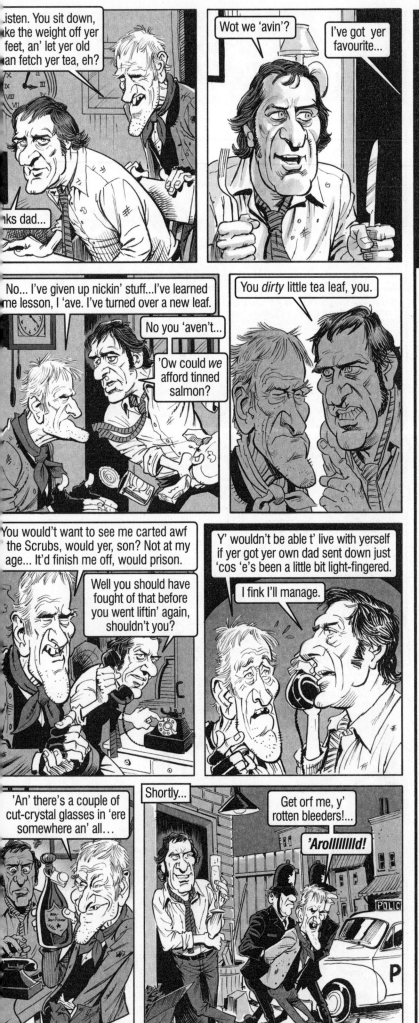

CURSE *OF THE* SWEAR-AOH!

ARCHAEOLOGISTS at Oxford's Ashmolean Museum reacted with shock yesterday after a long-dead Egyptian Pharaoh in their collection *rose from the dead!*

Rameses II: Egyptian potty mouth.

The Pharaoh, Rameses II, died in 1213BCE and since his tomb's discovery in 1928, his mummified remains have been on display in the town centre museum. Security guards on the night shift heard noises coming from the vicinity of the Egyptology department at around 3am on Tuesday.

"I've never been more frightened in all my life," said museum guard Frank Sludge. "We stood rooted to the spot in horror as the ghastly figure emerged from the tomb, his stinking bandages falling from his flesh as he moved."

shocked

CCTV footage shows the 3000-year-old figure emerging from his heiroglyph-decorated wooden sarcophagus. But it was what happened next that really shocked the museum's security staff.

"He opened his mouth and spoke," continued Sludge. "I don't know what I was expecting him to say, but I have to tell you, his language was a bit choice," he continued.

"The resurrected king let forth a stream of obscenities the like of which I have never heard in my fifty-eight years, and I've been in the army," Mr Sludge added. "The f-word, both the b-words, even the c-word."

pfeiffer

And it wasn't just the mummy's bad language that upset Frank, because the long-dead king, who became one with Orisir more than three thousand years ago, also displayed distinctly unacceptable behaviour when it came to women.

Mr Sludge told us: "As if the four letter words weren't bad enough, the undead mummy then started making inappropriate comments at my female colleague Janice, making a crude pun using the name of the wife of King Akhenaten in the 18th Dynasty."

"I told him that it wasn't on to talk like that in front of the ladies."

According to Professor Robert Everesley, Scealing Chair of Egyptology at St Cross College, this behaviour is not altogether surprising.

Foul-mouthed Mummy turns museum air Oxford blue

He told us: "In ancient Egypt, Pharoahs were seen as demi-gods. When he was alive more than three millennia ago, Rameses II would never have had to moderate his language in front of the ladies. He would have been able to eff and blind to his heart's content."

"When everyone around you believes you are literally descended from the sun, you don't really have to hold back."

"It's no surprise that some of the Pharoah's attitudes seem out of step with modern tastes and social mores," he continued. "There was no such thing as political correctness back in them times."

legrand

Others were quick to defend the Pharoah. "Yet again, the snowflake left castigate someone for speaking the truth," barked gobshite UKIP founder Nigel Farage.

"The usual carping voices will criticise, but I think that a lot of ordinary, hard working people will find that Rameses II's no-nonsense, speak-as-you-find tone and use of good old Anglo-Saxon language strike a chord with them," he added, whilst pretending to drink a pint of beer for photographers.

At time of going to press, the Ashmolean Museum refused to comment on rumours that Rameses II was considering an offer to take over LBC's *Drivetime* show.

GOVER-ACTIVE IMAGINATION!

A Breadsall father of three was last night said to be in a stable condition in Derby General Hospital …*after imagining what Michael Gove would look like having sex.*

Terry Rarebit, 52, was apparently in perfect health on Thursday morning, and was browsing through Twitter when he suddenly keeled over.

reading

Speaking to the *Derby Meatus & Banjo String*, Rarebit's wife Mary, 51 told reporters, 46, 38, 26 and 61: "Terry was reading something about Sarah Vine's latest poisonous Daily Mail column. He was going on about how dreadful she was. Then, quite without thinking, I mentioned that she is married to that awful Michael Gove."

round

A tearful Mrs Rarebit continued: "Terry chuckled and said: 'Christ, imagine the two of them going at it.' Then suddenly there was this almighty crash. When I looked round, Terry was twitching on the kitchen floor, white as a sheet, with his face twisted into a grotesque rictus of terror."

"I thought at first he was simply having a heart attack, but then I heard him mumbling: 'Just imagine it... Just imagine the two of them...! Oh Christ, the horror… the horror!' and I realised he was picturing the Chancellor of the Duchy of Lancaster, mid-coitus."

roses

Mary frantically attempted to shake her husband out of his fit, but his disturbing vision only grew stronger.

"He began retching wildly, and then I heard him hiss: 'Imagine his cum face… Oh, Jesus! No!'," she said. "I was screaming and begging him to think of something else, but it wasn't working. I can only suppose that the image of Gove's face in the throes of ecstasy, all twisted in rapture, with his glasses and those lips, must have been burned into his brain," she added.

"Then Terry's eyes snapped shut and he lay completely still."

terrys

A petrified Mary phoned for an ambulance, and Terry was rushed to the A&E department at Derby Hospital.

Chief surgeon Dr Charles de Villefort told reporters: "Mr Rare-

Derby man in critical condition after conjuring up MP's sex face

Leg Gover: Rarebit imagined Gove's face (top) during coitus, and (above) some normal, attractive people enjoying sex yesterday.

bit is extremely lucky to be alive. The mental image he conjured of Michael Gove achieving orgasm caused his vital organs and motor functions to start shutting down."

"We were able to bring him back from the brink, and I'm happy to report he is now in a stable condition. But someone less strong may not have been so lucky," he added.

alberts

And Dr de Villefort had this advice for anyone else wondering what the guppy-faced Tory MP would look like on the nest: "Don't go there. It's as simple as that," he warned. "Picturing the act of sexual congress between Michael Gove and Sarah Vine can only have a bad outcome."

"If you feel your brain drifting towards a vision of Gove in the vinegar strokes, simply ask a friend or relative to slap you hard in the face until it stops," he added.

LETTERBOCKS

Viz Comic, P.O. Box 841 Whitley Bay, NE26 9EQ : letters@viz.co.uk

AN archaeologist on telly the other day said that he had found a caveman settlement in Sussex that was 26 km long. He must think I was born yesterday, as we all know that the kilometre was invented in the 18th century by the French. If these so called scientists are going to make things up, they should at least try to make it a bit believable.

Dave Gibbs, Biscuit Mowbray

I HAVE just found out my brother-in-law was born in the Chinese year of the pig, and he ended up being a police officer. I was going to have a good laugh telling him, but unfortunately I was born in the year of the cock, which rather ended that particular comedic avenue.

Hammo, Harrow

PRIME Minister Boris Johnson was sacked from *The Times* because he made up a quote in one of his articles. But if reporters want to speak to somebody who does not want to comment, what are they supposed to do?

Baxter Twinhorns, Bude

MY cat is 13-years-old and its favourite song is *Won't get Fooled Again* by The Who. Beat that, you wankers.

Tim Buktu, Timbuktu

∗ Well, readers, Mr Buktu has certainly thrown down the gauntlet there. Can any of our readers who are wankers beat that?

WHOEVER said a dog is a man's best friend has never met my dog. It's a complete cunt. As am I.

Dangerous Andy, Wokingham

I THINK kids would eat more fruit if it was injected with artificial flavours. Perhaps they could inject oranges with strawberry flavouring, or apples with tangy mango. Come on, fruit growers. Get with the trends.

Terry Farricker, Blackpool

WHILST strolling up Blackpool promenade last night, I thought of a new attraction mixing the annual autumn light show with the world of Greek hard cheese, called 'Blackpool Hallouminations'. I'm not sure how many tourists this would pull in, but it's a difficult time for the hospitality industry, so it has to be worth a try.

Jim H, Blackpool

THE letter about deeley boppers (*page 165*) got me thinking. Are cats named after Cat Deeley, or is it the other way around?

Bill Harford, Hall Green

THESE people who talk about 'living like a king' forget that Richard the Lionheart had no central heating and had to shit out of a hole in the side of his castle.

Christina Martin, Bexhill-on-Sea

I'VE NO doubt that global warming is true, as I'm sure summers are much hotter now than they were when I was a child. Admittedly I grew up in Wales and now live in Malta, but still.

D Cooper, Malta

SCIENTISTS say that the human eye sees things upside down, but the brain converts them to be the right way round. If that is the case, how come the soup I had for lunch yesterday didn't fall out of the bowl? Do these boffins honestly expect us to believe the rubbish they come out with? And these are the people we are trusting to rid the world of Coronavirus.

Tim Buktu, Timbuktu

HAVE any of your readers lost a pigeon, only there's one that's been hanging around outside my local Greggs for a couple of days. It's grey in colour with a shiny neck and walks with a limp.

Johnny Turnbull, Hartlepool

APART from the Binars on *Star Trek*, why is it that all aliens on the telly speak very slowly and use the English language in an excessively pedantic way? And can any readers who have been abducted by real aliens tell us what their language sounds like when they are arguing about which probe gets inserted where?

Stew, email

I KNOW that 'snurgling' is the act of sniffing a lady's recently vacated bicycle seat, but is the word for the person performing the act spelt 'snurglar' like burglar, or the more traditional 'snurgler'? Can you confirm which it is, because I don't really want to make any spelling mistakes on this job application form, even if it is only the Hobbies & Interests section.

Clifton Bellsend, Manchester

I'D be celebrating my 100th birthday this year if I had been born in 1923. But I'm not as I was actually born in 1964.

Tim Steel, Hornchurch

I AM really glad the man from Del Monte always says "yes," otherwise all of those impoverished Latin American subsistence farmers and their children would be plunged into poverty and starvation. Good on him, I say!

Rev. Ken Curious, email

SOME say that philately is a lost art, whilst others say that collecting stamps can hardly be considered an art at all. Personally I couldn't give a shit either way.

Arthur C. Cardboard, Staines

THE number of times people ask "have you any common sense?" surely means that it's not actually that common. They ought to change it to something more fitting like "rare sense" or "uncommon sense."

Barry Berry, York

CUNT DRACULA

SUPERMARKET

I'M SORRY, SIR - I CAN'T LET YOU IN UNLESS YOU'RE WEARING A MASK...

YOU VILL LET ME IN VITHOUT VEARING A MASK!

YES, I WILL LET YOU IN WITHOUT WEARING A MASK...

FRUIT AND VEG

COUGH COUGH!

IN 1665, the University of Cambridge closed due to the Bubonic Plague and Isaac Newton had to work from home. During his time in lockdown he developed calculus, the theory of gravity and his 3 laws of motion. My routine of watching *Tipping Point* and eating Pringles seems like a wasted opportunity on reflection.

Siggy, Pudsey

DOES anybody have the address of the *Guinness Book of Records*, as I think I might have grown the world's smallest tomato.

Tom Thumbgreen, Derby

I SUSPECT Mr Thumbgreen (*above*) may have jumped to conclusions, somewhat. How can he be sure that he hasn't got the world's largest 50p piece. Either way, I suppose, he's a tiny-solanaceous-fruit-growing/large heptagonal-coin-possessing record breaker!

Jack Druridge, Bath

ON the off-chance I need to appear on TV via Zoom or Teams, can any of your readers lend me some big books or fancy pictures to have on show behind me to make folk think I'm smart and all that?

Mike Tatham, St. Andrews

I WISH airline pilots would just fly their planes without showing off and doing a fucking wheelie every time they take off. What a bunch of one-trick ponies.

D Williams, Donegal

WHY do drivers always go the same way around roundabouts? It's conformity gone mad. Come on, British motorists. Show a bit of imagination for once!

Ben Nunn, Caterham

WHEN they show old TV programmes, why don't they also show the correct adverts from that time in the commercial breaks? It's daft seeing an advert for the latest iPhone during an episode of *Columbo* when he has to make do with a landline. Come on, TV people. Keep it real.

Hazel, Hitchin

IF these 'soaps' are so realistic, how come you never see anyone unsuccessfully trying to hold a shit in whilst watching *Homes Under the Hammer* because they can't be arsed getting up to go the bog?

M. Goodlet, Leeds

THEY used to do "man-sized" tissues for blowing your nose and stuff, but what about bog roll? There must be plenty of big-arsed bastards out there who need a hefty handful of bathroom tissue for each wipe. And let's face it, a four inch wide strip of gossamer thin paper often isn't up to the job, quilted or not. So come on, shit-scrape manufacturers. How about some wider and more heavy-duty bumwad for the wider and heavy-duty arseholes who live in the real world?

R. Pitt, Kendal

ARE boil-in-the-bag kippers bad for you? I really hope not because I love the fuckers.

Eric the Red, Halifax

AS an avid Tesco-goer, I have been telling all my friends for many years that "every little helps," as per their slogan. So imagine my horror when I read on Ralf Little's portfolio website that for seven years he has been doing voiceover work… for Asda! I for one hope that Tesco modify their slogan to "every little helps, except Ralf".

Ryan N, Mansfield

IF Banksy is reading this and is short on new ideas, how about giving us your version of that bloke kissing that bird's arse? I'm no connoisseur of these things, but I'm sure that the art world would go mad over that.

Iain Devenney, Abingdon

THIS morning I found a toilet wedged in a wheelie bin. Can any of your readers beat that?

Sam, London

THESE new-fangled dating sites tell their members that they should meet their prospective partners in a safe place. I think that's good advice. I met my wife at a Fire Assembly Point and we've married for over thirty years.

Magnus Dean Stanton, Monks Heath

I'VE been scared to step outside my front door during the pandemic. I'm not particularly worried about catching the virus, it's just that my house is teetering on a cliff as a result of coastal erosion.

Glen Hattersley, Broadchurch

IF I was Jesus, I would let everyone go through doors ahead of me just so I could make the 'before Christ' joke. I would also let everyone go through doors ahead of me because I was Jesus and therefore extremely nice.

Christina Martin, Bexhill-on-Sea

Pope For A Day

I **N OUR** more contemplative moments, every one of us has wondered what it would be like to be the infallible supreme leader of the worldwide Catholic Church. But if we actually DID get to be Bishop of Rome for 24 hours, what would we do with our time? We asked three of our favourite A-List celebs: *What would YOU do if YOU were Pope For A Day?*

NIGEL FARAGE, utter bellend
I LOVE smoking indoors, but due to the bonkers Brussels barmycrats, I'm not allowed to do it any more. So if I was Pope For A Day, I'd use the centuries-old loophole permitting the release of smoke from the Vatican when a new pope is announced to have a cheeky inside fag! I'd spend the whole day with my feet up in the Sistine Chapel, puffing away happily on my Lambert & Butlers, all under the guise of announcing my papal successor! How about *that* for two fingers up to the snowflake loony left? Then, if I had time, I'd sink a pint of good old British bitter and have my photo taken whilst laughing like a cunt.

P DIDDY, gangsta rap fave
IF I was Pope For A Day, I'd use my new power of papal infallibility to definitively proclaim that Come Back Mrs Noah is the greatest sitcom of all time. I fucking love Come Back Mrs Noah. It's so underrated, and - honestly - I think it's Mollie Sugden's finest hour. It really boils my piss that everyone goes on about Blackadder and Fawlty Towers and The Office, but Come Back Mrs Noah never even gets a fucking mention. So, as soon as I became Bishop of Rome, I'd sign the papal encyclical stating conclusively that Come Back Mrs Noah is the all-time best sitcom - no muthafuckin' question. And then I'd quickly get a Channel 5 show commissioned in its honour, with Stuart Maconie and Andrew Collins talking about how great Come Back Mrs Noah is.

RICHARD HAMMOND, short-arsed petrolhead
I'VE always wanted to see how the famous 'Popemobile' would fare on the Top Gear test track, so if I inexplicably became Pope For A Day, I think I'd give that a whirl. I'd don my cassock and hat, and then screech around the 1.75-mile road circuit in the iconic quirkily shaped papal vehicle, trying to rack up as quick a time as possible. Perhaps I would even create a new segment called 'Star In A Reasonably Priced Popemobile', and let the likes of Alan Davies or Jay Kay out of Jamiroquai have a bash, too. Obviously I'm not on Top Gear any more, but I'd be the Pope so they couldn't exactly tell me to fuck off, could they?

YOU ASK, WE ANSWER... ABOUT SIEVES!

WHEN was the sieve invented and by whom?

Mrs Agnes Mighty, Stapleton

*Believe it or not, Agnes, the sieve was invented by none other than Renaissance brainbox LEONARDO DA VINCI! In 1486, Da Vinci had been invited by fellow Italian egghead Michelangelo to attend a Doctor Who-themed fancy dress party. The Mona Lisa fave set about fashioning a rudimentary 'Dalek' outfit from a 15th century sink plunger and a metal bowl into which he drilled some holes. When he returned home later that night, he realised that the hole-riddled Dalek headpiece he'd created was perfect for straining pasta and rinsing salad. Hey presto! the modern colander was born!

* * * * * * * * * * * * * *

WHO owns the largest collection of sieves on Earth?

Mrs Ada Buck, Steubenville

* The person in possession of the most sieves on the planet is Harlem-born hip-hop fave P DIDDY. The Bad Boy For Life superstar owns a whopping 81,408 perforated kitchen filtering utensils, all of which are housed in an industrial-sized Big Yellow Storage unit in Skipton. "Sieves, colanders, straining spoons, zarus, riddles, tamis, tea strainers – you name it, if the muthafucka's got holes and it's used for cooking then it's in my collection," Diddy told Puzzler magazine.

* * * * * * * * * * * * * *

I WAS planning to ask about the smallest sieve in recorded history, but I would assume that it will have been owned by the world's smallest man Calvin Phillips and was probably the size of a contact lens case or some such bollocks. Am I right?

Mrs Deidre Apollo, New Brighton

* Yes, you are absolutely correct, Mrs Apollo.

DID lumpy-faced late Motörhead vocalist Lemmy ever own some sort of Nazi sieve? And if so, where is it now?

Mrs Mable Semen, Penge

* LEMMY did indeed count a National Socialist sieve amongst his vast collection of German fascist memorabilia, Mrs Truehorn. In 1986, the late Ace of Spades icon purchased a rolled aluminium colander that had belonged to none other than Chaplin-moustached despot ADOLF HITLER. The utensil had been used by the Führer to strain some pasta during his final days cowering in a bunker before shooting himself and setting himself on fire. It now resides in the Imperial War Museum, alongside Josef Goebbels' garlic press, Rudolph Hess's egg whisk and a set of measuring spoons belonging to convicted war criminal Martin Bormann.

● Have YOU got a question about sieves, colanders or strainers? Write in to the usual address: Viz Comic, PO Box 841, Whitley Bay, NE26 9EQ. Don't forget to mark your envelope 'I've got a question about sieves, colanders or strainers'

Bad Bob The Randy Wonder Dog

IT WAS the day of the Glenpeebles Agricultural Show, and Sergeant Greenock had entered his dog Bad Bob into the All Breeds Terrier race. But once again, the excitable mutt had disgraced himself in front of everyone. "Och, Bob. Fancy daein' that," sighed the policeman. "And with bairns watchin' an' a'… Ah didnae know where tae put ma' face."

THE embarrassed policeman went into the prize vegetable tent to see some of the monsters that the people of the village had grown that year. "That's a braw leek you've got their, Mr McCullough," said Sergeant Greenock. "Aye, that it is," replied the proud grower. "It's as big as a man's leg. If this disnae win first prize, I'd like tae see the one whit does."

"AH'VE grown if from a seed an' ah've nursed it like a baby," said Mr McCullough. Suddenly, he heard a commotion, and turned in horror to see the randy pooch up to his old tricks. "Och, yir hoond's at it again, Greenock!" he yelled. "Get if aff ma leek afore I snap its neck." "Nae! Bob. Nae!" Greenock cried angrily. "Bad laddie!"

SERGEANT Greenock struggled to remove his little dog from the prize leek. But the harder he pulled, the harder Bad Bob dug in his claws. Mr McCullough tried to knock him off with his walking stick, but only managed to bruise the beloved vegetable further. "Yon dog's a menace, Greenock!" he cried. "Ye should have the bluidy thing pit doon!"

"OCH, NO! Will ye look at the state of it, Greenock," cried the distraught McCullough. "Yir mutt's fucked ma leek tae ribbons… an' he's left his bluidy spongle all awa' it." The old man was almost in tears. "It's nae gaun tae win any prizes noo." Sergeant Greenock once more scolded his dog. "Ye're a bad, bad duig, Bob! Y've let me doon again!"

BUT Sergeant Greenock's harsh words didn't satisfy Mr McCullough. The devastated old man picked up a hoe and made towards Bob. The randy animal knew he was in trouble and ran out the tent with Mc-Cullough giving chase. "Come back here, ye filthy, wee bas!" he cried. "Ah'll hae yir baals aff!" The pair of them headed towards the livestock.

BOB RAN into a sheep pen, closely followed by Mr McCullough. "Got ye, y' wee fecker," he snarled. "Y've naewhere tae run noo!" But Mr Selkirk the shepherd looked on in horror. "Get oot, McCullough, quick!' he cried. "That's Big Tam, the ram's pen. He has nae had a tup for months, an' he's got bawbags like two tins o' Fussels milk!"

THE OLD man tried to escape, but the fifteen stone priapic ram easily caught him. "Ach! Get him aff me, Selkirk!" he cried. "He's broken through the cloth o' ma troosers!" But all the shepherd could do was shout. "Bad Tam! Nae sheep treats!" Sergeant Greenock, likewise, could do nothing to help. "Bad Bob! Bad Bob. Nae biscuit!"

RENOVATION NIGHTMARE AT YORKSHIRE TRAIN STATION

By our Train Spotting Correspondent **Sexton Case**

Off the rails: Confusing platform numbers and a lack of pedestrain bridges are just two of the many issues that have plagued Rotherham train station since the upgrade, leading to the Mayor, Edna Tripe (top right), denouncing the works.

OFFICIALS from Rotherham County Council have been left with egg on their faces after a £1.5 million investment to upgrade their railway station ended up creating anger and confusion amongst passengers. And the local mayor this week denounced the work, complaining that Rotherham Central Railway Station had been left in a far worse state than it was before.

Early last year, Rotherham Metropolitan Borough Council predicted a rise in tourism due to the death of **BARRY CHUCKLE**, and anticipated the influx of 5 million pilgrims flocking to the late comedian's home town. In response, it was decided to upgrade the local railway station, extending the number of platforms from two to fifteen.

Pilgrimage: Council planned for influx of tourism after death of Barry Chuckle.

At the time, many Rotherham residents were critical of the plan, pointing out that only five services presently run from the town's station, but the expansion plan was given the green light by councillors and the work commenced in November 2018.

blunder

However, even the most vocal of sceptics could not have anticipated the monumental blunder that was to come. "The platform numbers aren't even in the right order," said commuter Rick Crumbhorn, 38. "Platform four is next to platform seven, platform three is next to number twelve, platforms one and nine are the same platform, and there isn't a platform two. It's just ridiculous."

But the station's problems are not just confined to its platform-

Upgrade works at station lead to confusion and delay

sequentiality. The lack of bridges between the fifteen platforms means that passengers are now forced to run across the tracks in order to make their connections.

"It's an accident waiting to happen," said pensioner Iris Sourcream, 74. "I get the train to the Meadowhall Shopping Centre on a Thursday with my friend, Edna, and it used to go from the old platform two," she told us.

"Now it goes from platform fourteen, and the only way to get to it is by jumping down from platform six and walking across the lines. Well, I'm not as fast as I used to be, and I daren't think what will happen if there's a train coming."

trolley

And yet further confusion arose from the fact that two of the platforms are not situated in the train station at all. Platform eight, for services from Rotherham to London is on the other side of the River Don on Corporation Street, and platform eleven is over two

> *The only way to get to platform fourteen is by jumping down from platform six and walking across the lines*

miles away in a sheltered housing complex in Brinsworth.

"I got the train from King's Cross, expecting to get to Rotherham town centre, and I ended half an hour's walk away in the garden of some old folks' home," said angry local businessman Rod Fogg.

greyhound

"What sort of first impression of Rotherham is this? If anything, it'll scare visitors away," he added. Rotherham council have tried to placate critics, pointing out that only two platforms are remotely situated away from the station. But many people are still angry at their taxes being spent on what many consider a botched job.

"I missed my train because I couldn't find my platform," fumed disgruntled commuter, Angelica Pinpad, 38. "I followed signs for the information kiosk and found it three miles away behind the Holiday Inn in Canklow."

To make matters worse, a software error means that all the platform clocks are set to Moscow time, making the entire timetable confusing and unworkable.

"It's not ideal, but if passengers just remember to subtract three hours from the time displayed, four if it's not British Summer Time, then there's no need for anyone to miss their train," said Alderman Brian Snorkle.

"It's not rocket science."

But the The Mayor of Rotherham, Edna Tripe, disagreed in the strongest terms. "I disagree in the strongest terms," she told local paper *The Rotherham Banjo and Helmet.*

NORMAN THE DOORMAN

Going Against the Flow

BLACKPOOL Council chiefs were under pressure this week to respond to complaints from residents that the town's canal is *TOO CLEAN.*

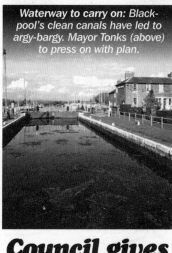

Waterway to carry on: Blackpool's clean canals have led to argy-bargy. Mayor Tonks (above) to press on with plan.

In 2015, after the stretch of the the Lancaster Canal running through the town was assessed as 'toxic' and given the lowest water quality rating possible, the local council began a clean-up campaign. The project resulted the waterway receiving a 2017 Clean Water Award and EU Clean Canal status in 2018.

canal

But the clean-up didn't stop there, and many campaigners believe that the council has gone *too far* in its efforts to purify the canal, with unintended consequences.

"The whole situation is deeply worrying," said local resident Douglas Fur. "The water is crystal clear, and you can see right to the bottom, which is all well and good. But they've cleaned it up to the point where it's acquired strange, ungodly properties."

He continued: "There's the immortality for starters. Anyone whosoever drinketh from its waters shall be blessed with life everlasting."

"I'm not saying we should go back to the state it was in before, with all car tyres and bike frames in it, but a canal so clean that its magical waters give eternal life? That can't be right," Mr Fur added.

coral

And other residents were quick to voice concerns that the canal was now so clean that anyone who caught sight of their reflection in its limpid waters would therein see the things that are yet to come.

"I don't want to see into the future, thank you very much," said local garage mechanic Frank Trabbsboy. "I went for a stroll along the towpath last Friday, and when I looked in the water, I saw I was going to die of a heart attack on June 14th, 2027."

"That foreknowledge of my own mortality completely spoilt my weekend, I can tell you," he added.

But Mayor Eric Tonks said that having a canal so clean that its wa-

Council gives green light to controversial canal project

ters had magical properties was a great boost for tourism in the area.

mill

"We get coachloads of old people in search of eternal life during the week," he told reporters. "And they all stop off for a cup of tea and a cake at the Copper Kettle before they go," he said.

"Although I have to admit, the man from William Hills isn't too pleased when his customers peer over the bank to see who's going to win the 3:30 at Chepstow."

barrier

However, despite protests from local residents and bookmakers, the council say they have no plans to scale down their clean-up act on the canal.

"We're going to press on," said Mr Tonks. "If we can get it a bit cleaner still, we reckon that it will make somebody fall in love with anyone who's reflection they see. Imagine what that'll do for the town centre on Valentine's Day."

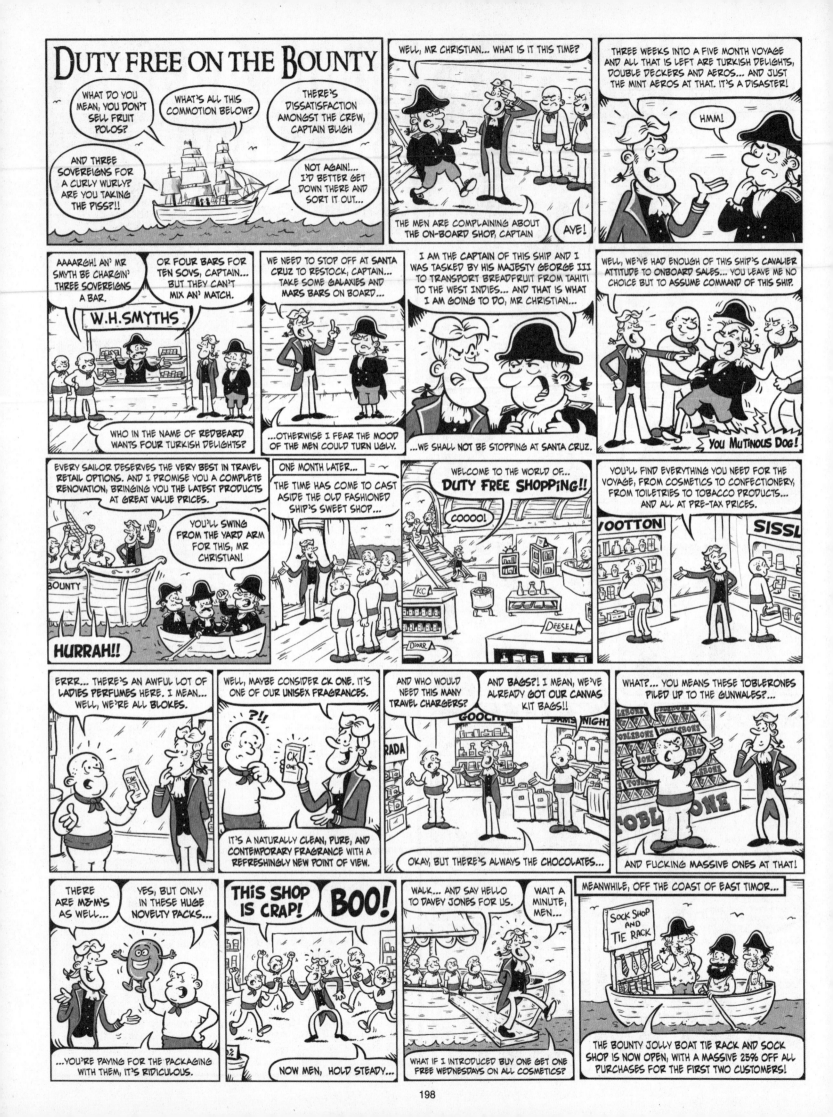

201

WHO'S THE MIG[

JAMES

SINCE making his TV debut on *Ready Steady Cook* in the mid-nineties, Yorkshire chef James has remained a steady fixture on Britain's small screens. The plain-speaking cuisinier has popped up on *Saturday Kitchen, Strictly Come Dancing* and *The One Show*, as well as releasing several cookbooks and volumes of autobiography, and performed a UK tour of his live show, *Plates, Mates and Automobiles*. It's a solid opening round for the hardest-working man in daytime cookery. **6**

IT'S THE RANCOROUS debate that's been raging through Britain's green and pleasant streets for centuries, destroying friendships and rending marriages in twain: *Who is the Best Martin?*

From Land's End to John O'Groats, each and every one of us has an unshakeable opinion on the subject, and we will all risk life, limb and legal action to defend our personal Martin preference. There are many Martins in the mix, but THREE names consistently top the popular polls.

First is cheeky, small screen gastronome *JAMES MARTIN*, who keeps us rolling in the aisles with his Yorkshire-based banter while he whips up mouth-watering treats on our tellies. The second is 'King of Cool' Rat Pack icon *DEAN MARTIN*, who wowed fifties audiences with his acting, singing and rib-tickling comedy antics. And the third is cap-wearing *Game of Thrones* author *GEORGE RR MARTIN*, who continues to amaze and arouse millions with his erotically charged fantasy novels.

But the time has come for the arguments to cease. We are finally putting our foot down and pitching these three titans of Martinhood head to head to head, to find out once and for all..

...Who is the Mightiest Martin?

WHETHER he's screeching around the *Top Gear* test track in a swish supercar, strutting through the Good Food Expo at the Birmingham NEC in a chic leather jacket, or exchanging cheeky banter with a D-List celebrity whilst cooking a quiche, Malton-born James is the undisputed Head Chef of Hip. In fact, the only time the unflappable gourmet loses his cool is when he spots a group of cyclists whilst out driving, and light-heartedly attempts to run them off the road into a hedge. All of which adds up to big points here for the Arthur Fonzarelli of weekend cookery programming. **7**

JAMES is a multi award-winning small screen icon, whose cheery daytime cooking shows have won him die-hard fans from Maltby to Catterick and from Pontefract to Wakefield. Unfortunately - or perhaps fortunately - at the time of going to press James has yet to simulate penetrative sexual intercourse on any of these programmes, and as such his score suffers severely in this round. **1**

TUNE into one of James Martin's numerous TV cookery shows and you can be sure that within seconds, the gastronome will somehow work the conversation around to his beloved place of birth - Yorkshire. The *Saturday Kitchen* fave was born and raised in Malton in the Ryedale district of the North Riding, and he regularly wows fans with his unerring ability to crowbar God's Own County into any televised discussion, no matter how non-Yorkshire-centric it may at first appear. **8**

IN 2011, as part of a TV series called *Operation Hospital Food*, kitchen whizz James was tasked with revamping the menu at Scarborough General Hospital. And you would think this would mean big points for him in this rather specific round. However, according to 17th Century French brainbox René Descartes, there are never any sure signs by which we can truly distinguish being awake from being asleep. Consequently we may simply have dreamed this show. **5**

THE sobriquet 'The Fifth Beatle' has been used to describe several people down the years - from luckless drummer Pete Best and ill-fated guitarist Stuart Sutcliffe, to plum-voiced producer George Martin. However, there is no proof whatsoever that TV cook James has ever attempted to distinguish himself from any of these almost-Mop-Tops. What's more, even if he wanted to, James couldn't use his middle initials, due to one very simple fact... he has no middle initials! It's a disastrous final round for the boy simply born 'James Martin'. **0**

HOW DID THEY DO?

JAMES

Eeh by gum! Yorkshire lad James has been given a "reet proper" shoeing off his two celebrity namesakes here, following a performance as flat as his vowels. When it comes to Martin match-ups, he obviously can't stand the heat... so he'd better get back in the kitchen! **27**

...TIEST MARTIN?

DEAN

ICONIC vocalist Dean boasts a discography so large that it requires its very own Wikipedia entry! And if his whopping six-decade musical career wasn't enough to swing it for him in this round, the multi-talented *Mambo Italiano* crooner also starred in countless films and TV series, and would almost certainly still be notching up credits if he hadn't chosen to take a well-earned step back from performing after dying in 1995. A stonking opening score for the deceased *It's Amore* idol. **9**

AT THE height of his fame in the 1950s, dapper Dean was nicknamed 'The King of Cool' for his effortless charm and charisma. And from *Hollywood or Bust* to *Ocean's 11*, a quick glance at any of the Rat Pack icon's films would suggest that the *Volare* crooner was the dictionary definition of 'with it'. Having said that, it is a sad yet unavoidable fact that every person on earth will experience 'explosive diarrhoea' at least once in their lifetime, and we have no reason to believe that Dean was exempt. Once we picture the supposedly suave actor bent double with his trousers round his ankles, groaning and sweating as he squirts rusty water through his inflamed sphincter, it's very difficult to associate him with any degree of coolness whatsoever. **2**

AS THE hottest male star in post-war Hollywood, Ohio-born Dean featured in more than his fair share of raunchy big screen adventures. From cavorting with a half-naked Marilyn Monroe in *Something's Got To Give* to smooching with Lana Turner in *Who's Got The Action?* the libidinous entertainer scores highly here. In fact, points are dropped in this round only because in none of his films do you ever actually see it going in. **6**

MOVIE star Dean was born and raised in Steubenville, Ohio, and while he displayed no evidence of a fanatical obsession with his hometown during his life, his hometown certainly seems guilty of a maniacal infatuation with him. The Dean-Martin-mad Steubenville residents chose to name one of their streets 'Dean Martin Boulevard' after the iconic Rat Packer, and the town also hosts an annual 'Dean Martin Festival', which is similarly named after Dean Martin, featuring numerous guest speakers going on and on about Dean Martin. **5**

THERE is no evidence that Dean Martin ever even visited the Yorkshire seaside town of Scarborough, let alone overhauled its hospital's culinary rota. That said, the *Ain't That A Kick In The Head* hit-maker did visit the UK back in 1983 for a 'Live In London' tour date, so it's not impossible that he may have taken some time off in order to nip up to North Yorkshire and revitalise the region's infirmary-based cuisine. With this posibility still out there, it's only fair to award him half marks here. **5**

DASHING Dean found fame many years before the Fab Four hit the sixties big time, and as such, he would have no need nor desire to distinguish himself from them, or any of their numerous nearly-men. Born Dino Paul Crocetti, the Italian-American idol could well have used these initials to set himself apart from any future Not-Quite-Beatles if he'd happened to choose a stage name like 'Chas Newby' or 'Brian Epstein'. But in the end, he picked 'Dean Martin', thus erasing any need whatsoever for Fifth Beatle distinction. **2**

GEORGE RR

CELEBRATED fantasy author George Raymond Richard Martin first took up the quill in the early seventies, and has since penned more than 200 short stories, TV scripts and novels. But in what could have been a strong round, the bearded writer drops points for keeping *Game of Thrones* fans waiting almost 10 years for the final instalment of his popular book series, after taking time out to pursue acting roles as a zombified version of himself in *Z Nation*, as well as a cameo alongside Jedward in *Sharknado 3*. **2**

WITH his scruffy fisherman's cap, unruly facial hair and Coke-bottle specs, dragon-obsessed George RR may not be the first name you think of when you hear the word 'cool'. That said, the OED defines 'cool' as 'easygoing, laid-back or mellow,' and when you consider that George has spent the thick of end a decade nonchalantly fannying about instead of finishing the hugely-anticipated final book in the *Game of Thrones* series, it's easy to see that the lackadaisical author may be significantly 'cooler' than one might think. As such, it's a decent haul for the easygoing, fanny-chopped procrastinator. **6**

GEORGE RR's bestselling *Game of Thrones* series is built around the four S's: Swords, Sorcery... and Steamy Sex! Whether it's Tyrion Lannister bedding whores in Littlefinger's brothel or his sister Cersei prancing about completely Billy Bollocks, any red-blooded male reading one of George's naughty novels will soon be reaching for the nearest cushion to conceal their excitement. It's a positively priapismic round for the coitus-crazed wordsmith. **8**

BORN in Bayonne, New Jersey in 1948, author George has always had little time for 'real' geographical locations, preferring instead to focus on strange and exotic fantasy lands with wondrous names like Essos, Westeros and Casterly Rock, in which hardened warriors battle ice zombies with flaming swords, and vast-titted women soar through the skies on scaly dragons. As such, it's a low-scoring round for the not-particularly-obsessed-with-Bayonne-New-Jersey wordsmith. **4**

HIRSUTE author George RR has concocted many iconic menus in his time: from the Bacchanalian fare served at GoT's 'Red Wedding' to the sumptuous spread laid out at the 'Feast of Winterfell'. However, at the time of writing, George has yet to pen any scene in which a Westeros resident journeys to Scarborough in order to upgrade its general hospital's in-house catering facilities, a fact that is duly reflected in his pitiful score in this round. **3**

GOOGLE the name 'George Martin' and the first entry that comes up is for the London-born producer, arranger, composer and 'Fifth Beatle', George Martin. In second place behind him is the lusty *Game of Thrones* scribe George RR Martin. In interviews, the latter has freely admitted incorporating his middle initials in order to avoid being confused with the ex-Mop-Top knob twiddler, which makes him a shoo-in for big points in this round. What's more, we cannot rule out the possibility that George RR might go on to pen future novels under other Fifth Beatle-distinguishing pseudonyms, such as 'Pete RR Best', 'Jimmie RR Nicol' or 'Yoko RR Ono'. As such it's a fab final round for the barbigerous novelist. **9**

DEAN

Well, ain't THAT a kick in the head?! Like "the fella once said", Hollywood heart-throb Dean has been sent (Rat) Pack-ing by his fellow Martins, bested at the last minute by a fanny-chopped septuagenarian scribbler. He may be the 'King of Cool' - but he sure ain't Monarch of the Martins! **29**

GEORGE RR

Winner is coming... and it's none other than George RR! As the smoke clears from a three-way fight-to-the-death that makes the Red Wedding look like Sesame Street, we can see that the bewhiskered *Game of Thrones* fave has left his opponents in a worse state than Theon Greyjoy's chopper. *All hail Good King George RR!* **32**

Take a Shit

SHOCK HORROR!

Bright Spark Frank's switch-on lights up Mayor

Shock and Aw! Amateur sparky Spongle (above) blames foul play and faulty wiring for onlookers disappointment and the injuries caused to Mayor Tonks (left)

AS the dark winter nights set in, many youngsters look forward to their parents taking them to see their town's Christmas illuminations. But the sparky who was put in charge of this year's Tipton Christmas Lumiere Festival has had the plug pulled on his services after the town's Lord Mayor suffered severe burns at the official switch-on.

Amateur electrician Frank Spongle had been given the contract to wire up the West Midlands town's annual festive lights and spent most of September and October setting up the display, which included illuminated figures of Snow White and the Seven Dwarves.

The council had originally approached comedian Jasper Carrott and one of the members of Steps to officially turn the lights on. But Carrott was self-isolating due to Covid, and the member of Steps allegedly asked for a two-figure appearance fee, so Lord Mayor Edward Tonks stepped into the breach.

But disaster struck on the night of the big switch-on, when councillor Tonks suffered a massive 2000 volt electric shock, burning his hand and arm, blowing off his ceremonial hat and causing the links of his chain of office to weld together.

"I think it was a faulty RCD that failed and allowed a hundred amps of current through the switch," Spongle told *Take a Shit*. "Whoever manufactured that unit should be prosecuted, not me. I had absolutely nothing to do with it."

However, a preliminary inquiry into the incident saw the Ghost of Christmas Past come back to haunt Spongle, as it emerged that the accident was only the latest in a series of botched light shows organised by the self-taught electrician.

As told to
Vaginia Discharge

And talking to reporters, Spongle admitted that previous displays he had set up had also suffered issues.

"There'd been an incident a few years back when I did the Christmas lights in Wednesbury," said Spongle. "I'd set up the display and earthed it to a nearby lampost correctly, but before switch-on, some vandals must have swapped the wires round. It worked okay, because they'd mixed up the live and neutral and it was AC. But one night during some particularly heavy rain, a 4000-volt electric arc suddenly shot out from Snow White and hit a passing tram."

"All but two passengers survived, so there was no harm done. But the subsequent inquiry concluded that I had got the old cable colours mixed up with the new EEC ones. Which I hadn't, even though you can see how someone could. I mean, brown's live or something these days, and that's just asking for trouble. But even though I was utterly blameless, as I say, I had to give an undertaking not to set up public illuminations again."

Apart from one or two times, Spongle kept his word. But the joy of seeing

> ***"I'd set up the display and earthed it to a nearby lampost correctly, but before switch-on, some vandals must have swapped the wires round"***

childrens' faces light up when they saw his Christmas displays drew him back in. The following November, against his better judgement, he volunteered to do the festive display at Walsall Arboretum.

"I set up what was the best display I had ever done," he said. "Snow White and the dwarves as usual, but this time there were reindeers too. And one of them had a red bulb on his nose that was wired up to some capacitors and things to make it flash. It was spectacular."

Fuse, what a scorcher: The charred evidence of what Spongle believes was someone changing the circuit breakers on his set-up

"But somebody, must have gone and changed the circuit breakers on my system after I set it up, replacing them with ones with too high an amp."

"There was no way that the Seven Dwarves could have exploded like that when they were switched on unless the electrics had been tampered with," said Frank.

"Whoever did it knew what they were doing."

Spongle believes that a qualified electrician, jealous of an amateur rival being given such a prestigious job, sabotaged his display. But his protestations fell on deaf ears amid an outcry from those watching, many of whose hair had caught fire, and he was given his marching orders by Walsall council.

Undeterred, the Christmas-loving sparky decided to head north to ply his trade, and quickly won the contract to set up the Roker and Seaburn Illuminations after tendering the lowest bid under an alias. And in September last year, he set up his Snow White and the Seven Dwarves display along the seafront.

"The dwarves were a bit melted and worse for wear after their last outing," he said. "But the electrics inside were basically sound. I tested them with a meter I got from Maplins and found they were good to go."

"I was going to give the people of Sunderland a festive display they would never forget."

Winter wonderland! A spectacular festive light display not entirely dissimilar to the one that Spongle was trying to achieve

But come switch-on night, the fairytale twinkling of illuminated figures was quickly replaced by the blue flashing lights of the fire brigade.

"The supply on the seafront was single-phase AC, but I'd spent hours rigging up the display on three-phase," said Frank. "It's no surprise to anyone with electrical knowhow that it went up like a rocket. You'd think the council's registered electricians would have thought to tell me."

"It was their fault, not mine."

A subsequent enquiry found Spongle responsible for the fire and barred him from practising as an electrician under his own name or any of his three professional aliases, and he headed back to his native West Midlands.

"I was gutted. All I could think of was how much I loved Christmas and helping people appreciate the joys of electricity in light form. I know it was wrong, but I decided to ignore the judgement of the inquiry, and I offered to do the lights for Tipton Council," he said.

"They jumped at the chance. Whether it was because they knew all the other incidents weren't my fault, or because I was using a fourth alias, I don't know, but I was grateful for another chance and determined to give them a light show like no other."

"I decided to go with Snow White and the Seven Dwarves again, and set the lights up all through the precinct, hanging them off the lampposts and shop-fronts. It was my biggest and most ambitious set-up ever. I couldn't wait for it to get dark so I could see it lit up in all its glory."

But this time Frank's high hopes were dashed after he was let down by faulty equipment. He told the paper: "During testing, every time I plugged it in and threw the switch, the fuse went."

"I knew it wasn't anything to do with the wiring, as I'd checked it all carefully after it caught fire the last time, and there was definitely nothing amiss. I could only conclude that the fuse I'd got in the plug simply wasn't big enough to handle all the bulbs in such a spectacular display."

"As I didn't have any fuses with bigger amps, I decided to simply stick a nail

between the live and the pin. It's an old sparky's trick for when plugs keep blowing for no reason."

But disaster struck Frank's plans once again at the switching on ceremony. In addition to the Mayor suffering his injuries, the display inexplicably caught fire for the fourth time. "I can only assume there was some sort of freak voltage surge in the mains, and it overloaded the bulb in Sneezy's head, which burst into flames. The burning plastic set fire to the wire, and before long the whole display was burning."

People in the crowd called the emergency services and the flames were soon extinguished, with the unfortunate Mayor on his way to hospital in an ambulance.

"Everybody seemed to think that my wiring was at fault," said Frank. "I suppose it was easier to blame me than looking for the real cause of the blaze, which was probably sabotage, lightning or a voltage spike in the mains."

Following the latest incident, Spongle was once again summoned to court to face charges under the Health and Safety at Work Act.

"It's no surprise to anyone with electrical knowhow that it went up like a rocket"

Magical! Not one of Spongle's displays, yesterday

"It seems unfair that someone can manufacture shoddy equipment and sell it to unsuspecting electricians at car boot sales, or change the colours of the wiring in plugs, yet it's my reputation that suffers when it keeps on going live or catching fire," he said. "And on top of that, I'm fast running out of aliases."

Take a Shit

Anger as Commons Soft Play Area Stays Open

MPs are being pressured to provide a proper explanation as to why soft play areas across the country are being forced to close due to the Covid pandemic, whilst the Indoor Play Centre at the House of Commons remains open.

And regional mayors are furious that the Palace of Westminster is continuing to flout its own lockdown rules, seemingly able to stay open at all hours with little or no concern for the restrictions imposed on the rest of the country.

bouncy

The parliamentary soft play area, called Big Bens, features slides, climbing frames and a bouncy castle, and is popular amongst MPs wanting to let off steam after a long debate or gruelling select committee meeting.

"It's 'one-for-rule-for-us and another-rule-for-them'," said Eric Tonks, mayor of Blackpool which, under Tier Three restrictions, has seen soft play areas closed for months.

"We need parity in the UK with restrictions," he added, "Children in England and Wales are being stopped from visiting a supervised soft play area. Yet after a day at the despatch box, the Prime Minister or the Leader of the Opposition can clown around on the slides, tumble mats and ball pool for as long as they want."

"It shows utter contempt for the British people," he added.

cwix

And Manchester mayor Andy Burnham added his voice to the growing chorus of criticism levelled at the government. "I would love to take my shoes off and throw myself around on some big foam mats," he told the BBCs Laura Kuenssberg. "But I respect the laws this government has implemented. It's just a pity that they do not. It's not faor."

Letterbocks

Viz Comic, P.O. Box 841 Whitley Bay, NE26 9EQ   letters@viz.co.uk

ON a recent trip to Germany I visited the town of Bad Krozingen, and to my surprise it was actually a rather pleasant place. I really don't see why they feel the need to denigrate themselves like this and risk putting off tourists. Mind you, the French probably went too far the other way in calling their town 'Nice.' Nobody likes boastfulness.

Ben Nunn, Caterham

WHEN I see the career Derren Brown has made for himself using his photographic memory, I sometimes feel a bit guilty that I have a very similar talent, yet I have only really used it to create the most impressive wank bank in Britain. Still, I may not have made his millions, but I've had fun and that's what's important.

Torbjorn Wells, Leeds

I WAS recently informed that owls have 8-times better eyesight than humans, yet my ophthalmologist reckons my eyesight is perfect. I'd like to see David Attenborough explain that one.

Boon, Cardross

I HAD my septic tank emptied by an engineer called Thomas Moore. I was about make a very clever play on words by remarking "who will rid me of this turbulent piss," when I remembered that was Thomas Becket, not Thomas More, and so narrowly avoided a potentially embarrassing moment.

Persemillion Jones, email

I'VE often heard that women are most sexually attracted to men who can make them laugh. But when I copped off with a woman last weekend, she took one look at my cock, burst into hysterical laughter, and that was that.

Crosby Fibreboard, Luton

SO multi-millionaire property developer and Conservative party donor Tony Gallagher has been given a knighthood in the Queen's Birthday Honours List "for services to land development and the property business". Well, if that's the case, why is it that… actually, no. Fuck the punchline. "Services to land development and the property business" is funny enough as it is.

Stan Magnusson, Tooting

MY vegan neighbour farted himself off his bike and broke his hip. Healthy diet my foot.

Grant McBurnie, Malvern East

STAR LETTER

IF I ever get to work in one of those factories that make bubble wrap, I'd fart in every bubble so that when they were popped they would smell of my bowel fragrance. Come to think of it, I don't know why bubble wrap factories don't put smells in their bubbles already and use it as a marketing gimmick. It's madness if you ask me.

Tim Buktu, Timbuktu

DURING the 80s, we wagged school a lot and watched a mate's dad's stash of pornos. Once a German said "Dat izt fantastisch, Angie." I'll never forget our shared euphoria at becoming bilingual without going to school.

Mark Hunt, Beeston

WHY is 'hard cheese' used as a term of commiseration to someone when something unfortunate or unpleasant happens to them? Hard cheeses, such as Cheddar, Comté and Provolone, are delicious. And I'm rather partial to a Manchego.

Gerry Paton, London

I'D JUST like to say that I find *Viz* about as amusing as having my genitals trapped in a car door. However, I have a rare fetish where I do actually find it amusing to trap my genitals in car doors, so keep up the good work!

Darren Singleton, Belper

A MATE of mine says it is the law that you have to put your dipped headlights on when it's raining in Sweden. How the fuck am I supposed to know when it's raining in Sweden?

Millsy, Newcastle

THEY say the Royal children are born with silver spoons in their mouths, but if I lost some cutlery up my wife's fanny, I'd think of a better way to retrieve it than getting her pregnant.

Pat Bricklayer, email

WE'RE always being told that regular exercise is the key to long life. But whenever you see people on the news for reaching 100, they're never jogging or at the gym, they're usually just sitting in an armchair staring at the TV. That's the approach I'm going with, and it's worked okay so far. I'll keep you posted.

Hector Crumbs, Tring

I CELEBRATED our tenth wedding anniversary by visiting Marks and Spencers and buying some French knickers to give my husband a thrill. But on reading the label, I was upset to discover that they were made in China. If I had wanted Chinese knickers, I would have bought some. I had hoped that Brexit would sort this kind of thing out, but Nigel Farage is a cunt so I'm not holding my breath.

Beverly Hills, Orkney

IN a recent issue of *Viz*, a reader mentioned the saying 'if at first you don't succeed try, try again'. Since childhood I have thought the saying had three 'try's in it, not two. Can you imagine my disbelief when I realised I had been over-trying everything by fifty percent for decades? From now on I'm only going to try things twice instead of thrice before giving up.

Tristan Tricep, Tring

"YOU'RE not going out of the house dressed like that! You look like a porn star!" shouted my Dad. I had to laugh, because I am a porn star, and I was on my way to shoot a film called *Piss Orgy*.

L. Lovelace, Hollywood

THEY say "seeing is believing" but it's not. It's when you look at something.

Lenny Sherman, London

AS I am now retired, I can watch telly all day and I have been staggered to see the number of adverts for products aimed at women who piss themselves.

Stephen Gordon, London

'NO CONFERRING' CORNER

I ONCE let out a bottom burp that sounded just like the buzzer from *University Challenge*, and quick as a flash I said "Samson, Cambridge." Unfortunately there's was no one around to hear the amusing sound and subsequent witty remark, but I'm certain it would have made my wife laugh had she been there. Have any other readers managed to make a well known sound when trumping, followed by a witty remark?

Matt Varnish, Staines

I WAS recently watching an edition of *University Challenge* and was astonished to hear that one of the Oxford University contestants was studying 'modern history'. What utter nonsense. History cannot be 'modern' any more than water can be dry. I understand that Boris Johnson attended the same institution, so it's little wonder that he turned out to be a wrong 'un.

Eric Nipples, Orkney

FLEABAGPUSS...

Brian Kelly

DID YOU GO OUT WITH MADELEINE THE RAG DOLL LAST NIGHT?

FUCKED HER UP THE ARSE.

ON a recent trip to my local nature reserve I was appalled to see this murmuration in the form of a phallus. Suffice to say I put my foot through the hide and sent Terry Nutkins the bill.

Miss S E Hall, Jesmond

MY wife recently bought me some expensive white underpants from John Lewis, and I wondered why anyone would wear white underpants, on which any faecal, urinary or spermatic misdemeanour could so instantly be spotted? TKMaxx sell brown undercrackers for half the price, and nobody suspects a thing.

David Haslam, Datchworth

HOW ABOUT this for a tall shed?

R.R. Rasputin, email

WHY is it that, when people see a ghost, it's always a lady in a grey dress, slowly walking down the stairs? Why is it never a middle-aged, balding man in a tank top pottering about in the shed? Come on, ghosts. Try to show a bit of diversity.

Reginald Meringue, Luton

"WELL, I wish it could be Christmas every day" went the lyrics of Wizzard's famous single. Well, it's not far off, since the BBC start playing it non-stop from November.

Andy Mac, Trumpton

AFTER hearing about the way they treated Rudolph and then gathered round to lick his arse, I'd say the rest of Santa's reindeer are a load of cunts.

Jim Allsopp's pal, Haverfordwest

IN the 1970s children's programme *Bagpuss*, does anyone know Emily's business model? She seems to be able to keep a small retail business open simply by putting shit she found on the street in her shop window.

Dave Slade, Stevenage

MY four-year-old showed me a picture she drew of our family which was in fact just a few blue scribbles and a purple dog. I told her that dogs aren't purple and the picture was complete and utter shit. I was always taught that honesty is the best policy.

Lee, email

THERE are twelve stairs in my house, then a ninety degree turn onto a thirteenth stair. I've just blown off on every one of them whilst going upstairs. Surely this must be some kind of record?

Fat Al White, Wrenthorpe

CAN any of your readers tell me if the saying is "for fucks sake" or "for fuck sake"? It's for a work email, so it needs to sound professional.

Dr T. Uke, email

I HAD a beefburger the other night and I have to say, it tasted lovely. I don't know what these vegans are complaining about.

Gal Postans, Hereford

IN response to Mike Tatham's request for a backdrop of books to make him look smart should he be invited onto a Zoom call (*page 187*), please feel free to use this photograph, which can be easily set as his background. Happy to help. Mike.

Kevin Caswell-Jones, email

ToP TIPS

VICARS. Don't spend all that donated cash on restoring the belfry and training bell-ringers, simply drop a few scaffolding poles off the vestry roof on Sunday mornings.

Mark Glover, Coventry

MEN. Make hoovering more fun by doing it with one hand and having a wank with the other.

Seb Placebo, Bow

ATTRACT more health-conscious garden birds this winter by replacing fatballs with tangerines.

Phil Kitching, Isle of Jura

CRIMINALS. Avoid being caught by deliberately wearing the wrong-sized shoes when committing a crime.

Rob Powell, Welshpool

CAN'T be arsed to wait for a decent lightning storm? Simply wait until it's dark, then turn your living room light on and off really quickly.

Dave Edwards, Bridport Parkway

OFF-ROAD enthusiasts. Test your skills as a driver and the performance of your vehicle by driving along the pothole-filled, challenging terrain of the A82 main road through the town of Clydebank.

T.O'Neill, Glasgow

QUIZ show contestants. Interrupt any question which begins "Which famous graffitti artist..?" It's Banksy, 100% of the time.

Rich Karslake, Oxon.

ENJOY the experience of fishing without the ballache of buying expensive equipment by simply sitting by the river and watching anglers looking bored and catching fuck all. When you've had enough of the ennui, you can simply leave without having to pack away all that kit.

Zarg the Splendid, Norwich

toptips@viz.co.uk

NORMAN THE DOORMAN

Man Bemoans 'Wrong' Lottery Numbers Again

Buttocks: Fuming, yesterday

A DERBYSHIRE man has sent an official complaint to National Lottery organisers Camelot after the incorrect lottery numbers came out of the machine for the 4000th consecutive time.

Harold Buttocks, 62, said that he watched the draw on Saturday evening and was left fuming that the wrong numbers were once again selected, whilst the balls with the numbers he had chosen were left tumbling around the machine.

saturday

"I mean, how hard can it be," screamed the former gas fitter from Mickleover. "I choose the correct numbers every Saturday morning and they are clearly the numbers that should come out. It makes absolutely no sense that they don't."

Buttocks, who spends around £200 on lottery tickets and scratchcards each week, says he has a foolproof way of choosing the winning numbers, but Camelot just keep getting it wrong.

atonement

"I've got a system, and if Camelot did their job proper it would work," he told us. "But they just bugger it up, week after week. If they were in charge of any other business, they'd be sacked."

"Like I was when I was a bus driver and I turned up for work pissed," he added.

NEW YEAR'S RES

WE **ALL** love making our New Year's Resolutions. Whether we're cutting out carbs, stopping smoking or taking up the trombone, there's nothing Brits love more than starting the year with a solemn, life-enhancing vow.

But statistics show that most of our good intentions fizzle out before the first month draws to a close. By January 12th or thereabouts, we're all back to stuffing our faces with doughnuts and puffing away on 40 cigs a day, whilst our new musical instruments sit untouched in the corner of the room, silently judging us.

But as ordinary members of the public, we are mere mortals. *For the A-List stars, it's a different story.*

Celebrities are the godlike idols we look up to, using them as yardsticks for how to live our pathetic, meaningless lives. It is their superhuman drive, dedication and willpower that has propelled them to the top of the tree. *So, if one thing's for sure, it's that when these showbiz icons make a New Year's Resolution, they stick to it...*

...or so you might think.

Award-winning *Viz* investigative reporter **MAHATMA MACAROON** went undercover to find out whether today's celebs are *really* capable of keeping the promises they make each new year. And what he uncovered will make every right-thinking Brit feel physically sick and spiritually bilious.

New Year's Resolutions? For the stars, it's more like *New Year's Swizz-olutions.*

BY Viz UNDERCOVER REPORTER MAHATMA MACAROON

PROFESSOR BRIAN COX

Occupation: Scientist

Resolution: Spend less time using technology

GADGET-MAD Brian is famous for his obsession with all things hi-tech. Whether he's prodding his 'synthesizer', twiddling the knobs on a space telescope or tapping away at his 3G mobile to send a 'Tweet' to his 2.95 million followers, there's nothing this tousle-haired egghead likes more than fannying about with space-age machinery.

But too much 'screen time' can have a detrimental effect on everything from our eyesight and mental health to our social life and sperm count. We're all on the lookout for ways to cut down our use of technology to spend more quality time with friends and family, so it's fair to assume that computer-crazy Brian might well have put 'logging off' at the top of his 2020 Resolutions list.

It's a noble – albeit hypothetical – vow. *But can the tech-bonkers boffin stick to it?*

I book a flight to Geneva on January 2nd, and head for CERN, home of Cox's Large Hadron Collider. In the dead of night, I disguise myself as a CERN technician, dressing up in a Village People-style 'construction worker' costume bought off eBay. The gullible security guard is instantly taken in by my hard hat, tight grey vest and tool belt, and I step right past him with no questions asked, once I've hit him several times with a large bit of wood.

I make my way to Cox's private quarters, and bearing in mind the New Year's Resolution I've imagined, I am expecting to find a Luddite-esque haven full of textbooks, candlelight and simple wooden trinkets. As I peer through the crack in the door, however, I'm immediately disappointed. There is computerised gadgetry *everywhere* – tablets, laptops, Kindle e-readers – and the floor is a veritable jungle of computer cables and wires. Clearly the bed-headed physicist has shattered his supposed January oath within just *hours* of potentially making it. To add insult to injury, Cox is even jabbering away into his high-tech mobile phone as I approach. I see him through the door, whispering: "Hello. Police?... I think someone's broken in... Come as quick as you can."

As I leave, I feel sick to my stomach at the small screen scientist's despicable lack of willpower. To make it look like a genuine break-in, rather than a respectable reporter on the hunt for hypocrisy, I do a quick shit in the Hadron Collider before making my escape.

The Professor famously sang, "Things can only get better." Well, Brian, when you break your New Year's Resolution on JANUARY 2ND, they can't get much worse.

TRACEY EMIN

Occupation: Sort of artist

Resolution: Be a bit tidier

CROYDON-BORN Tracey is admired by art lovers for her iconic 1998 installation of her own shitted bed with all used johnnies in it. But while her natural messiness may have won her critical plaudits from Tyneside to Timbuktu, it won't have won her any new house guests.

So it's safe to assume that every January, the famously slovenly 'artist' resolves to keep her home neater and tidier – and this year is unlikely to be any different.

The question is: how long can the 'enfant terrible' of British art stick to her pledge?

Done up as a plumber in a bright red 'Super Mario' outfit from a pound shop, I knock at Emin's door on January 10th. When there's no answer, I shin up the drainpipe and let myself in. A neighbour pops out to ask what I'm doing, but after clocking my disguise, and being knocked unconscious and locked in my car boot, he enquires no further.

I jemmy open Emin's bedroom window and, at first glance, everything *seems* spick and span. The bed appears beautifully made, the carpet spotless and there's not a single spunk-encrusted tissue or empty fag packet in sight.

However, before I can carry out a full inspection to determine whether the YBA wild child has stuck to her hypothetical cleanliness regime, disaster strikes. I leap into the room to find that my oversized blue dungarees have caught on the window latch, throwing me off balance. I career wildly into the bookshelf, and then stagger backwards into the dressing table with my arms flailing, before spinning head-first into the mantelpiece.

As I stand up, a glance around the room causes my heart to sink. My eyes must have initially deceived me, because this bedroom is a *bombsite*. There are tattered books and broken ornaments scattered everywhere, shattered glass all over the floor, and muddy bootprints covering the carpet.

I shake my head in disgust that Emin has not even made it *a fortnight* into 2020 before allowing her house to fall into unhygienic disrepair. I hear sirens wailing in the distance, and realise that the neighbour must have woken up and phoned the filth. To make it look like an innocent robbery, I steal some of her knickers before doing a shit in the drawer. But in truth, the mess in here is so overwhelming, I'm not sure Emin will even notice

Tracey is renowned for her 'confessional' style of art. But here's one confession she SHOULD be making: "I can't keep my New Year's Resolutions."

JANUARY 1

O-LETDOWNS!

We uncover the SHAME of the January-promise-breaking stars

DAVID MITCHELL

Occupation: TV funnyman

Resolution: Learn to speak fluent Latin

CAMBRIDGE-educated brainbox David loves to show off his impressive vocabulary and lightning quick wit on popular TV panel shows such as *Would I Lie To You?*, *QI* and *Have I Got News For You*.

He keeps viewers rolling in the aisles with his highbrow quips on everything from literature and history to science and maths. However, there's one intellectual mountain he has yet to climb: *mastering the long-dead language of Latin.*

Speaking Latin is the widely accepted pinnacle of cleverness, and only the most brilliant and perceptive thinkers – such as MP Jacob Rees-Mogg – are capable of it. With that in mind, it's almost certain that cerebral funnyman Mitchell has etched 'Learn to speak fluent Latin' firmly at number one on his list of resolutions for 2020.

It's a bold theoretical pledge that will take months of hard work. But can he really pull it off?

On January 6th, I make my way to the *Would I Lie To You?* studios in central London. I am dressed as a delivery man, in blue shorts and a peaked cap, with a leather satchel over my shoulder.

The security guard falls for my disguise, and once I've wrestled him to the floor and held a chloroform-soaked rag to his face, I'm able to waltz straight past him.

I knock at Mitchell's dressing room and enter. *"Veniam in me, Dominus Mitchell,"* I chirp. *"Sarcina pro vobis."* The *Peep Show* jester looks frightened and confused. "Er, sorry... what?" he splutters.

Oh dear. Not a good start.

I've just said, *"Excuse me, Mr Mitchell, I've got a package for you,"* in Latin. A relatively straightforward statement, but the supposedly 'intelligent' comedian clearly hasn't understood a single word. He's had *six whole days* to get cracking on the hypothetical New Year's Resolution I've conceived for him, and yet he doesn't appear to have learnt *a single Latin phrase*.

Being a good sport, I decide to give the *Upstart Crow* icon a second chance. I hand him a parcel, which he opens to reveal a large Latin dictionary. But instead of saying, "Great, just what I need for my New Year's Resolution," Mitchell simply stares at me. "I didn't order this," he mutters.

He goes to call security, and I'm left to reflect on the bitter disappointment of discovering that yet another A-List star has thrown their January promise out of the window within days of making it. I don't want Mitchell realising that a top reporter is on his trail, so to make myself seem like an ordinary stalker, I do a shit in his costume cupboard before jumping out of the window.

We all love Mitchell's erudite quips on Would I Lie To You? But when it comes to making New Year's Resolutions, the weak-willed wisecracker is only lying to HIMSELF.

DAVID CAMERON

Occupation: Former Premier

Resolution: Go vegan

WHILST he is best remembered for being the brave leader that united our country with the Brexit referendum, David Cameron's reign as prime minister was marred by some unfair – and possibly untrue – allegations about him sticking his cock in a pig.

Since these rumours of youthful swine-fucking continue to dog him to this day, it's highly likely that Cameron will have chosen to distance himself from meat entirely this year by pledging to *go vegan* for 2020.

It's an admirable intention, and the health benefits of a plant-based diet are well recorded. *But the question is: can Dave really go the meat-and-dairy-free distance?*

To find out, I arrive in the Cotswolds town of Chipping Norton on January 14th. I'm here for a private barbecue held at the home of Cameron's close friend and neighbour, Jeremy Clarkson. Motormouthed Clarkson famously loves meat so much that he punched his producer for failing to get him a steak, so if there's anywhere Cameron's speculative New Year's 'Vegan-lution' will be tested, it's here.

The event is invite-only and security is tight, so to gain entry I disguise myself as another member of the Cotswolds celebrity set: cheese-mongering Blur bassist Alex James. Wearing a Beatles wig and with an inflatable bass guitar slung around my shoulders and a fag dangling from my lip, I saunter up to Clarkson's gate. "I'm Alex James out of Blur," I tell the doorman. "I'm here for the barbecue."

"Yes, of course, come on through," I imagine the guard is thinking, and after a brief scuffle in which I immobilize him with a Taser I

bought on the internet, he allows me to pass.

Striding through the star-studded gathering, I spot ex-PM Cameron making his way towards a 'bra and pants' apron-clad Clarkson, who is manning the barbecue. Bearing in mind the resolution I'm assuming he's made, I expect to see the former Tory leader walking away with a slice of nut roast and a bowl of lentils. To my surprise, however, Cameron asks the *Grand Tour* icon to serve him up the juiciest *beefburger* on the griddle – with a *slab of grilled cheese* on top!

As the allegedly pig-bothering ex-PM takes a bite, I shudder in horror. January is not even *halfway* over and already the hypothetically 'vegan' premier is stuffing his face with dead flesh and dairy produce. We are used to politicians breaking their promises to the public, but Cameron can't even keep one to *himself*.

Disappointment courses through my veins, and when I see several security guards approaching – along with the real Alex James – I decide it's time to make my exit. Before I go, I sneak into the kitchen and perform a sex act in the potato salad to make them think I was a crank with a grudge against Clarkson, rather than an award-winning undercover journalist.

In his days as PM, Cameron was often referred to as a 'right honourable gentleman'. But clearly, when it comes to keeping his Resolutions, he's nothing of the fucking sort.

NEXT ISSUE: ROMANCING THE CLONE – *Mahatma kidnaps five celebrity spouses and then assumes their identities, in order to see how well the stars REALLY treat their loved ones on Valentine's Day.*

214

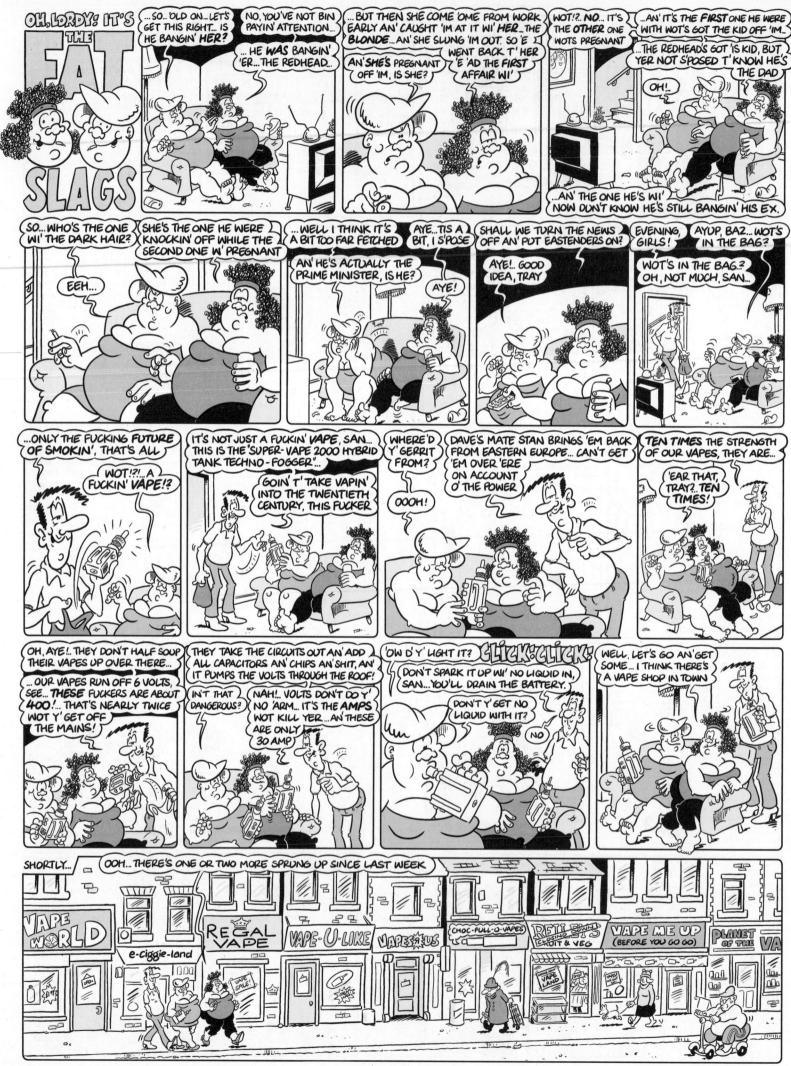

So you THINK you want... a Cup of Tea?

TEA. It's the best drink of the day, and on average, every Brit glugs down three or four steaming mugs of our delicious national beverage between getting up and going to bed. Rich in vitamins, nutrients and antioxidants, the good old cuppa puts a spring in our step and a healthy glow in our cheeks; it's undeniably a good thing. *Or is it?* It's time to take off your Rosy-Lee-tinted spectacles and take a cool and dispassionate look at this hot drink, before asking yourself...
...do you really want a cup of tea?

A SPILT cuppa isn't a problem, right? Wrong. According to the experts, tea is best drunk at a piping 98°C - that's just 2° off boiling point, the highest temperature possible for water at atmospheric pressure. If you're drinking your tea in a sitting position and the handle comes off your cup, that's 330ml of scalding liquid falling directly into your lap. Your trousers and underpants may take a degree or two off the temperature, but nevertheless the skin on your scrotum, penile shaft and glans will blister and peel off like a tangerine. You're looking at a month in a burns unit and at least a year of painful skin grafts. Of course, during your course of treatment, sex will be out of the question, and your wife - full of pent-up unfulfilled sexual desires - will almost certainly go elsewhere in search of physical gratification.

TEA has always been a quintessentially British drink, so you may be surprised to learn that it is actually grown in foreign countries - places that teem with venomous insects and aggressive creepy-crawly parasites who regard human beings as their hosts. And despite stringent precautions at the teabag plant, some of these lethal mini-beasts could get into the packaging... and into your home. Your wife could be innocently opening a pack of teabags to make your morning cuppa, only to be attacked by a four-inch wide black and yellow tarantula, hungry to sink its fangs into her finger and send its lethal toxin coursing through her veins. Even worse, your daughter could be stang off a tropical wasp, only to find - perhaps months later - that it has laid its eggs under her skin, when a giant 'boil' on her arm swells up and erupts into a writhing mass of flesh-eating maggots.

NOTHING breaks up a long, boring car journey like pulling over to enjoy a refreshing drink of tea. And if you pack a flask, you can enjoy your favourite brew wherever you like. But think! In your eagerness to pull over for a cuppa, you might miss a roadside sign, warning that you are inadvertently entering Ministry of Defence Property... during a *Live Firing Exercise!* You may be licking your lips at the prospect of a brew, but your love of tea has put you in mortal danger. Travelling at supersonic speed, the Sidewinder Air Ordnance missile will hit you before the noise of the Tornado jet that fired it reaches your ears. You, your family, and your cups of tea will never know what hit you.

BREWING a cuppa using teabags is easy, with none of the mess of pots, strainers and leaves. But next time you reach for a box of those oh-so-convenient little perforated sachets, stop and think. What if you forget to take the bag out of the cup and it accidentally slips into your throat? It will lodge in your windpipe, preventing you from breathing, and every attempt to remove the lethal blockage will only serve to push it further down your trachea. And as the fluids in the moist lining of your windpipe are absorbed, the leaves in the bag will expand, lodging it ever tighter. As your life slips away over the course of a few terrifying minutes of blind panic, you will have time to reflect that, had you decided to have a drink of safe orange squash instead of tea, you would still be looking forward to many decades of happy life.

WHAT do you do when you run out of tea? The answer's simple - you pop to the shop to buy a fresh supply. But if the shopkeeper only accepts card payments for transactions of £5 or more, and you have no money on you, you've only got one choice. You'll have to go to the nearest cashpoint. But as you stand by the machine, innocently typing in your PIN number and thinking of that delicious cuppa, chances are you're being watched by a street tough lurking in the shadows. And before you take your money - he'll strike - punching you hard in the temple. If you're lucky, you might get away with a black eye, a perforated eardrum, and concussion. But if your bank card is one with fingerprint recognition, things could take a darker turn. When you wake up, it might not just be your card that is missing, but also your right thumb, crudely hacked off to allow the miscreant to drain your bank account.

So next time you're a bit parched and you automatically reach for the teapot... **STOP!** *Think once... Think twice... **Think have a nice glass of orange squash instead.***

NEXT WEEK: *So you think you want... a Glass of Orange Squash?*